Manual of
Lathing and Plastering

MANUAL of LATHING and PLASTERING

John R. Diehl **A. I. A.**

Author

Project conceived by

NATIONAL BUREAU FOR LATHING AND PLASTERING

Designed and produced by Stahley Thompson Associates, New York

ACKNOWLEDGMENTS

The Lathing and Plastering Industry Committee, composed of the National Bureau for Lathing and Plastering and the Manufacturers Association Committee, gratefully acknowledges the contribution made by the officers, staffs and members of the following organizations:

NATIONAL BUREAU FOR LATHING AND PLASTERING

Representing

CONTRACTING PLASTERERS' AND LATHERS' INTERNATIONAL ASSOCIATION
WOOD, WIRE AND METAL LATHERS INTERNATIONAL UNION
OPERATIVE PLASTERERS AND CEMENT MASONS INTERNATIONAL ASSOCIATION
BRICKLAYERS', MASONS' AND PLASTERERS' INTERNATIONAL UNION

MANUFACTURERS ASSOCIATION COMMITTEE

Representing

THE FINISHING LIME ASSOCIATION OF OHIO
GYPSUM ASSOCIATION
METAL LATH MANUFACTURERS ASSOCIATION
PERLITE INSTITUTE
VERMICULITE INSTITUTE

Manufactured in the United States of America

FOREWORD

One of the most imposing challenges to the architectural and engineering professions is to keep abreast of the constantly changing materials, systems, ratings and techniques involved in the design and construction of better, safer shelter for whatever man chooses to do.

To assist in meeting this challenge in the knowledge of lath and plaster is the basic objective of this manual.

For the first time, in one industry-wide project, the labor unions, contractors and manufacturers have directed their efforts to this one recording of combined knowledge. Prior to this time, such knowledge was contained only in thousands of pieces of literature, catalogs, technical journals, and in the minds of hundreds of individual men.

It is an effort to treat the aesthetic and the practical aspects of uses and applications — the problems and limitations — the performance and results — of materials, techniques and manpower.

LATHING AND PLASTERING INDUSTRY COMMITTEE

Table of Contents

CHAPTER THREE

LATHING AND THE PREPARATION FOR PLASTERING

CHAPTER FOUR

PLASTERING

CHAPTER FIVE

LATH AND PLASTER SYSTEMS AND ASSEMBLIES

CHAPTER SIX

FUNCTIONS AND QUALITY OF LATH AND PLASTER WORK

CHAPTER EIGHT

ACOUSTICAL AND THERMAL CHARACTERISTICS OF PLASTERWORK AND RADIANT HEATING

CHAPTER NINE

FIRE RESISTANCE IN BUILDING CONSTRUCTION

Manual of
Lathing and Plastering

CHAPTER 1

ARCHITECTURAL CONSIDERATIONS

I. USES OF LATH AND PLASTER

A trend in contemporary design that is currently noticeable indicates an increasing interest in plaster and the plastic building arts in general. Although the venerable plastering and lathing crafts — particularly the decorative plaster arts — may have received less attention than they deserve in modern architecture, and may have been abused during earlier periods, there remains the versatility of the materials and skills of these trades which neither misuse nor changing fashions in design can obliterate. There is hardly an enclosure or a surface requirement to which some aspect of these crafts may not be applied to architectural advantage.

Present uses. The current use of plasterwork in the United States can be estimated to range from three to four hundred million square yards each year. That is enough to plaster both sides of a wall ten feet high, and approximately thirty thousand miles long. Although traditionally thought of as a finishing material, new multi-purpose uses are continually being developed as are improvements in existing materials and methods so that each day lath and plaster become more useful and more funda-

mental to the building industry. Few other architectural materials combine properties useful to the same extent.

Finish. As shown in Chapter 6, the functions performed by plaster fall into several major classes, some of which are visual while others are not. Among the visual functions is finish. By finish, one may mean the function of hiding or masking, as in the case of concealing mechanical service lines or rough structural elements. Such a finish, of course, must have structure of its own and, unlike paint, must exist independently of that which it conceals, One might also think of finish as a means of refinement, or the opportunity to embellish or to control color, texture and surface shape. In the lath and plaster crafts can be found materials and methods for the performance of any of these tasks.

Ornamental and decorative plasterwork. Among the visual functions which plaster can perform is that of ornamentation. Plaster, being a material readily modeled or cast, lends itself well to sculpture, moulding work, texturing and contouring. Ornamental plasterwork is an art in itself which has devel-

1

oped special techniques and skills. Owing to the decline in use of classic architectural detail during the past thirty years, contracting ornamental shops have become relatively rare; they are, however, by no means extinct. Commercial shops capable of high-quality production still exist in a number of American and European cities, and very active plying of the trade still goes on in the theatrical and motion picture production industries. A revival of architectural interest in ornament, of which there are current indications, would probably find the capacity of this segment of the industry low but with facility for growth.

In addition to its use in sculpture, plaster is a primary material used in several other art media. Most notable of these are the mural arts in which both the techniques of *graffito* and *fresco* make use of plaster, each in its own way, as a working base. These media are considered to be among the most permanent known.

Space definition. Lath and plaster are commonly used as primary architectural materials, which is to say they can be used in combination as the major component of a space enclosing or dividing element such as a partition, a screen, a wall, or a ceiling. Solid and hollow partitions, as well as many single-surface furred constructions, are made of lathing and plastering materials.

These are all multi-purpose systems widely used in building design for a variety of purposes such as concealment, formation of ductways, the partitioning of interior space, non-loadbearing exterior walls, acoustical treatments, formed and suspended ceilings, and many other uses. The various systems available are described in detail in Chapter 5.

Structural uses. Lath and plaster work, as such, is not commonly used in architecture for purely structural purposes, although some experimental and development work has been done along these lines, with good prospects, by Hobson and McNulty in the Plastering Development Center at Chicago, O. Huntley of St. Louis, the Venzie Corporation of

Philadelphia, and others. The materials and methods are, however, regularly employed as primary elements of load-bearing structures in theatrical and display construction work. Traditionally, stage scenery, amusement parks and expositions of various types have made wide use of plaster where the structural versatility and economy of the craft have been exploited fully. For example, much of the delightful fantasy of Disneyland in Southern California, would have been impossible without stucco, lath and plaster. Many exposition buildings primarily constructed of plasterwork have long outlived their original temporary purpose, and many such buildings have had major influence on the development of architectural design.

Metal lath, of course, is widely used as combined reinforcement and centering for concrete floor decks, and is installed by lathers. Similarly, gypsum and portland cement, both of which are plaster cements, are used in structural concretes and deck construction. It can be noted that the materials and methods employed by these crafts do produce structural characteristics of great value which are used architecturally in semi-structural forms such as walls, partitions, and the like. Farther on in this chapter an extended discussion of potential structural uses of lath and plaster work will be found.

Fire protection and other special uses. Membrane fireproofing (this is discussed in detail in Chapter 9) is one of the most important uses of lath and plaster. Excellent protective performance is obtained with great economy in material, labor and structural weight. To the designer, maximum flexibility and multi-purpose employment of materials are among the important advantages of lath and plaster. With proper calculation and control, fire protection, acoustical treatment, sound isolation and some degree of thermal insulation can be incorporated into a finished structure serving other architectural purposes as well. Plaster is also commonly used as the panel material for radiant heating systems in ceilings and walls. Acoustics, thermal characteristics and radiant heating are discussed in detail in Chapter 8.

Possible future uses

Without presuming insight into the yet unexplored, an extension of construction application can easily be envisioned for lath and plaster that would include most of the structural and semi-structural functions of enclosure. With architectural imagination unrestricted by lack of technical reference, the plastic wonders that might thus be created appear to be limited only by the time and funds available for development. The opportunities offered in plaster for economical, mechanical placement of mass in an enclosure utilizing materials in their most elementary forms, water, cement and aggregate, over lath reinforcement armatures — seem to offer new avenues to the complete "industralization" of building construction. There appears to be no limit to the design uses that can be made of these materials as a primary building element; in fact, there seems to be no real obstacle to the construction of entire buildings in this way.

There are aesthetic as well as utilitarian needs for plaster. Recent developments in architectural philosophy place new emphasis on form and space and less on sentimental regard for the distinctive characteristics of particular materials. Plaster, in turn, is now being used in ways recognizing its own distinctive, intrinsic qualities. In addition to a purer interest in the relationships of form and space, some influential contemporary designers have begun a return to ornament. To be sure, not to the stereotyped forms of the traditional styles; rather, the movement constitutes a protest against the endless monotony of severely simple planar surfaces and the unselected, uncontrolled textures of so-called "natural materials". The first examples of this trend that come to mind are to be seen in the grill work of the U.S. Embassy in Bangkok, Thailand, designed by John Carl Warnecke and in recent buildings by architect Edward D. Stone. Other examples can be observed in the increasing use of mosaic tile and other colorful materials in surface decoration, masonry shadow patterns, and embossed metal curtain walls.

Notwithstanding the increased usefulness of plaster to architecture in conventional construction, the most exciting prospect of all is the impact these materials are destined to have on the future of design. The so-called plastic design theories are drawing an ever-increasing interest from the profession. The architectural desire for freedom from rectilinear form imposed by the sticks and stones of conventional construction methods is persistent and fundamental. In the directions indicated by Le Corbusier in his Chapel at Ronchamps, France, (Fig. 6) we can sense the formulation of a new set of aesthetic values which may well be of historical importance.

This possibility is further dramatized by the work of the thin-shell structural experimentalists — engineer Felix Candela and others — as well as the many possibilities for freedom of space definition and plasticity of form to be seen in the recent work of Kiesler and Johansen (Figs. 1 and 2). The attention of architects and architectural scholars to the opportunities offered by this approach to design is apparent not only in the increasing space devoted to the subject in architectural journals, but also in the work of design students in schools of architecture all over the world. The trends in student design work have long been accepted as a barometer of design fashion, and it is unimportant to us whether this phenomenon is the result of the influence of their advanced thinking teachers or whether it is of indigenous origin. What *is* important is that many architectural scholars agree that the familiar formed, reinforced concrete construction is not the method by which the ultimate fruits of this movement will be borne. Conventionally placed concrete is not, in the true sense of the word, a plastic form material. Its plasticity of form is completely limited by the containing formwork into which it is poured. It is obvious that while the currently fashionable long-span, concrete thin-shell expresses economy in the use of material, any actual economic advantage is offset by the cost of the formwork required to support the curvilinear surface while it cures, and by the expensive field precision required for the placement of reinforcing metal.

The construction methods already developed and regularly employed in the lathing and plastering trades on the other hand, provide an opportunity to eliminate formwork completely by using the reinforcement itself as a form, after the manner of the sculptor's armature. Those architects who have depended repeatedly on the ingenuity of the lather to improvise complex interior structures know well that he has the skills and enthusiasm for the fundamental act of construction. It was the lather who built, often without the architect's instruction, the false vaults placed in the rectangular spaces of our cathedrals. It is also he who produces formed ceilings and constructs the imaginative display work of our amusement parks and theaters. The lather belongs to one of the few remaining trades that can, as a matter of course, establish lines and levels, lay out work and engineer methods of assembly.

With the increasing prevalence of mechanical application methods and continued improvement in these techniques, there is good reason for hoping that one direction toward the industrialization of the building process lies somewhere within reach of architects by way of the lathing and plastering trades. In fact, if we agree that the industrialization of the building process and the resulting economies in the cost of enclosure are necessary and inevitable, we can ignore neither the plastic form theories of design nor, therefore, these skills and materials. From disappointing experience with current central prefabrication methods and other similar attempts at the industrialization of building, we can expect much from this approach which places no weight-strength limitation upon the mass of the enclosure. This industrial method may be able to produce buildings which do not resemble vehicles, since they will not have been produced by methods originally conceived for that purpose. For while aesthetic judgments normally associated with the airplane may permit, or demand, the frank expression in design of the light, flexible construction required of this vehicle's function, we normally require of our buildings a stouter sense of shelter and security.

The total efficiency of an enclosure of light structural framework, shipped to the job collapsed and then quickly erected, upon which the covering mass is sprayed while in the cheapest and most rudimentary state of the materials, appears obvious and presents a challenge to the designer difficult for him to ignore.

The wholesale abandonment by architects of traditional aesthetic values and established design principles that would apparently be necessary to the immediate and complete exploitation of plastic form construction, is neither advocated nor anticipated. Furthermore, extension of the usefulness to architects of the skills and materials of these trades does not depend upon so drastic a revolution. Many aesthetic and philosophical considerations of importance, which concern far more conventional design matters, can be explored in terms of the influence that lath and plaster have had, and can have, on the development of architecture. Some of these are discussed in the essay written expressly for this manual by the perceptive architectural critic, Dr. Charles W. Moore.

II. PLASTER IN ARCHITECTURE

An Illustrated Essay by Charles W. Moore, Associate Professor, College of Architecture, University of California

This essay is written in the conviction that we can learn from the past — indeed, that it is already a part of us, and that we cannot avoid learning from it. It follows that a look at the uses of plaster in the past should throw light onto our own attempts to benefit from new uses of it in the future. None of us, certainly, is interested in historical material assembled into a source convenient to copy from. Nor is it necessary to establish plaster's legitimacy by belaboring its antiquity (the Egyptians used it). If, however, a look at its uses in the past can point to some needs that these uses were created

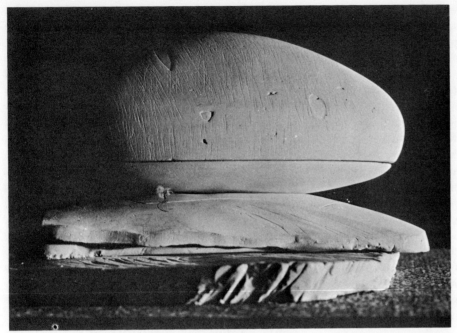

Photograph by Percy Rainford

Fig. 1 — The Endless House — Architect, Frederick Kiesler

Fig. 2 — Spray Form House No. 2 — Architect, John M. Johansen

to fill, and if the needs in some measure coincide with our own, as we might expect them to, we may well be able to benefit from the experience of others.

The experience of others with plastic materials extends over a long period. Plastic materials and "plastic form" must have entered the human consciousness when someone discovered that a handful of moist clay would change its form under the pressure of his fingers, and then would retain the form that bore his imprint. Since the first discovery that a layer of plastic material spread over a rough surface would create a smooth one, or that a layer of plastic material spread over a complicated set of shapes would simplify them, plastic material has been applied, indoors and out. And since someone first discovered, on the other hand, that these same plastic materials could be fashioned into shapes which could make building surfaces more interesting, they have been pressed or cast into decorative shapes, and applied to enrich the simplicity of architectural forms.

Plaster is one of the most important of these plastic materials. As a building material, its special quality is its ability to take and retain the form impressed upon it, or upon which it is impressed. As it happens, during the last half-century architects and critics have been paying particular attention to the "nature of materials" and its expression in architecture. There has been strong insistence on the need for a stone building to demonstrate its stoniness, or a brick building its brickiness. Into such an atmosphere, plaster does not fit very well; its essential quality is not its "plasteriness", but its ability to take — and make — architectural forms. Our own development of the uses of plaster, it seems likely, will then be a product of an interest in and a search for form, at least partly for its own sake. This search for form — on the one hand, through the simplification and clarification of shapes that are complex or confusing, and on the other, through the enrichment of shapes that are too simple to interest us — should be our concern here. Examples are available to us from a wide variety of times and places: through the ancient Near East

and in Egypt, plaster was used to make surfaces smooth for decoration. The Romans used it both in smooth walls, and to make sculptured relief. It appears in Romanesque churches and in Renaissance palaces. Finally, in the late Baroque and Rococo periods in western Europe and America it became the basis for a whole system of design, even as much earlier the Moors in Spain had based an entirely different system of design on its use. Chronologically, we should note, the development of our own plastering traditions seemed, to late nineteenth century historians of the craft, no development at all, but rather a retrogression from the exuberant heights of expression reached late in the Middle Ages by the plasterer himself. Gradually since then, they lamented, designs had become more and more specific when they came from the architect until, in the nineteenth century, ready-cast plaster decorative elements which the plasterer on the job needed only to install, and the craftsman's initiative has almost vanished. Now, with handicraft processes stifled more than ever by the increasing industrialization of the entire building industry, we are in need of a whole new evaluation, the tear shed so eloquently by the nineteenth century for the departure of the "happy" medieval craftsman need not be shed again. Our own techniques can scarcely be turned backward in time. But the ways people in the past (and the past extends up to the present moment) have used plaster in their search for architectural form, and the successes which met their efforts are nonetheless illuminating. We are fortunate that there are so many examples to look among.

The creation of plastic form, and the articulation of form

As we have noted, there seem to be two principal ways to compose buildings. There seem too, to be two ways to make use of materials: whether buildings are composed by simplifying complex forms, or by enriching simple ones they are either put together of separate pieces, or they are made of something continuous. Ordinarily, the separate pieces fastened together best result in a series of straight line forms, distinguished from one another; that is to say, the forms are "articulated". On the other hand, it seems desirable to emphasize the continuity of continuous materials, so that smooth curves lead from one surface to another, and angles do not break the flow of the eye over the form. The resultant curved continuous shapes may thus express the quality of plasticity which was the original nature of the material, and reinforce the impression that the material has been squeezed into place. A piece of plastic material squeezed into a round ball is a very different thing from a Chinese wood-block puzzle whose separate pieces interlock into a round ball. Although they have the same shape, only the former is "plastic". And even plastic materials, like poured concrete, which are put into place between forms of non-plastic materials, are apt to seem non-plastic, as they retain the shape imposed on them.

In the American past, which offers mostly examples of buildings made of pieces of wood, masonry, or metal, it would not be difficult to conclude that articulated form, resulting from the expression of pieces put together, was the norm, and plastic form an aberration. The 1957 Progressive Architecture Award Jury, for instance, thought it wise to withhold prizes from two buildings by John M. Johansen which it admired, because their plastic forms, so different from standard building shapes, seemed to the Jury to be fraught with the danger of being repeated by unskilled hands (Fig. 2). This conclusion, though, would be hasty; the history of American building is full of examples of continuous form. The Southwest American tradition of building, for example, with adobe bricks covered with renewed layers of mud plaster, has for centuries produced buildings with curved surfaces, rounded at the corners, which look as though they had been modeled or squeezed into shape. The Ranchos de Taos church in New Mexico, built in 1776 (Fig. 3) is such an example. In the Eastern United States, especially in the decades following 1870, even wood shingles were applied as a continuous flowing skin, which created the impression of plastic forms (Fig. 4). Contemporary with these plastic forms of shingle, the heavy masonry forms of H. H. Richardson, Furness and Hewitt, and other architects, though they were pieced together of separate stones, created forms which seemed carved from a single block, and therefore seemed continuous. Techniques following on the development of metal lath and new methods of blowing concrete and plaster onto it might well give new importance to plastic forms in the architecture of our own time.

The use of plaster does not depend entirely on the creation of plastic form. Today, in fact, plaster appears in millions of houses and offices on planar surfaces divided by angular corners; it appears, in fact much more frequently this way than as a material which creates plastic forms. But if we are to distinguish the ways plaster has been used in the past, and could be used to advantage in our own work, the differences between the two uses become important. New techniques increase our ability to create plastic forms, and a glance at the architectural periodicals indicates a growing interest in these forms during the last several years. Just possibly, this is happening because the designer, separated by a lengthening set of mechanical processes from a finished product, feels the need to achieve the same kind of immediacy as exists between the hands of the potter and the work that takes shape under his fingers. The creation of a set of forms which seem as though they had been squeezed and patted into place helps fill this need. Then, for the designer, there are still other reasons to create plastic forms: these forms create a continuity of structure, of experience, and of movement of light; they intensify a sense of enclosure, while they render unclear the relation of the observer to the space he is in; and they can heighten a sense of movement.

Continuity of structure is important even in stressed-skin systems made of plywood and other unit materials. It is generally essential to a structure made of plastic materials. In such a structure, as we know, stresses do not act neatly at right angles to one

Charles W. Moore

Fig. 3 — Front — Ranchos DeTaos Church, New Mexico

another, around right-angled corners. Instead, a force applied at any point in the system creates lines of force which flow through the structure. Natural forms such as morning glories, turtles and walnuts, as the structural engineer Fred Severud has pointed out, are curved; and while "we cannot . . . completely abandon right angles and straight lines in favor of nature's curves . . . what we can and should do is to understand that her use of curves is merely the expression of a principle of structural continuity; and this latter quality is what distinguishes her de-

signs". A multi-story rectilinear cage, on the one hand, which is an adequate demonstration of the structural nature of steel is not a particularly reasonable form in concrete, because it is unrelated to the structural nature of the plastic material; and for people in the middle of the twentieth century, interested in an honest indication of the nature of the structure, a serious dilemma has appeared, which must be resolved. In the works of such engineers as Pierluigi Nervi, (Fig. 5) on the other hand, or of others interested in the structural properties of con-

Photo by Berenice Abbott

Fig. 4 — Stoughton House, Cambridge, Mass. — Architect, H. H. Richardson

From *Structures*, Nervi, P. L., New York, © 1956 F. W. Dodge Corp.

Fig. 5 — Turin Exhibition Building Pier Luigi Nervi

crete, men like Felix Candela or Eduardo Torroja, the shapes are related to the curved lines of flow of the stresses, and are generally continuous; the plastic form works to indicate the nature of the structure.

Another characteristic beginning to emerge in the middle of the twentieth century is a special concern with the observer's reaction to a building over a period of time, so that the whole process of arriving at a building, of seeing it from far away and up close, from a variety of angles, represents part of one continuing experience, in which the forms instigate the observer's movement, so that one view slides into another. At Le Corbusier's chapel at Ronchamp, for instance, (Fig. 6) each façade folds into the next, and even the façade full of windows set into deep reveals is arranged so that the observer inside, drawn by the desire to see through each window, is impelled from place to place. The curved tower, on the left as one approaches, turns around the corner to become, with only the slightest break in the continuity, the gargoyle-accented west wall, which in turn slides smoothly around a curve to become a tower

Photo Lucien Hervé. Courtesy Frederick A. Praeger, Inc.

Fig. 6 — Wall, Chapel at Ronchamps — Architect, Le Corbusier

for the smaller chapel. This simple continuous experience of one surface is enlivened by variations in the texture of the plaster, and by the constant modulation of the light that falls on it.

A third concern, which is only now beginning to interest us is for the continuity of movement of light; if movement of light is to have continuity, a continuous plastic form for it to fall on is strongly indicated.

Earlier in this century, it was as if light and the sun had .newly been discovered; glass walls opened up to face the sun, and the more light that came in, the better. Now the decorative screen has intervened, so that the light from the outdoors is tempered, and patterns of light and shade are formed on the walls and floors inside, as they had been in the eighteenth century church at Wies, in Southern Germany (Fig. 7). When patterns of light fall, the nature of the surface they fall on becomes important; it can be smooth and simple, as at Wies, to emphasize the pattern falling; it can be smooth but not planar, as is evident in other parts of the picture of Wies, so as to add variations to the patterns; or it can introduce, as the Alhambra in Granada, a pattern in counterpoint to the pattern of light (Fig. 8). In any of these cases, an important characteristic of the light that makes the patterns, if it is sunlight, is that it changes its direction from minute to minute, from hour to hour, and from season to season. Here the continuity of plastic form again offers the opportunity to take advantage of movement of light, as it slides gradually from surface to surface. The interlocking plastic forms of the light-intercepting screens of Erwin Hauer are among the very few contemporary attempts to take advantage of this opportunity (Fig. 9). For decades, though, the apse of the church at Ranchos de Taos, New Mexico (Fig. 10) has been a favorite subject for painters because of the way the sun slides across its surface during the day, forming changing shadows and picking out, as its rays become almost parallel with the wall, the concavities and the subtle curves of the adobe plaster, and its irregular texture. The

Charles W. Moore

Fig. 7 – Detail, 18th Century Church at Wies, Southern Germany

nave at Wies (Fig. 11) is an even subtler demonstration: here a pattern of light shining past other forms falls onto the multiple surfaces of the wall, creating a fascinating double modulation of the pattern. The same kind of effect occurs at a larger scale, as the light, patterned by the shape of the South windows of the nave, the floor, and the wall beyond, and picks up the leading edges of plaster decorations, so that even within a few minutes, as the sun moves through the sky, the movement of light on the plaster forms makes the space come alive.

Charles W. Moore

Fig. 8 — Alhambra, Granada, Patio De Los Leones Cupola

Fig. 9 — Concrete Trellises, Architect, Erwin Hauer

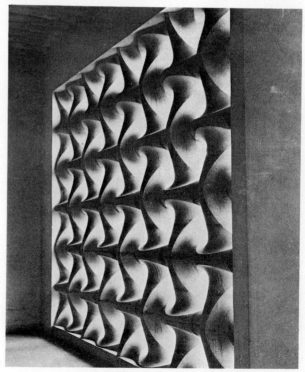

Courtesy Erwin Hauer

Charles W. Moore

*Fig. 10 — Apse, Rancho
De Taos Church*

Fig. 11 — Nave, 18th Century Church at Wies

Charles W. Moore

A second reason to create plastic form is in order to intensify enclosure, to create areas in which the intellectual relation of the observer to the space around him is destroyed, but his emotional relation to the space in enhanced. "There is," as Heinrich Wölfflin pointed out, "a beauty which has its roots just in the not fully comprehensible, in the mystery which never quite unveils its face, in the unassimilable which seems to change at every moment." Trinity Church in Newport, Rhode Island, built in 1725 and Touro Synagogue, also in Newport, built in 1763, create in their beautifully proportioned interiors such a dissolution of intellectual relationship with the space. In each of them a system of columns and entablature, painted white, rises for perhaps three-fourths the height of the space. The carefully defined members of this trabeated system bear, down to the last molding, a directly measurable relation one to another, and to the human observer. But above these columns and entablatures there is, in each building, a simple smooth blue-green plaster vault, which suggests a vast indefinite incommensurable space very like the sky, a kind of reasonable infinity.

Plastic forms, as well as rendering unclear the sense of forms receding, can intensify the sense of enclosure. The cave-like, womb-like form seems more effective than any other for providing the reassuring sense of solidity at one's back, a sense whose absence is suddenly coming to be noticed. John MacL. Johansen's project for a house with a plastic shape, mentioned before (Fig. 2), or especially Frederick Kiesler's "Endless House," (Fig. 1) illustrate the ability of plastic forms to produce buildings which, though small, are not oppressive because their size is unclear. Because of their cave-like continuous forms, they provide a sense of enclosure which is phenomenal.

A third reason to create plastic forms, a reason which other times have understood, perhaps better than our own does, is in order to suggest movement, or to abstract the movement which our eyes and minds experience when they search out a space, and imagine themselves around it and through it. Our reaction to spaces can be explained by this empathetic process, through which we imagine ourselves, when we enter a space, projected up and out into the space, searching out its farthest dimensions. This empathetic process causes us, too, to project ourselves into the structure, which perhaps helps account for our thinking of Gothic piers as rising, rather than as pressing down into the ground as they actually do. The imagined motion, like expressed lines of stress, is likely to have a pattern of flow made up of curves rather than of angles and straight lines. Such suggested motion can flow around the outside of a curved form as well as into or through an enclosure, as the example from Ronchamp (Fig. 6) demonstrates.

The next step in the suggestion of movement comes with the desire to get the forms themselves into apparent motion. It is a desire, surprisingly, which our own architecture does not yet often show, although the sweeping forms of our new superhighways have a hold on the public imagination which the static "architectural" forms at their sides do not possess. (On the highways, to be sure, the mind's imagined sweep through space can be physically duplicated at the wheel of a car.) Some new buildings come, ostensibly by way of structure, to forms which seem to move: Eero Saarinen's hockey rink at Yale University, for instance, (Fig. 12) suggests rather more motion even than the very plastic Einstein Tower of Eric Mendelsohn, built in 1921. But in order best to discover the conscious development of forms which seem to move, we must look to the buildings of central Europe of the seventeenth and especially the eighteenth centuries, when the plaster masterpieces of the later Baroque and Rococo periods were conceived. In the Würzburg Residenz, for example, are pilasters and a cartouche, (Fig. 13) delicately formed of plaster, but caught up nonetheless in an illusion of wild writhing. The background of the cartouche swells broadly, then divides itself with fine furrows and curls up again. Consoles curl over the cornice, and feathery leaf forms flutter down over the doorway; other forms slide and dance down the pilasters, and whirl around the candelabra, while out from behind the swelling cartouche prickle spiked objects. More than that, in the architecture of this period, whole interiors swirl into motion: the nave of the pilgrimage church of Vierzehnheiligen, in Southern Germany (Fig. 14), comes into moving life, and the façade of San Carlo alle Quattro Fontane, in Rome, (Fig. 15) symmetrically organized as it is, weaves in and out. In the nineteenth and early twentieth century work of Gaudi, such as the Casa Botllo, in Barcelona, (Fig. 16) as symmetrical organization and simple geometric forms are discarded, and the plastic shapes become more free,

the movement becomes more complex — and more violent — than ever.

Movement is reason, then, for the creation of plastic form; the provision of aggressive enclosure, with a simultaneous unclearness of the space enclosed, is a second reason; and the desire for continuity of structure, of experience, and of movement of light is a third reason for the creation of such forms. The creation of plastic form is by no means synonymous with the use of plaster; stone, concrete, clay and many other materials beside plaster can create such form, and the use of plaster on forms which are not plastic is, as we have noted,

Baltazar Korab

Fig. 12 — Hockey Rink, Yale University — Architect, Eero Saarinen

Charles W. Moore

Fig. 13 — Cartouche, Würzburg Residenz

As soon as forms begin to take shape in the mind of the designer, then the development process begins, either simplifying complex ideas and forms to bring order and clarity to them, or amplifying simple forms, to bring richness to them. Through both these processes, the neutral material can give form to the designer's idea.

The clarification of form

In a complex world, a world of complex architectural programs and a riot of complex forms, the process of simplification should be of vast importance to the designer. The plan complexity of a hospital program, for instance, demands an orderly modular repetitive unit if the solution is to be comprehensible to the eye and the mind. Just so, the visual complexity of almost any urban scene requires simplification and organization, if the eye and the mind of the observer are to be satisfied. Articulated forms can be simplified ordinarily so as to emphasize whatever rhythm is inherent in the way the pieces are put together; plastic forms can be simplified, too, so as to emphasize basic rhythms and relationships in space.

For the clarification of articulate form there is required the establishment of an order in which parts maintain their own identity, but are organized into units, which in turn are combined (without loss of the identity of the unit) into the whole. It is important, for clarity, that the parts be commensurate, and that their relation to the unit of which they are a part be understandable. The Chinese long ago formulated for these purposes the "law of five". In a set of observations corresponding closely with those of more recent Gestalt psychologists, they noted that it is impossible instantly to understand a relationship among more than five objects. It would follow, then, that for clarity each unit should be made up of not more than five separate parts, and should combine into a larger unit of not more than five such parts. For clarity, too, the identities of the separate units must be maintained, and insisted on. The recessed joint, increasingly in evidence, is a

common. It is important to us, however, to distinguish between the kind of desires which produce plastic forms, and those which produce articulated forms just because plaster is such an extremely flexible material, because it can do, and has done such a wide variety of things that its use does not suggest specific forms. Indeed, instead of letting his material determine the form, as a steel beam or rough stone determines form, the designer using plaster must decide himself, on these other bases, what kind of forms he wants. If there is in these pages a particular emphasis of plastic form, it is because recently it has received little emphasis elsewhere and because the future of plaster in its creation looks particularly promising.

Charles W. Moore

Fig. 14 — Nave, Church of Vierzehnheiligen, Southern Germany

Fig. 15 — Facade, San Carlo Alle Quattro Fontane, Rome

Reprinted by permission of the publishers. From Sigfried Gideon's *Space Time and Architecture, the Growth of a New Tradition*, Third Edition, Enlarged and Revised; Cambridge, Mass. Harvard University Press, Copyright 1941, 1949, 1954 by the President and Fellows of Harvard College.

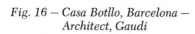

Fig. 16 — Casa Botllo, Barcelona —
Architect, Gaudi

means for separating panels from one another by a small recess, instead of hiding the separation with a molding. In this way the panel is established as surface in its own right, so that attention falls onto its proportions and on the plane of its surface. In an example in Los Angeles by Richard Neutra, (Fig. 17) the proportions and the plane surfaces of the plaster shapes are emphasized by their isolation from one another, either in depth or, when they occur in the same plane, by the glass walls. In a Japanese example, (Fig. 18) on the other hand, a complex wall surface achieves clarity by its use of plaster wall panels as negative elements. No clear planes of plaster are established by any definition at the edges; instead the insistence is entirely on the dark wood forms, balancing one another in acrobatic symmetry. Numerous examples in western Europe since the Renaissance have used the same negative quality of plaster panels, by putting them between pilasters of the same material, in order to throw emphasis onto the proportions of the pilastered bays, onto their relation to the window openings within them, and onto the proportions of the whole façade, of which the bays are a part.

To clarify plastic forms, the designer must shift his attention from planes and their edges to volumes, so that the attention of the observer will be drawn to the relationships of solid forms in space. Greek island villages, such as Mykonos, (Fig. 19) are, for their size, extremely complex aggregations of tiny dwelling units and even tinier churches, with tortuous paths of circulation winding among them. If these complexes were built of a variety of materials, or even of a few materials which called attention to themselves, the visual result would be sheer chaos. As it is, however, a coat of plaster painted white is applied to almost all the surfaces and the result is an exciting kind of visual order. In Alberobello, in Southern Italy, the coating is simply a lime wash, applied frequently. The result at both places is that the emphasis is all on the forms themselves, and on their relationships in space. Added to this is the tactile pleasure suggested by the plaster; it acts as though it has been patted into place, and wel-

comes further patting. The very whiteness, accented by an occasional blue door or window frame, increases the contrast between sun and shadow, so as to put more emphasis than ever on forms standing in space. The detailing is crucial to this impression of solid forms: in contradistinction to the kind of recessed joint which emphasizes the fragmentation of planes, at Mykonos the planes merge into one another, so that a sharp angle is avoided, the juncture is almost lost, and the sense, as at the Ranchos de Taos church, (Fig. 10) is not of planes but of solids. Even when changes of material occur, as they occasionally do in Greek island villages such as Mykonos, the order brought about by the continuous surface material persists. Often, for instance, the whitewash on parts of a wall of rubble stone merges with the white plaster areas of wall, so that in the bright sun the only variation is the appearance of shadows where the rubble walls cut back out of the sun. The sense of order which comes from the continuous material brings visual calm to the riot of complex form.

A sophisticated version of this play of forms in space against the unifying element of a single plaster texture, used almost everywhere, appears in the rear view of Le Corbusier's Chapel at Ronchamp, (Fig. 6) where sun, shadow and oblique light play on the plastic forms of the curving wall and on the bulge in it. Here the strong sense of the total form is modified but not destroyed by the recessed joints where the curved wall meets the towers. The recesses create a sense of separation among the varying shapes of the wall, so that there does not seem to be one surface with an irregular bit taken out of it, as the absolutely unbroken combination of towers and wall would otherwise have produced. On the other hand, these recesses are not so strong that they overcome the powerful continuous curved flow of the wall and tower; they do not fragment the sense of the whole as one plastic solid. They modulate it without destroying it, which is a very sophisticated accomplishment indeed. The same subtlety of modulation without contrast is to be seen in the introduction of unsurfaced concrete forms under the

Courtesy Richard Neutra

Fig. 17 — Heath House, Los Angeles — Architect, Richard Neutra

Fig. 18 — Japanese House

Courtesy Norman F. Carver, Jr.

Fig. 19 —
Island of Mykonos —
Double Vaulted Church
and House (Foreground)

Dan Branch

downspout. The color and texture of the exposed concrete underline the fact that the walls are not concrete but rough-textured plaster. The plaster, therefore, is not the negative foil for the positive wood, as it was in our Japanese example, (Fig. 18). Instead it receives some attention for itself as well as for the form it creates — but not very much. It is the form which is important.

The work of some twentieth-century sculptors, particularly Constantin Nivola, illustrates the same unification of disparate forms with a consistent negative material, a sand-textured plaster. As it is used at the Olivetti showroom, in New York (whose architects were Belgioloso, Peressutti and Rogers) joints between plaster panels establish a rhythm in the wall without destroying the powerful plastic continuity of the sculptural forms.

A much different use of a plastic volume, designed to show itself as the simplest possible mass in bright desert sunshine, occurs in a new store for Joseph Magnin in Las Vegas, Nevada (Fig. 20) by Victor Gruen. Here the problem was to try to vie with an urgent and chaotic set of roadside signs; the solution was the simplest possible block, with an overall plaster texture, and with surfaces merging into one another, so as to emphasize their solidity (against the dancing signs nearby) and to create an almost primitive strength of presence which, like the buildings of Mykonos, would carry a sense of calm, as an antidote to the chaos around. A complex program housed in a smooth plastered shell has been rendered almost as simple as it can become.

The enrichment of form

Architecture complicated by budgets, schedules, limited land, and other restrictions of space, time and money is, in our own day, rather more in need of simplification and clarification than of the counter processes, amplification and enrichment. But our age has developed a set of "pure" and simple forms, and now we feel strongly the need

to enrich these forms, to make the simple complex. At this juncture we run headlong into three problems, whose common quality seems to be that they all have to do with time. There is first, the problem of the value of the craftsman's time, second, the problem introduced by the need we feel for expressing the relationship of the product to the time during which it was created, and third, the problem of the changes wrought by time and the elements after the building is built.

To an historian of the plasterer's trade, such as William Millar, the whole "development" of English plaster from late medieval times to the twentieth century is in some important ways no development at all, but rather a decline, as the freedom of the early plasterer to create his patterns as he worked was gradually removed. The early designs of the English plasterer were his own creation (Fig. 21); he was artist as well as executor. Then some of the design initiative was taken from him, and he was put to work interpreting the design of someone else, an architect. Finally, the crucial parts of the design became prefabricated units, which the plasterer merely inserted, and he was left with only the simpler routine areas to work. It is easy enough to regard the process as inexorable decline, and to regard the mid-twentieth century state of affairs, which would hardly allow for any hand-done ornamental plasterwork at all, as the absolute end of the art. What has happened, of course, is a decline only from one point of view. The emphasis has shifted; the plasterer, like everyone else in industry and the building trades, must produce a great deal more than his medieval counterpart did if he is to earn the correspondingly greater return which is his in our society. Some sort of multiple production does seem indicated. Richard Neutra points out in *Survival Through Design* that our society, unlike former ones, does not regard uniqueness as essential to quality. An item of value in the Renaissance was the only one of its kind; our machines turn out quantities of identical products, all of them "perfect" within extremely close tolerances, so that the perfection which resulted from extreme manual skill

Fig. 20 — Joseph Magnin Store, Las Vegas — Architect, Victor Gruen

creating the unique object has lost some of its value. Indeed, as Neutra notes, although the pre-machine craftsman applied his labors toward making a round pot perfectly round, we are frighteningly likely to make the round pot lopsided, in order to make clear that it has been "hand-crafted". A plasterer cannot ordinarily work all day perfecting the surface of a tiny area, by hand, if his day's labors are to earn him the house, car, washing machine, steak, and other manifestations of the "good life" which can be his.

In this situation, one of the notions which has disappeared is that plaster is useful to imitate some more expensive material, like marble. It is simply not worthwhile for a well-paid man to work the imitative material by hand. Unfortunately, no such restriction applies to products of the machine, and we have an increasing array of surface materials in imitation of everything from wood to gold mosaic. But, during the last century the notion has gained force that the "nature of materials" is worth considering, so in our best work what looks like wood is wood, and what looks like stone is really stone. This was not always the case, and numberless historical

From *Plastering, Plain & Decorative,* Wm. Millar, London, Batsford, 1899

Fig. 21 — Early Designs of the English Plasterer

examples exist of plaster carefully formed and painted to look like wood or marble, as well as of stone carefully cut and joined to look very much like plaster.

Beside the kind of time for which the craftsman is so well paid, there is a second kind of time, the time required for the creative act, which seems to be more important to us, perhaps on account of the remarkably accelerated tempi of our lives, than it has ever been before in the West. Since in China for centuries the visual arts have been intimately related to the passage of time, it is there that we can turn for some parallels with our own urgencies. In China, for instance, the media used for painting — brush, ink and silk or absorbent paper — establish that the visual form of a painting will be determined by the speed of its creation, since an ink-loaded brush drawn swiftly across the paper produces a very different shape from the one that results if the brush is allowed to hesitate. It is not impossible that this whole set of materials was found sympathetic because the painters were likely to be not humble craftsmen, but calligrapher-litterateur-courtier-officials, whose time, however calmly passed, was valuable. Chinese stories abound in which the famous painter, ordered by the Emperor to paint a thousand miles of Yangtze scenery, spent years in thoughtful reflection (with perhaps a province or two to run on the side) until at length, the night before the Emperor's patience was about to run out, he suddenly painted a shorthand representation which so evoked all that stretch of Yangtze that the Emperor was speechless with amazement.

This kind of urgency of activity is evident in some of the work of Picasso or Matisse or Klee and seems to be of special interest to our high-speed generation. Even the Western past, moreover, offers examples of artistic activity conditioned by time, when time influenced the medium itself. In such a technique as fresco, for example, tempera colors are applied to plaster while it is still wet; plaster background and applied colors then dry together. This ordinarily produces a far different expression from, say, oil paint on canvas, which can be worked and reworked over an indefinite period of time. The Roman "Impressionistic" technique, for instance, in the Yellow Frieze in the House of Livia (Fig. 22) with such realistic sparkle at a distance is evidently,

a top layer of plaster is spread over an underlayer of contrasting color, and then while the upper layer is still wet, portions of it are scraped away to reveal the color of the layer below. The plaster façades of

From *Plastering, Plain & Decorative*, Wm. Millar, London, Batsford, 1899

Fig. 22 — Yellow Frieze — House of Livia

from close up, the product of a shorthand technique eminently suited to the relatively quick-setting medium. The simplicity of a Giotto fresco, too, may well be regarded as stemming from the techniques required by the plaster and the tempera, as they quickly set together (Fig. 23).

Another technique of surface decoration depending on the drying of plaster is graffito, in which

late Medieval English houses often used this technique. A recent example, a labyrinth at the Milan Triennale, designed by Belgioioso, Peressutti and Rogers, contains a graffito mural by Saul Steinberg (Fig. 24) which illustrates well the headlong quality that the drying plaster seems to generate.

In addition to the time contributed by the workmen, and the time of creation expressed in the

Fig. 23 — *Joachim & Anna Meet at the Golden Gate of Jerusalem — Giotto*

Fig. 24 — *Graffito Mural by Saul Steinberg, Labyrinth at Milan Triennale*

Courtesy Architectural Review

work of art itself, there is a third kind of time which must be considered in connection with the enrichment of form. That is the time which will pass after the building is built, while obsolescence sets in (which happens very rapidly, in our time), and while at the same speed as they always have, water, the sun, and dirt act on the building.

Plaster does not have, in our minds, the symbolic permanence of stone, although some extant plaster surfaces are thousands of years old, and even exterior plaster exposed to the English climate has lasted since the Middle Ages. We are more likely to remember what a plaster wall meant to be temporary, as on a world's fair building, looks like the year after (or what a struggle San Franciscans have had with the temporary plaster Palace of Fine Arts built for the season in 1915, and too beloved to be torn down yet). In other circumstances, however, plaster rather more protected from the elements, or of a more permanent sort, can improve its looks with age since simple unbroken surfaces can give rich play to the discolorations and textures of time. On simple buildings, such as the plastered adobes of the Southwest (Fig. 25) the very texture of time, the patterns made by waterborne dirt become a part of the enrichment. If the texture of the plaster is rough, as at Ronchamp, the accumulation of dirt assumes particular importance. And if the relation of the wall to the weather can undergo variations, on account of overhang, or change of exposure, patterns to enrich the surface are introduced at an entirely different scale.

With the three kinds of time in mind which can allow us to consider the enrichment of simple forms, we have occasion to note that, as buildings are "articulated" or "plastic," so the enrichment of them can be either, and plaster can be used in either way. Applied to surfaces either with traditional plasterer's tools, or with a machine, it can serve as plastic enrichment; and cast in blocks, it can be assembled as a set of interchangeable pieces. Mayan temples in Yucatan used stone in this way, in a series of blocks cut in a very limited number of standard shapes which functioned as abstract decoration, or

as the eyes, nose, mouth, and ears of a ritual mask when they are properly assembled. This system is of obvious interest to us on account of its simple interchangeable parts (parts whose counterparts could easily be made by us by machine) and the enrichment these simple parts are capable of producing. Perhaps the most impressive development of this idea occurred among the Moors in Spain. At the Alhambra, in Granada, the Court of the Two Sisters has a fantastically elaborated faceted ceiling composed of 5000 precast plaster blocks. The 5000 blocks which create this richly elaborated effect are of only seven different shapes, based on just three plan forms with similar curves in elevation, so that the pieces fit together in an incredible variety of ways (Fig. 26). The process, of achieving almost infinite variety from a set of almost identical parts, is of direct interest to us, as we begin to look, within the limits of the three kinds of time which concern us, toward the enrichment of our simple forms.

One of the recurring twentieth-century notions which could slow down this kind of enrichment is a narrow interpretation of the dictum that the "nature of materials" should be "expressed". This can mean that natural materials must be put together as little changed by the hand of man as possible; rubble stone wall and untreated wood, preferably sawn rough, are most acceptable. There is a curious notion based on this dictum that even manufactured materials, like steel I-beams, must manifest themselves as decorative as well as structural elements, undeviating from the state in which the standard product comes from the steel mill. But plaster does not come in any standard shape, so the import of this approach is to doubt that it has any nature and to mistrust it therefore. Central to plaster's nature, of course, is its ability to take almost any form, and it is this interest in *form,* succeeding the prejudices hinging on a narrow interpretation of the "nature of materials", which bodes well for a new understanding of neutral materials like plaster, materials which are capable of taking almost any form, without themselves attracting much attention.

Charles W. Moore

Fig. 25 — Plastered Adobes of the Southwest

Our interest in enriched form leads us, along the way, to an interest in the unadorned surface, calculated to give importance, by contrast, to enriched areas. Here the ability to create surfaces unbroken by joints is essential, since the forms of the enrichment must establish their own relationships of size and scale, and plaster, not subject to any modular unit size, is able to be formed into whatever surrounding the enrichment requires. At the Joseph Magnin store in Las Vegas, too (Fig. 20), the absence of visible joints, again contributes to the almost primitive monolithic strength of the statement.

With time in mind, and the weather, the faceting of surfaces implied in, for instance, the Alhambra becomes of particular importance, since the play of light and shadow is augmented by the play of dirty surfaces, where dirt can land but water cannot fall, against neutral surfaces, where dirt can cling but cannot settle, and water cannot fall, against clean surfaces, washed by the rain. These variations carefully exploited can bring added interest to the surface, and minimize the adverse effects of weathering and decay.

Articulated enrichment is of particular interest to us, because of the possibilities inherent in it for

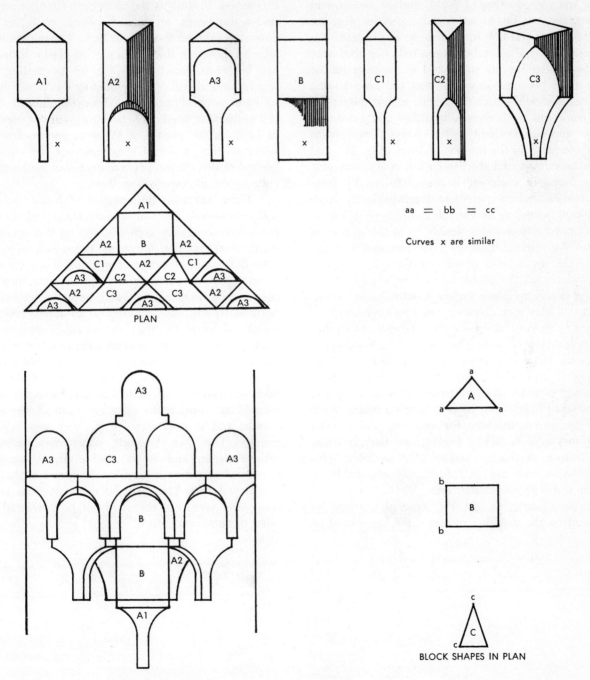

aa = bb = cc

Curves x are similar

BLOCK SHAPES IN PLAN

The Architectural Review

Fig. 26 — Component Blocks — Ceiling, Court of the Two Sisters, The Alhambra, Granada

the mass production of parts, and its consequent congruence with our industrial capacities. But the possibilities and the importance to us of plastic enrichment should not be minimized. For the same reasons that we are interested in creating plastic forms, it becomes important that the same plastic material should enrich the forms, so that the nature of the forms themselves is amplified and enhanced. The sense of continuity of the forms then remains unbroken, as in the interior of Wies (Fig. 11) and the movement of light becomes a continuous one. The sense of enclosure is not destroyed by fragmentation, and the movement suggested by the large building forms, as at Vierzehnheiligen (Fig. 14), is continued into the very details, as in the cartouche from Würzsburg which we have examined (Fig 13).

This continuous plastic enrichment, however, introduces all the problems in time which enrichment brings up in our society. Continuity of enrichment of this sort demands one-of-a-kind creation, since by its very nature it cannot be pieced together of prefabricated parts. The value of the craftsman's time becomes important, therefore, and the need arises to express his creative art as something happening in time. The craftsman, of course, is not limited to hand tools; he is as much a craftsman if he operates a machine for spraying plaster onto surfaces as if he held a trowel; and the variations of texture, of shadow and of form achieved with the larger tool are as full of meaning as those achieved with the smaller one.

As a matter of fact, the sense of urgency induced by the machine recreates the same kind of excitement in time as the absorbent Chinese paper under the brush, or the soft plaster changing its consistency under the graffito tools. The enrichment which follows on the techniques of plastic forming can be, as at Ronchamp, (Fig. 6) as exciting, as urgent, and as full of movement as the forms done by hand in another era, at Wies or Würzburg. But the underlying needs are the same, and the control of light on the plaster at Wies, or the control of water on the plaster of Ronchamp, or the built-in control of dirt on the plastered walls of an English cottage are all responses to them.

These notes on the creation of forms, plastic and articulated, on their simplification and clarification when they are complex, and on their enrichment when they are simple, are not meant to make rigid definitions of modes of working. They are not meant either to promote any special new uses of plaster. Since, on the one hand, however, plaster is particularly capable of taking on an almost infinite variety of forms (so that the design process must start with forms more especially than with the limitations of material) and since, on the other hand, plaster is an old material, and the world is full of its uses in response to demands for forms, it has seemed appropriate to examine some of the demands, and to note some of plaster's uses which resulted. Our own demands, which may be very much the same, and our own techniques, which will be very different, will suggest new uses for plaster, and new forms. They will be different from anything ever seen; but they will not be unrelated to what has gone on before.

CHAPTER 2

BASIC PLASTERING AND LATHING MATERIALS

The capabilities of lath and plaster are constantly expanding as new products and systems are introduced. The purpose of this chapter is to facilitate the selection of those materials most appropriate to specific needs by classifying and describing the types available. Further information of a more specific and proprietary nature may be found in the descriptive literature published by manufacturers' associations and individual manufacturers within the lathing and plastering industry.

It must be understood that abstract consideration of individual plastering and lathing components provides only an approximate knowledge of their behavior when chemically or physically combined with other components. Such an approximation, though extremely useful for initial selection, must be supplemented by further specific information before final appraisal of material selections can be made. These details are provided in later chapters. Plaster is composed basically of three materials: the cementitious material or binder, an inert filler

material or aggregate, and water. Occasionally other materials, termed admixtures, are added to modify the properties of plaster so that the material will conform more closely to particular requirements.

CEMENTITIOUS MATERIALS

The cementitious material is the active ingredient of a plaster mix since it undergoes a change in physical or chemical form during mixing and after application. The properties of the cementitious material determine to a large extent the characteristic qualities of the plaster mix.

Most plaster used today contains either gypsum, lime, or portland cement as the principal cementitious material. However, certain clays and other materials are used as the binder in some acoustical materials and other specialized products.

Gypsum. Gypsum is a naturally occurring sedimentary rock, gray, white or pink in color, that has been deposited in vast beds by the precipitation of calcium sulphate crystals from evaporating sea water. Deposits are found in abundance throughout the world and are either quarried in open pits or mined underground. The term "plaster of Paris," which denotes calcined gypsum, was derived from an unusually large bed of very pure gypsum which underlies the city of Paris, France. Large gypsum deposits of varying purity exist throughout the United States; those used for plaster production are between 85 per cent and 97 per cent pure.

The word "gypsum" is derived from the Greek *gypsos*, meaning gypsum or chalk. The first recorded use of gypsum plaster was that by the Egyptians who around 4000 B.C. applied it to the interior and exterior of the pyramids. In 1760 Benjamin Franklin first brought gypsum to notice in this country in the form of "land plaster," a coarsely ground gypsum used agriculturally as a soil conditioner.[1] But it was not until early in the twentieth century that gypsum came to be used extensively for building plaster. Prior to this time, no practicable commercial means had been found to control the time of set.

Between 8 and 9 million short tons of raw gypsum are mined or quarried annually in approximately 57 mines or quarries throughout this country, with Michigan, California, and Iowa ranking among the largest producing states.[2] Approximately 90 per cent of the gypsum produced is ultimately used in the building industries.

Manufacture of gypsum plaster from gypsum rock involves calcining or heating the previously crushed rock to temperatures of 250 to 300 degrees Fahrenheit. At these temperatures the combined water of crystallization, accounting for approximately 20 per cent by weight of the rock, dissociates. The process is usually continued until three-quarters of the combined water is driven off.

Keene's cement, used mainly in finishing plasters to obtain particularly dense, hard surfaces, is produced by heating crushed gypsum rock between 1000° F and 1400° F. At this temperature virtually all the water of crystallization is driven off. At this stage the product is termed anhydrous or "hard-burned" gypsum. In 1838 an Englishman, R. W. Keene, patented the process of adding small quantities of alum to this material to accelerate its otherwise extremely slow set. This modification of setting time made the material practical for general use and it became known as Keene's cement.

Recently it was discovered that gypsum calcined in the presence of water vapor, or aged artificially by adding certain salts during calcining, produces an extremely strong cement which makes it possible for plasters to have compressive strengths well in excess of 10,000 psi. This material is termed Alpha gypsum and from an experimental design point of view, represents a development of considerable interest.

After calcination, most gypsum designated for use as wall plaster is passed through a tube mill where it is ground uniformly to a fine powder. The plasticity or working quality of the plaster mortar is largely related to this milling operation. Additives to control set, stabilization, and other physical or chemical characteristics are thoroughly blended with the gypsum before packaging.

Gypsum is hydrous calcium sulphate in the dihydrate form. After losing three-quarters of its combined water during calcination it is termed hemihydrate. Hemihydrate, when mixed with water, recombines with approximately the same amount of water lost during calcination and reverts to the hard, rock-like crystalline form. This rehydration is called *setting action,* and the time which elapses between the addition of water to the gypsum and the start of the recrystallization is called *setting time.*

Other forms of gypsum occurring in nature are alabaster and selenite. Alabaster is a dense marble-like material, while selenite is a transparent substance of laminar construction. In certain sections of the United States, notably in the Southwest, a form of gypsum called "gypsite" is manufactured into plaster. Except for a red or brown color produced by a percentage of clay, plaster made from this material has properties approximating those of other gypsum plaster.

General Uses and Characteristics of Gypsum Plasters. Calcined gypsum is used both in basecoat and finish coat plasters. In basecoat work, calcined gypsum is combined with either sand or a lightweight aggregate or sometimes with a small amount of wood fiber. Gypsum basecoat plasters are available neat (that is, without aggregate) for job mixing or ready-mixed with aggregate, so that only water need be added at the job. The various gypsum basecoat plasters, their characteristics and uses are described farther on in this section.

In finish coat work calcined gypsum is used with lime putty as gauging to provide set and early strength, or is used alone either with or without addition of fine aggregate. Usually, Keene's cement is used in combination with lime putty for finish coats, but it has been used for basecoat work as well.

Gypsum plasters are suitable for all interior plastering uses except when they are exposed to free water or severe moisture conditions. Gypsum plaster can also be used in exterior locations such as ceilings of open porches and carports or eave soffits where it will not be directly exposed to water.

All gypsum plasters possess setting characteristics. The time of set is controlled during manufacture, usually by adding a *retarder,* so that after mixing, sufficient time will be provided for handling, application and finishing before the material begins to change from the plastic to the rigid state. It is believed that when water and calcined gypsum are mixed together a portion of the hemihydrate is dissolved. As solution continues, dihydrate crystals, similar to those in gypsum rock, precipitate out and, becoming more numerous, begin to interlock causing the mix to stiffen and finally harden.

Except for Keene's cement plaster, once gypsum plaster has started to harden, it cannot be retempered (that is, re-mixed with water). This agitation disturbs and disrupts crystal formation and results in greatly reduced strength.

Extension of time of set on the job by adding a retarder to the mortar must always be avoided ex-cept in rare instances where time or conditions absolutely preclude all other alternatives. Very small amounts of commercial retarder added to gypsum plaster will significantly alter time of set, but at the same time will significantly lower compressive and tensile strengths. Excessive addition of retarder will drastically reduce strength thereby impairing the integrity of the finished work and may also contribute to the defect known as "dryout" (see Chapter 6).

Gypsum, like all conventional plastering materials, is incombustible. In addition, the liberation of its chemically combined water at low temperatures enables it to prevent passage of intense heat for long periods. This property makes gypsum plaster particularly valuable as a fire retardant capable of preventing spread of fire and structural failure. The subject of membrane fireproofing with gypsum plaster is discussed in detail in Chapter 9.

Four types of Gypsum basecoat plasters.

Gypsum neat plaster is used for job mixing with aggregate and may be obtained fibered or unfibered, or specially formulated for use with lightweight aggregates and machine application.

Gypsum ready-mixed plaster consists of calcined gypsum and an aggregate (usually perlite) combined at the mill. At the job it requires addition of water only. It can be obtained for trowel or machine application to gypsum or metal laths and masonry.

Gypsum wood-fibered plaster may be used either as it comes from the bag or may be mixed with one part of sand to produce basecoats of superior strength and hardness. It consists of calcined gypsum combined with not less than 0.75 per cent (by weight) of non-staining wood fibers.

Gypsum bond plaster is a specially formulated plaster designed for basecoat use over properly prepared monolithic concrete. This material consists essentially of calcined gypsum with 2-5 per cent lime by weight. Preparation of a monolithic concrete surface to receive bond plaster is described in Chapter 3.

Table I. General Properties of Gypsum Basecoat Plasters

Material	Compressive Strength PSI (Dry)	Tensile Strength PSI (Dry)	Weight per Cubic Foot	Time of Set (Hrs.)	Unique Properties
Gypsum ready-mixed plaster (Perlite)	675 average[a] 400 minimum (ASTM C28)	155 average[a]	52 lb.	1½-8 (ASTM C28) 4 Max. (ASA A42.1)	K−1. 40 or 3½ times better insulator than sanded plaster. Closely controlled quality.
Gypsum Neat Plaster	900 average with 2 parts sand	175 average with 2 parts sand	104-120 lbs. with 2 parts sand	2-32 (ASTM C28) 4 Max. (ASA A42.1)	–
Gypsum wood-fibered plaster	2,100-2,500 average 1200 minimum (ASTM C28)	400-500 average	80 lbs.	1½-16 (ASTM C28) 4 Max. (ASA A42.1)	Approximately 50% greater surface hardness than sanded plaster. Higher strain and strength values.
Gypsum Bond Plaster	2,300 average	400 average	75-80 lbs.	2-10 (ASTM C28)	Bonds with monolithic concrete.

[a] Not applicable to ready-mix plaster for masonry bases.

Note: Figures are averages, and may vary by locality.

Five types of Gypsum finish coat plasters.

Ready-mix gypsum finish plasters are designed for use over gypsum plaster basecoats. All these materials are proprietary products consisting of finely ground calcined gypsum with or without fine aggregate. At the job they require addition of water only. They are available as white or gray trowel finish, sand-float finish, and colored float or textured finish.

Gypsum acoustical plasters are proprietary materials designed to reduce sound reverberation. The effects and applications of these materials are discussed in greater detail later in this section and also in Chapter 8.

Gypsum gauging plasters are combined with lime putty to provide setting properties, to increase dimensional stability during drying, and to provide initial surface hardness in lime finish coats. Gauging plasters are obtainable as slow-set, quick-set, and special high strength.

Gypsum molding plaster is a more finely ground form of calcined gypsum than gauging plaster. This material is used primarily in casting and in ornamental plasterwork. Molding plaster is used neat or with lime.

Keene's cement is a fine, high density plaster capable of receiving a highly polished surface. Usually, Keene's cement is used with lime putty, and like lime may be reworked after it has started to harden. Addition of fine sand to a mixture of Keene's cement and lime putty, and subsequent floating, produces a finish having a high resistance to cracking (see Chapter 6). Due to the density normally developed in a highly trowelled Keene's ce-

Table II.

General Properties of Gypsum Finish Coat Plasters

Materials	Compressive Strength PSI (Dry)	Setting Time	Surface Hardness	Working Properties	Unique Properties
Ready-mix gypsum finish plaster	—	—	Moderately hard.	Not as plastic as lime putty	May be painted as soon as set. No alkali reaction with paint.
Gypsum acoustical plasters	Lower than other gypsum finish plasters.	—	Moderately soft.	More difficult to apply than conventional plasters.	More effective than conventional plaster in sound absorption. Negligible effect in reducing sound transmission. (See Chapter 8)
Gypsum gauging-lime putty plasters a. Regular	2,000-3,000 average 1,200 minimum (ASTM C28)	20-40 minutes. (ASTM C28)	Varies with lime proportions	Good; improves as lime proportion increases.	—
b. Special High Strength	5,000 minimum	20-40 minutes (ASTM C28)	Very hard; similar to Keene's cement under similar conditions.	Good	Low consistency (i.e. requires less mixing water to provide workability than standard gauging plaster.)
Keene's Cement	4,000-5,000 average 2,500 minimum (ASTM C61)	20 minutes — 6 hours (ASTM C61)	Very hard; becomes softer as lime proportion increases.	Fair to poor — improves as more lime is added.	Can be re-tempered. Strong-dense-hard. Can be polished. Less susceptible to moisture than regular calcined gypsum.

ment — lime finish, and the relatively low permeability of such a finish to water, it is somewhat less susceptible to deterioration by water than an ordinary gypsum gauged-lime putty finish. For this reason it is often used in bathrooms and other areas where conditions of high humidity prevail. While under limited conditions of exposure to moisture the finish, properly painted, performs satisfactorily, it is prone to deterioration from prolonged or frequent wetting. Keene's cement should not be used as a finish coat over a portland cement plaster basecoat, or on monolithic concrete, due to the probability of unsatisfactory bond between gypsum and portland cement materials.

Proportioning and mixing procedures for the materials that have been described, and recommendations for suitable bases for their application, are discussed in Chapters 3 and 4.

Lime. Lime is obtained principally from the burning of limestone, a very common mineral consisting mainly of calcium or magnesium carbonate, or both, and existing in many forms having widely varying physical and chemical characteristics. Marble, chalk and marl are forms of limestone and may be used for producing lime. The lime derived from them, however, is generally not suitable for construction purposes. Lime produced in the United States comes principally from dolomitic or calcitic limestones. Dolomitic deposits in northwest Ohio are the largest single sources of finishing lime. Commercially important calcitic deposits exist in several states, including Missouri, Pennsylvania, Texas, and Virginia. Only limestones of extremely high purity (97 per cent to 99 per cent) are used for producing building lime.

During the burning or calcining process, limestone gives off carbon dioxide, and changes from the carbonate form to calcium or magnesium oxide, or both, the product being termed quicklime.

The use of lime plaster dates back to the earliest known civilizations. Knowledge of its properties and uses came to North America with some of the first immigrants. There are numerous examples of lime used as exterior plaster in New Orleans, Charleston, and Quebec. Many of these examples exist today in virtually the same condition as when they were applied almost three hundred years ago.

Until early in the current century, virtually all plaster, both interior and exterior, contained lime as the binder material. With the advent of gypsum plaster with a controlled time of set, the use of lime plaster for interior basecoat work has declined. Today, lime plaster is used principally for interior finish coats, as exterior plaster, and as a plasticizing agent for portland cement plasters and masonry mortars. Present-day uses are extensive with respect to the total volume of the product consumed (see Chapter 7).

Unlike gypsum, the use of lime is not primarily confined to the construction industry. A large proportion of the total production is consumed by the steel industry. Also, significant quantities are used in paper and glass manufacturing, in agriculture, and for other non-building purposes.

Prior to calcination, dolomitic limestone is quarried or mined and crushed into a size optimum for burning. The crushed material is placed in either vertical or rotary kilns, where it is burned at 2,000° F. The product then becomes quicklime, which may be processed and sold for either industrial or building uses. Usually the building product is further processed and ultimately sold as normal (Type N) or special (Type S) hydrated lime. In the case of high calcium lime, both pulverized quicklime and hydrate are used in building.

Building limes are classified as finishing lime or mason's lime. The finishing type has working characteristics that make it more suitable for plaster than the mason's type which is designed for use in masonry mortars.

The physical and chemical properties of a lime depend largely upon the limestone from which it was derived. Calcitic limestone contains principally calcium carbonate and produces "high calcium" lime, while dolomitic limestone consists of calcium carbonate and from 43 per cent to 46 per cent magnesium carbonate and produces "dolomitic" lime. The magnesium content produces a unique property in dolomitic limes which improves their working quality as plaster mortar. Before being used for plastering, quicklime must be slaked. Slaking consists of adding the quicklime to water and involves a rather violent exothermic reaction which transforms the quicklime to the more stable hydroxide state and is followed by an extended soaking period to complete the transformation. Most building lime is hydrated at the mill and usually is soaked on the job to produce a plastic putty.

Like calcined gypsum, lime plaster tends to return to its original rock-like state after application to a surface. The process of hardening is termed *recarbonation* and involves absorption of atmospheric carbon dioxide to replace that lost during calcination. Under natural conditions, recarbonation never proceeds far beyond the exposed surface of the plaster since it becomes increasingly difficult for carbon dioxide to penetrate as the surface recarbonates.

General uses and characteristics of lime plasters. Lime plaster may be used on either the exterior or interior, and for basecoat and finish coat work. For basecoats and some finish coats, lime, either in the form of putty or dry hydrate, is mixed with sand, water, and a gauging material. The gauging may be either gypsum gauging plaster or Keene's cement for interior work or portland cement for exterior work. It is added to produce early strength and to counteract the shrinkage characteristic of lime plaster as it dries.

Lime putty, the material resulting from slaking quicklime or soaking finishing hydrated lime, is the most plastic and workable of the standard cementitious materials used in plaster. Because of this property, it is often added to other less workable plaster materials to provide necessary plasticity.

Both dolomitic and high-calcium limes are used for plastering; the latter principally in localities where the dolomitic type is not available.

Due to its relatively short "shelf life" and the time consumed by the slaking process, slaked quicklime, as a plastering material, has been to a large extent replaced by plastic hydrated lime of either the normal or special type. The principal difference between the two types of hydrate lies in the method of preparation at the job site prior to use in plaster. The normal type requires soaking in water for 12 to 16 hours prior to use to develop plasticity. The special type is mill-hydrated under pressure and need only be mixed with water to develop its plasticity. Therefore, it may be combined with other plaster components while dry, and used immediately after being mixed with water.

Lime, unlike calcined gypsum or portland cement may be "retempered," or recombined with water, and used after it has initially hardened. For this reason, it is possible, and sometimes practicable, to mix enough lime putty for an entire job in one operation for storage and use as necessary. Sand may be combined at the outset of the soaking period or "cut in" along with gauging material just before the plaster is to be used.

Because lime plaster is strongly alkaline, it prevents or retards corrosion of any ferrous metal embedded within it.

Types of lime plasters. Lime plasters, regardless of type or locality of use, all contain finishing hydrated lime. Except for mill-fibered hydrate which is produced for basecoat work, all finishing lime, when in the form of putty, may be used for any plastering purpose.

The kind of gauging material used with lime to produce the many different types of finish and basecoat plasters, largely determines where and how the plaster should be used. These plasters and their formulation are described in Chapter 4.

Portland cement. Portland cement does not occur naturally; it is produced primarily from a combination of limestone and an argillaceous or clay-like substance both of which are found in abundance throughout the world. More than 50 million tons of portland cement are produced annually in the United States. It is used predominantly for concrete, only a small percentage of the total output being consumed by the plastering industry.

Portland cement was first made and patented in 1824 by Joseph Aspdin, a bricklayer of Leeds, England. The first record of its use in the United States was in 1868. European manufacturers began shipping it here as ballast in tramp steamers, thus enabling shipment at very low freight rates.[3] Production began in the United States during the 1870's.

The first operation in the manufacture of portland cement consists of quarrying and crushing the raw materials. After crushing and mixing in the proper proportions, water may be added to form a slurry, although sometimes the materials are kept in a dry powder state. The slurry or powder is then fed into kilns which raise its temperature to approximately 2,700° F. The raw ingredients combine at this temperature to form a new substance which is subsequently discharged in the form of clinkers. The clinkers are then ground to an extremely fine powder and a small quantity of gypsum added to control the setting properties of the material.

Chemically, portland cement is essentially a combination of various silicates and calcium aluminates. Addition of water starts a complex reaction which ends as certain crystalline substances are formed in an amorphous gel. Both crystals and gel contain combined water, and eventually set into a dense, hard mass.

The hydration or hardening process requires the presence of water for several days after mixing and placement. Like lime, portland cement is alkaline. **General uses and characteristics of portland cement plaster.** Portland cement plaster is used primarily for exterior plastering and for interior uses where wetting or severe dampness are likely to occur. It is very durable, relatively unaffected by water, and capable of withstanding repeated cycles of severe freezing, thawing, wetting and drying over relatively long periods without damage. For exterior plastering and most interior uses, portland cement is combined with sand and usually with lime. Lightweight aggregated mixes may be used on the interior and have been used experimentally on the exterior, but sufficient performance data are not currently available to warrant acceptance as general practice.

Portland cement plaster mortar containing only cement and sand is more difficult to manipulate with the trowel than lime or gypsum plaster mortars. For this reason, often a plastic hydrated lime, ground asbestos, or other plasticizing material is added, usually in relatively small amounts, to improve workability. A characteristic of portland cement after application is its tendency to shrink as it dries. Unless this initial dimensional change is allowed for through proper detailing at the membrane perimeter, provision of expansion-contraction joints, and so on, the forces set up by shrinkage may produce cracks. This subject is discussed further in Chapters 4 and 6.

Portland cement plaster may be applied to all metallic plaster bases as well as masonry and rough monolithic concrete. It should not be applied to gypsum lath or used in direct contact with gypsum plasters, because the two materials may react chemically so that bond between them is destroyed.

Types of portland cement used in plastering. Portland cement is manufactured in five types designated I, II, III, IV, and V. Type I is the standard product and is generally used except when special properties possessed by the other four types are required. Types I and II are those generally used in plaster work.

Type I portland cement is generally used in plasterwork for both basecoats and finish coats. It is available in natural gray color or in white. The white material is particularly useful in finish coats where integral coloring or colored aggregates are used. Type 1-A or air-entraining cement is coming into wider use in plastering; it has the advantage over the regular type of providing improved workability, durability, and resistance to "bleeding" (that is, concentration of fine material at the surface).

Type II portland cement is similar to Type I, except that it has greater resistance to decomposition by reason of sulphates and higher heat of hydration. Resistance to sulphate attack may be a useful property in cases where portland cement plaster is applied to certain types of brick or block containing soluble sulphate materials. The greater heat developed during hydration is useful when the ambient temperature during application and curing may drop below freezing. Type II-A (air-entraining) cement is also available.

Ready-mixed finish coat materials. Several proprietary finish coat materials are manufactured for application over exterior or interior portland cement plaster basecoats. These materials are obtainable in white or a variety of colors, and in general provide more satisfactory results than those produced by addition of pigments on the job. Most ready-mixed products of this type are designed for a float or textured finish, and are not recommended for smooth trowel work.

AGGREGATES

Aggregates perform several functions in plasterwork. Probably the most important of these is to provide dimensional stability in the plaster during and after the hardening or setting process. Volume changes in plaster are primarily attributable to the cementitious material which, in the case of lime and portland cement, shrinks as it loses water after placement and expands and shrinks cyclically thereafter due to changing moisture and temperature conditions. By comparison, the aggregate is generally stable and if added in proper quantity provides a cushioning effect in the plaster and tends to prevent excessive dimensional change, which is one cause of cracking.

A second function of aggregate is to provide bulk which has economic implications. Since usually the most expensive plaster ingredient is the cementitious material, aggregate by displacing it serves to reduce the cost of materials. The significance of this function varies according to type of aggregate used, size of the job, and many other factors. In addition to stability and economy, aggregate is often used to produce texture or color effects in the finish coat. This function is described in Chapter 4.

Most aggregates are inert mineral materials which affect the properties of plaster according to their physical characteristics. Chemical effects are possible where organic or chemical impurities are present on the particle surfaces of the aggregate. This is particularly true of sand. Since the effects and their magnitude cannot be accurately predicted, and are therefore undesirable, only sand meeting recognized standards for purity should be used in plaster.

These physical properties of aggregates have the most pronounced effect on the plaster: gradation from coarse to fine particles, shape and density of particles, and particle surface characteristics such as roughness and porosity.

SAND

Natural deposits are the source of most plastering sands. These deposits are the result of gradual breakdown of rock by wind and water erosion, or by the grinding action of glaciers. Artificially produced sand or stone screenings, of the proper size and gradation are also suitable for use in plaster. Except for stone screenings, sand processing is confined to procurement, grading according to particle size, and washing if the source is known to produce impure sand.

Most sands consist primarily of quartz and silica with small percentages of mica, feldspar, clay and miscellaneous impurities. Sand weighs from 80 to 110 pounds per cubic foot. Probably the most pronounced characteristic of sand is the extremely wide variation in composition and gradation encountered among different local deposits.

Since a small amount of dissolved chemicals or organic impurities can have considerable effect on set time and plaster strength, this variation has provided one of the greatest obstacles to establishment of standardized plastering procedures. To overcome this difficulty, the ASTM and ASA recommend certain limitations on gradation and percentage of impurities that may be permitted, and have set forth testing procedures to measure these factors. Sieve analysis (ASTM designation C35) is used universally to determine gradation; a colorimetric test (ASTM designation C40) is used to determine the amount of organic impurities; and a water soluble impurities test (ASTM designation C37) is used to determine the presence of harmful chemicals in solution. In addition, most gypsum plaster is formulated for use with the sand generally used in the region where the gypsum is to be sold. Usually this process consists of varying the amount of stabilizing agents added to counteract the retarding or accelerating tendencies of the sand.

The character of individual sand particles can affect the strength and workability of plaster. Sharp, rough, angular particles generally produce a stronger plaster than smooth, round ones.

General uses and characteristics of sand in plasters. Sand is used with all three of the standard cementitious materials. It may be incorporated in both basecoats and finish coats and for both interior and exterior use.

In comparable proportions, sanded basecoat plasters are generally stronger than lightweight aggregate mixes but have a higher modulus of elasticity. The significance of this relationship with regard to cracking is discussed in Chapter 6.

VERMICULITE

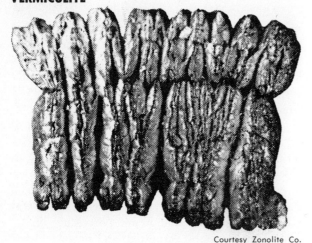

Courtesy Zonolite Co.

Fig. 1 – Particle of Expanded Vermiculite Magnified

Vermiculite is a micaceous mineral consisting of a series of parallel plates or laminae. Minute amounts of water, between the laminae, turn to steam when exposed to intense heat. The steam expands to force the laminae apart, causing the particle to increase from six to twenty times in volume. Most of the vermiculite ore mined in the United States comes from Libby, Montana, or Travellers Rest, South Carolina. From these points it is shipped as ore to processing plants throughout the country where it is expanded and bagged.

The term "vermiculite" was originated by Thomas W. Webb in 1824, and is based on the peculiar vermicular or worm-like movement of the material as it exfoliates. Commercial production of vermiculite did not begin until about one hundred years later when the deposit at Libby was discovered.[4]

Approximately 200,000 short tons of vermiculite are produced annually in the United States.[5] In addition to its use in plaster and acoustical plastic, vermiculite is employed as concrete aggregate, loose fill insulation, and for miscellaneous industrial, chemical and agricultural purposes.

The manufacturing process consists of first quarrying and crushing the raw ore. Prior to exfoliation, the material is graded as to particle size, impurities are removed by air separation, and much of the combined water is removed by heating. Exfoliation is produced by heating from 1,600 to 2,000 degrees F in a vertical shaft furnace. Heat is applied for four to eight seconds, after which the material is cooled rapidly to impart pliability and toughness to the expanded particle. As the material is cooled it is air-lifted to remove unexpanded rock particles, to accelerate cooling, and to classify the vermiculite according to particle sizes.

Vermiculite consists basically of silica, magnesium and aluminum oxides with small percentages of several other minerals. Combined water accounts for approximately five to nine per cent by weight of the ore and less than one per cent of the expanded product.[6] The expanded material is soft and pliable. Its color varies from silvery to golden, depending on the composition of the ore.

General uses and characteristics of vermiculite in plaster. Vermiculite is used for interior plastering and is usually combined with calcined gypsum, or with a special binder material to produce acoustical plastic. It is used both in conventional basecoat work and as the aggregate in a special sound-absorbing material. Fine particles of vermiculite may also be added to gauged lime and gypsum finish coat plasters.

Expanded vermiculite is manufactured in five types (I, II, III, IV and V), classified according to particle size. Type III is used in plastering. It is the lightest of the standard plaster aggregates, weighing from six to ten pounds per cubic foot. The approximate dry weight of a cubic foot of 1:2 gypsum-vermiculite plaster is 50 to 55 pounds; the dry weight of a cubic foot of comparable sanded plaster is 104 to 120 pounds. In many instances this weight differential may have a considerable effect on the overall weight of a building and the sizes of its structural members, as well as on the economics of handling materials during application.

The cellular structure of the expanded particles makes them considerably more effective than sand in plaster when used as membrane fireproofing.

PERLITE

Raw perlite is a volcanic glass which, when flash-roasted, expands to form frothy particles of irregular shape that contain countless minute air cells. The sources of crude perlite ore are confined to the western part of the United States. From these points raw ore is shipped to processing plants located throughout the country.

Expanded perlite is the newest of the basic plastering materials. The industry has been in existence since 1948. Approximately 246,000 short tons of expanded perlite are produced annually in the United States. The largest single use of perlite is as a plaster aggregate, accounting for more than 75 per cent of total production.[7] Between 10 and 15 per cent more is used as concrete aggregate; the remainder is used in oil well drilling, filtration, agricultural and for miscellaneous purposes.

Fig. 2 – Particle of Expanded Perlite Magnified

Virtually all perlite ore is mined by open pit methods. After being mined, the crude ore is crushed and various particle sizes segregated by screening. The material is then ready for expansion which is accomplished in either vertical or horizontal furnaces maintained at 1,400 to 2,000 degrees F. At this temperature the glassy ore particles approach the melting point and begin to soften. As they soften, a small amount of combined water is converted to steam. The steam, suddenly able to expand, causes the particle to "pop," forming a frothy mass of glass bubbles, which is four to twenty times the volume of the raw particle. After expansion, the particles are conveyed by air blast to a cyclone system where they are finally collected according to particle size.

Chemically, perlite is primarily silica and alumina with four to six per cent combined water and various trace elements. The material is generally considered to be chemically inert and free from impurities that could alter the setting properties of gypsum plaster.

Fig. 3 — Comparison of Perlite: Crude Ore — Crushed — Expanded

The color of expanded perlite ranges from pearly white to grayish white, depending on ore composition and processing. Particles are of irregular shape and of varying surface roughness. Rough surfaced particles will generally provide higher plaster strength, but somewhat lower mortar workability, than smooth particles.

General uses and characteristics of perlite in plaster. Perlite is used with calcined gypsum or portland cement for interior plastering. It is also used with various conventional and non-conventional binders in acoustical plasters. Perlite "fines" are used in some finish coat plasters.

Expanded perlite used in basecoat plastering weighs from 7.5 to 15 pounds per cubic foot. The approximate dry weight of a cubic foot of 1:2 gypsum-perlite plaster is 50 to 55 pounds, or approximately half the weight of a cubic foot of a comparable sanded mix. Perlite is a very effective fire retardant. Fire resistance ratings for perlite plaster constructions are usually considerably higher than equivalent constructions in which sanded plasters are used.

In the past, isolated instances have been reported where unsatisfactory results have been attributed to expansion of perlite in hardened plaster. Investigation by the industry of these cases disclosed that in virtually all instances other contributing factors were present. Some laboratory evidence of the expansion of unrestrained specimens of perlite plaster has been produced. However, continuous testing of restrained specimens by various segments of the industry in this country has disclosed no condition that would induce the Perlite Institute or other authoritative agencies to recommend precautionary or preventative measures other than good job practices and proper use of related materials.[8]

OTHER AGGREGATES

Although sand, vermiculite and perlite account for the great preponderance of plaster aggregate used, occasionally certain other materials are employed. This is done to provide special properties or because of a favorable local procurement condition.

Wood fiber added to neat gypsum plaster at the time of manufacture is considered an aggregate. Its addition improves the working properties of neat calcined gypsum. Although believed by some plasterers to produce a sticky mortar, the working quality of the modern wood fiber plaster is much improved over that of the earlier product. It may be applied very satisfactorily either by hand or by machine. This type of plaster produces the strongest of the commonly used gypsum basecoat materials. Added during manufacture, wood fiber must account for not less than .75 per cent by weight of the plaster according to ASTM C28.

The composition of pumice, a naturally foamed volcanic glass, is similar to perlite, but generally it weighs 28 to 32 pounds per cubic foot against 7.5 to 15 pounds per cubic foot for perlite. The weight differential affords a definite economic advantage for perlite and limits the use of pumice to localities near where it is produced.

AGGREGATE GRADATION

One of the prime determinants of the quality of plaster is the proper gradation of aggregate used in its formulation. Proper gradation of aggregate particle size from coarse to fine influences plaster strength and workability, and its tendency to shrink or expand.

The maximum aggregate particle size recommended for plaster by ASTM specifications is that which will pass a No. 4 standard sieve. It is further recommended that the amount of very fine material, or "fines" (that is, material readily passing a No. 200 sieve) be limited, in the case of sand, to five per cent by weight. Within these limits, the maximum and minimum percentage of aggregate material retained on each of six standard sieves is also specified by ASTM C35 for interior plastering, and by the American Standard specifications for portland cement plaster and stucco, ASA A42.2.

Plaster strength is reduced if excessive fine aggregate material is present in a mix. The greater quantity of mixing water required raises the water-cement ratio, thereby reducing the dry set density. The cementitious material becomes overextended since it must coat a relatively greater overall aggregate surface.

Mortar workability is adversely affected by the presence of a preponderance of coarse particles. The mix becomes "harsh working" and is difficult to apply.

Plaster shrinkage during drying and subsequent cyclical movements often is increased by a predominance of either fine or coarse particles. As previously seen, an excessive proportion of fine material greatly increases the total surface area of the aggregate. This requires a greater quantity of binder paste to completely coat all particles and ultimately results in a mix which, by weight, is too rich in

Table III.

Sieve Analysis of Aggregates for Gypsum Plaster (ASTM C35)

| | Percentage Retained on Each Sieve | | | | | |
| | Perlite by Volume | | Vermiculite by Volume | | Sand by Weight | |
Sieve Size	Max.	Min.	Max.	Min.	Max.	Min.
No. 4	0	–	0	–	0	–
No. 8	5	0	10	0	5	0
No. 16	60	10	75	40	30	5
No. 30	95	45	95	65	65	30
No. 50	98	75	98	75	95	65
No. 100	100	88	100	90	100	90

Table IV.

Sieve Analysis of Sand for Exterior Plaster (ASA A42.2)

| | Percentage Retained on each Sieve (by weight) | |
Sieve Size	Minimum	Maximum
No. 4	—	0
No. 8	0	10
No. 16	10	40
No. 30	30	65
No. 50	70	90
No. 100	95	100

cementitious material. Therefore, it becomes subject to relatively greater shrinkage or expansion, or both, after application. In addition, sand "fines" usually contain a high percentage of clay which upon drying shrinks excessively.

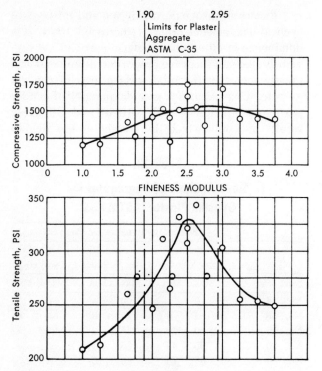

Fig. 4 — Effect of Sand Gradation on the Strength of Plaster Mixes. (2:1 Sand-Plaster Ratio Normal Consistency)[9]

If an aggregate consists almost exclusively of coarse particles, much the same effect will result. Since fine material is not present to fill the voids between the larger particles, these voids must be filled with cementitious material. Again the result is a rich and relatively unstable material.

WATER

Mixing water performs a dual function in plastering. Through its addition the dry powdery mixture of cementitious material and aggregate is transformed into a workable, plastic mass. Water also combines mechanically and chemically with the cementitious material during hydration. Although, unlike gypsum and portland cement, lime plaster does not contain water of crystallization, a certain water content is necessary for recarbonation to occur.

In all mixing, more water is added to plaster mortar than is necessary to provide for hydration of the binder material. The excess is necessary to bring the mix to a workable consistency. Prime determinants of the quantity of water that must be added for workability are the basic characteristics and age of the cementitious material, the method of application, the suction of the plaster base on which it is applied, and the drying conditions. High suction bases, such as porous masonry, draw an appreciable part of the water out of a mortar soon after it is applied. If insufficient water remains for hydration of gypsum, "dryout" will occur; in the case of portland cement, the result will be incomplete curing.

As a general rule, only that amount of water should be added that is necessary to render a mortar workable, and no more, because plaster strength is drastically lowered by excessive additions. Excess water tends to produce a porous material that has high initial shrinkage and usually with insufficient strength to resist the stresses thus produced without cracking.

Water for mixing should be clean, fresh and potable. In addition it must contain no dissolved chemicals in quantity sufficient to accelerate or retard set. Water that has previously been used to wash plastering tools must never be used. It may contain particles of set gypsum, a powerful and unpredictable accelerator. Stagnant water should also be avoided since organic materials are often present that may retard setting and occasionally cause staining.

ADMIXTURES

An admixture is any substance, other than binder, aggregate and water, that is added to plaster during manufacture or during mixing on the job for altering the properties of the mix. For many reasons, addition during manufacture is more desirable than field addition. Product uniformity is more readily controlled by the manufacturer. It may be assumed that his choice of a particular additive and the amount to be used is based on experience that would be too costly to acquire through field experimentation.

If there is one characteristic common to all admixtures, it is the very small quantity necessary to produce significant changes in mix properties. Many materials, when added to plaster for a particular purpose at the job, will produce other effects which may be undesirable to an extent that the benefits gained are outweighed. An example is the common practice of retarding gypsum plaster during mixing, whereby plaster strength is lowered considerably and the possibility of dryouts arises. This is to be avoided particularly where lightweight aggregates are used.

ACOUSTICAL MATERIALS

Several manufacturers produce plaster-like materials designed primarily to absorb sound. Without exception these materials are proprietary ready-mixed products requiring only the addition of water.

Most materials of this type are termed acoustical plasters or acoustical plastics. They may contain conventional binders such as gypsum or lime, or they may utilize clay-like materials similar to Bentonite. Acoustical materials generally contain, in addition to the binder, a lightweight aggregate and a foaming or air-entraining agent to provide low density and cellular characteristics necessary for sound absorption. Depending upon their formulation, acoustical materials may be applied by hand or by machine, either as a conventional finish coat or direct to the plaster base. Some types may be sprayed directly to the underside of galvanized steel decks, concrete slabs, and the like, or direct to structural members.

Chapter 8 describes in detail the various types of plastering materials used primarily for sound absorption. In general, noise reduction coefficients that may be obtained with these materials vary from .40 to .60. The outstanding advantage of acoustical plasters over the other acoustical materials is their fire endurance value.

Acoustical plasters are generally softer and more friable than a conventional finish coat. For this reason their use usually is confined to ceilings and the upper parts of walls where abrasion is not likely to be encountered. The various surface textures that can be produced with acoustical plasters are described and illustrated in Chapter 4, as well as the materials and procedures used to obtain them.

LATH

The primary function of lath is to span the open spaces between the structural framing and provide a surface to which the plasterer can apply his mortar. Lath must be able to receive and support wet plaster and provide support or reinforcement for the first plaster application.

Ideally, lath and plaster combine to form an integral unit. This unity depends on the type and effectiveness of the bond between the two materials. Bond is obtained either through formation of keys which embed metal lath, or by absorption or suction on the surface of gypsum lath which draws in some of the dissolved cementitious material during plaster application. As the plaster sets, crystals which have formed within the gypsum lath surface interlock with those in the plaster, to produce a continuous bond.

The use of lath dates back to prehistoric daub and wattle huts made by applying mud and clay to a woven framework of saplings and reeds. Other elementary materials such as wickerwood, burlap and hand-split wood lath have also been employed.

Sawed wood lath, used almost universally through the early twentieth century, has today been replaced almost completely by metal and gypsum laths. Their great advantages over wood lath are incombustibility, ease of application, stability, uniformity of units, availability, and generally improved results.

Expanded metal lath. The basic material in metal lath is cold-rolled, copper-bearing steel. Mild low carbon steel with approximately .25 per cent copper added is generally used.

In 1839 an American, Peter Naylor, developed and patented a process whereby sheets of metal were perforated to be used as a plaster base.[10] Later, in 1884, J. F. Golding developed a process of cutting parallel, staggered slits in sheets of metal which were then expanded to form diamond-shaped openings. This material was the prototype from which have developed the expanded types of metal lath manufactured today.

Prior to 1923, 125 varieties of expanded metal lath were manufactured and sold. Many of these laths were almost identical. Realizing the difficulties in production, marketing, specification and installation imposed by such a large line of materials, the Associated Metal Lath Manufacturers (now the Metal Lath Manufacturers Association) initiated proceedings culminating in promulgation by the U. S. Department of Commerce of Simplified Practice Recommendation No. 3, which recommended only 24 varieties, with minimum requirements for each. Subsequent amendments by the Department to SPR No. 3, and its widespread acceptance throughout the industry, resulted in further simplification. Today, seven major types of metal lath are manufactured. These are described in the pages that follow.

Subsequent to fabrication, all metal lath except the galvanized type is coated with a rust-inhibitive paint. Although copper-bearing steel is the standard material for metal lath manufacture, stainless steel, zinc alloys, copper and aluminum can be fabricated for special orders to satisfy unusual requirements.

General uses and characteristics of metal lath. Metal lath is the most versatile of lathing materials. It may be used as a base for all types of plaster materials and in its various forms may be used either on interiors or exteriors. It is also the most suitable plaster base for creating plastic forms that involve compound curvatures.

The bond between metal lath and plaster is created when mortar is forced through lath openings to form keys which slump down over and around the metal strands embedding them. As the mortar hardens or sets, the two materials become rigidly interlocked, the lath acting as a steel armature. When diamond mesh metal lath is used, more than 1,000 plaster keys are formed within each square foot of lath surface.

In addition to its use as a plaster base, metal lath is employed as a base for mortar setting beds for ceramic tile and centering for concrete floor and roof decks.

Types of metal lath. The types of metal lath available may be classified as flat expanded laths, expanded rib laths, and sheet laths. All types may be used as plaster bases.

Flat expanded laths. *Diamond mesh lath* (Fig. 6) is suitable for all types of plastering. It is fabricated in weights of 2.5 or 3.4 pounds per square yard from copper alloy steel, and then painted. It is also available galvanized in the 3.4 pound weight. Standard sheet sizes are 24″ x 96″ and 27″ x 96″.

Self-furring diamond mesh (Fig. 7) consists of diamond mesh with dimples that hold it ¼″ away from a surface to which it is applied. This lath may also be used for all types of plastering and is particularly useful where furring is necessary. It may be nailed to smooth reinforced concrete or masonry, or wrapped around structural steel and the plaster applied direct. Self-furring diamond mesh is widely used for replastering old walls and ceilings where the original surfaces are not removed. It is available in the same weights and sheet sizes as diamond mesh.

Paper-backed diamond mesh. A diamond mesh with paper strips attached to the back surface is produced primarily for machine application of plaster by means other than with a nozzle specifically designed for plaster application over metal lath. Spaces are provided between paper strips to permit fastening through to studs or other supporting components.

Stucco mesh (Fig. 8). While similar in pattern to diamond mesh, stucco mesh has larger openings approximately 1½″ by 3″. It is designed pri-

Fig. 5 — How Metal Lath Is Expanded From Steel

marily as a base for exterior plastering and is available painted in weights of 1.8 or 3.6 pounds per square yard.

Rib laths (Fig. 9). Rib laths, like diamond mesh, are expanded. However, the V-shaped integrally formed ribs provide greater stiffness and permit wide spacing of lath supports. (See Chapter 5.) Three types of rib laths are available.

Flat rib lath is formed with ribs ⅛″ deep and is manufactured in weights of 2.75 and 3.4 pounds per square yard from copper alloy steel, and then painted. Sheet sizes are 24″ by 96″ and 27″ by 96″.

⅜″ rib lath is normally fabricated with ribs ⅜″ deep in weights of 3.4 and 4.0 pounds per square yard from copper alloy steel, and then painted. Sheet sizes are 24″ by 96″ and 27″ by 96″, al-

Fig. 6 — Diamond Mesh

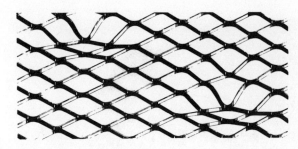

Fig. 7 — Self-Furring Diamond Mesh

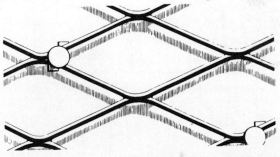

Fig. 8 — Stucco Mesh

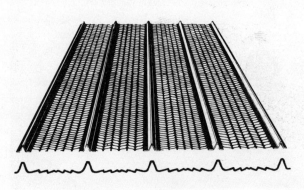

Fig. 9 — Rib Laths

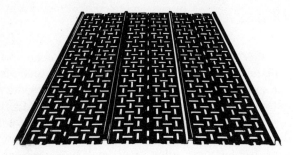

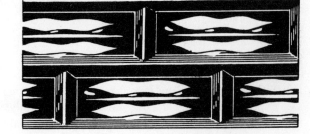

Fig. 10 — Sheet Laths

though lengths in excess of 96 inches may be obtained on special order.

¾″ rib lath, like the other rib laths, is also made from copper alloy steel, and then painted. Weights available are .60 and .75 pounds per square foot. Sheet lengths are 8′, 10′ and 12′. This type is used primarily for top lathing, and as forms and reinforcement for concrete slabs.

Sheet laths (Fig. 10). Sheet laths are not expanded, but are fabricated by punching geometrical perforations in copper alloy steel, and are then painted. Weights available are 4.5 pounds per square yard or more, as required. The stiffness of this material makes it appropriate for use as concrete slab centering and ceramic tile back-up as well as for a plaster base. Because of the sectional configuration and the greater quantity of metal per unit of area, this type of lath is also considered very effective as tensile reinforcement when used as concrete deck centering.

Other metallic plaster bases. In certain sections of the United States wire lath is used to some extent as a base for interior and exterior plastering. Wire lath is formed by weaving or welding steel wire of various gauges into either hexagonal or rectangular mesh. Keys are formed as the mortar is applied.

The ASA specifications for interior lathing and furring (A42.4) thus defines wire lath: "*Wire lath shall be not lighter than No. 19 U. S. gage wire, 2½ meshes per inch, coated with zinc or rust-inhibitive paint.*"

There is available a paper-backed wire fabric consisting of wire mesh with an integrally woven paper backing. This material is used in certain sections of the United States as reinforcement for interior and exterior plastering.

Gypsum Lath. Gypsum lath consists of a core of gypsum plaster sandwiched between two sheets of a fibrous, absorbent paper. The gypsum core usually contains entrained air and may contain up to 15 per cent of fiber by weight.

During the 1890's Augustine Sackett invented a material called "Sackettboard," which consisted of three layers of plaster placed between four plies of wool felt paper. This board was difficult to produce and cumbersome to use because it was heavy and the corners and edges crumbled readily. In 1910 a method was devised whereby a gypsum core could be wrapped with paper mechanically, eliminating the need for the layers of felt within the core. During the early 1920's development of the air-entrained or foamed core produced a much lighter material which ultimately evolved into the standard size of 16 inches by 48 inches produced today. Concurrently, the wrapped edge was developed to minimize edge damage. Variations on the basic material such as foil-backed or insulation lath and perforated lath were invented and developed during the 1930's.

Gypsum lath is now produced by a continuous process. The plaster core is formulated and poured onto a continuous moving paper strip. Top paper is fed from rolls above the plaster core. During this process, the top and bottom papers are wrapped around the edges. The final operation cuts the material to length. Perforated lath is further processed by drilling or punching three-quarter inch holes on approximately four inch centers in each direction. Insulating gypsum lath is manufactured by bonding a layer of aluminum foil to the back of plain gypsum lath. All types of gypsum lath are used as a base for gypsum plaster.

Types of gypsum lath. *Plain gypsum lath* (Fig. 11) is available in ⅜″ or ½″ thickness. Sheet size is 16″ x 48″ except in western United States, where it has been standardized at 16⅕″ x 48″.

Perforated gypsum lath (Fig. 12) is a plain gypsum lath with ¾ inch holes punched on 4 inch centers in both directions. The mechanical key provided by the perforations generally produces slightly better fire resistance ratings than plain gypsum lath. Otherwise there is little difference in performance between the two types.

Insulating gypsum lath (Fig. 13) is plain gypsum lath with aluminum foil bonded to the back

Fig. 11 — Plain Gypsum Lath

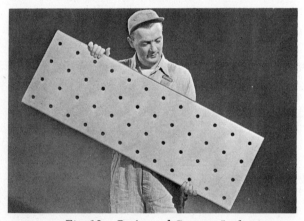

Fig. 12 — Perforated Gypsum Lath

Fig. 13 — Insulating Gypsum Lath

surface. This material provides thermal insulation and also serves as a vapor barrier.

Long length gypsum lath (Fig. 14) is available in ⅜ inch or ½ inch thickness. Sheet sizes are 16 inches or 24 inches wide and any length up to 12′ can be cut as required. Edges are usually either square or are formed with V tongue and groove. Plain, long length lath is used primarily in solid plaster partitions. Insulating long length lath is also available and is used on the inside face of exterior walls.

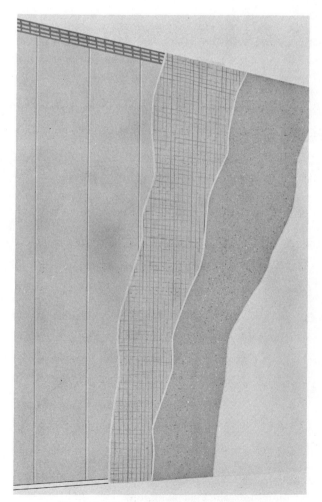

Fig. 14 — Long Length Gypsum Lath

LATHING ACCESSORIES

Lath and plaster manufacturers produce a wide variety of metal accessories to facilitate and complement a plaster job.

A plastering accessory is any device, usually installed prior to plastering, which defines a corner, serves as grounds, lends structural support, or other similar function.

Accessories may be broadly classified into two categories: structural components, and miscellaneous accessories.

Structural components. *Channels* (Fig. 15). One of the most versatile of all plastering accessories is the steel channel. Channels are used as main runners and cross furring in ceiling construction, as studs, furring and bracing in many wall and partition constructions, and for miscellaneous purposes.

Channels are available either hot- or cold-rolled. Cold-rolled channels are generally preferred because they are more easily cut and bent.

Cold-rolled channels are available in three stock sizes:

Table V.

Sizes and Weights of Cold-Rolled Channels

Width	Weight (lb. per 1000 Lin. Ft.)	Lengths (Ft.)
¾	300	16 and 20
1½	475	16 and 20
2	590	16 and 20

Design tables for channels appear in Chapter 5.

Round rods. Hot-rolled rods of circular cross section are available in a variety of sizes with ³⁄₁₆″, ¼″ and ⅜″ the most common. They are used to fur lath out from structural members and are frequently used for cross furring in plaster membranes having double curvatures.

Prefabricated metal studs (Fig. 16) are used as the supporting elements of lath and plaster hollow partitions. They are available in 1⅝″, 2″, 2½″, 3¼″, 4″ and 6″ widths. Lengths are available in

increments up to 24 feet. Prefabricated studs are usually of the non-load bearing type, but load-bearing metal studs also are manufactured. The hollow space provided within the partition serves as a raceway.

Fig. 15 — Channels

Designs vary with each manufacturer, and most produce a line of related accessories such as clips, runners, and stud shoes, and similar articles.

Floor and ceiling runner tracks (Fig. 17) are used in conjunction with prefabricated metal or channel studs to provide floor and ceiling anchorage. Many are formed with slots or receptacles to receive the studs.

Fig. 16 — Prefabricated Metal Studs

Metal base and base clip (Fig. 18) are used in conjunction with the prefabricated stud to form a baseboard.

Hangers are used in suspended ceiling construction to tie the main runner channels into the structure above. When used, wires should be Class I, galvanized as per Federal Specifications *QQ-W-461e*, "Wire, Steel, Carbon, (Round, Bare and Coated)."

Wire hanger sizes are generally U. S. steel wire gage No. 8 or gage No. 9. Sometimes mild steel rods or flat hangers are used when the supported ceiling area is greater than 16 square feet and in certain building code jurisdictions. Areas of more than 25 square feet require special provision in the design of the hanger assembly and main runners.

Two methods of installing hangers in concrete slabs are commonly used. In the first, inserts are placed in the forms prior to pouring concrete. Inserts are usually of either the toggle type (6 inch and 7 inch pieces of flat steel stock bolted together to form a T with a hole in the vertical 6 inch leg for attachment of either wire or flat hanger extensions); or one of several patented devices which are laid flat on the bottom of the forms and subsequently dropped to receive a hanger extension after the forms have been stripped.

The second method utilizes single pieces of wire of length necessary to suspend the ceiling at the required height. The upper end of the hanger is formed into at least three loops having minimum diameters of 3 inches, and is hooked over the nearest reinforcing rod. A hanger design table is shown in Chapter 5.

Tie wires are used in practically every instance where metal is attached to metal — as with metal lath to supports, bracing to supports, cross furring to main runners, and other like connections. The lather is highly skilled in the use of wire forming, and uses a variety of ties for various connection conditions.

Nails and staples are usually used to attach gypsum lath and metal lath to wood supports. Those nails most commonly used are: *for gypsum lath,* 1⅛″, 13 gage, $^{19}\!/_{64}$″ diameter flat head, blued nails for ⅜″ lath (1¼″ for ½″ lath); *for metal lath and wire lath,* 4d nails, common blued or bright for verto wood, to metal, or to masonry supports. Usually these accessories are related to a particular partition or ceiling system, and manufacturers' catalogues must be consulted. Clips are particularly appropriate where gypsum lath is used in suspended ceilings and metal stud systems, whereas metal lath is usually attached by wire ties. Resilient clips are produced by several manufacturers and are recommended to enhance sound transmission loss ratings and to help isolate a plaster panel from structural movement.

Furring clips generally serve two functions: to act as horizontal braces for a panel of wall furring, and to hold the panel a prescribed distance from the base wall. A wide variety of devices may be used that may be fabricated either on or away from the site.

Miscellaneous Accessories. *Corner beads* (Fig. 20) are straight strips of perforated or expanded metal with a V cross section and a bead at the vertex. Primarily, they define and reinforce a plaster corner. During application, they also aid the mechanic in bringing the plaster up to its grounds and providing a true straight corner.

Corner beads are available in two types: the small-nose bead, and the bullnose bead. Each type

Fig. 17 — Runner Track

tical wood supports, 1½", 11 gage ⁷⁄₁₆" diameter head, barbed roofing nails for horizontal wood supports.

Power driven staples used to attach ⅜" gypsum lath to wood framing members should be of No. 16 U.S. gage flattened galvanized wire formed with a ⁷⁄₁₆" wide crown (outside measure) and ⅞" legs with divergent points. For ½" gypsum lath, staples are the same except that legs are 1" long.

Power driven staples for attaching metal lath to wood supports should be used in accordance with the manufacturer's recommendations.

The lathing section of Chapter 3 includes further specific information on attaching lath with nails and staples.

Special clips (Fig. 19). A variety of clips is produced for attaching metal lath and gypsum lath

Fig. 18 — Installation of Metal Base & Base Clip

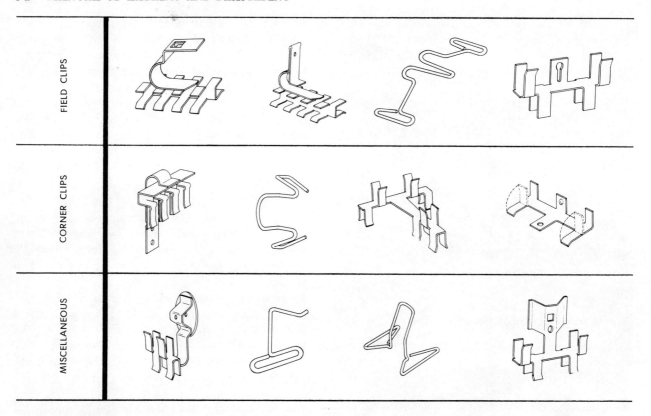

FIELD CLIPS

CORNER CLIPS

MISCELLANEOUS

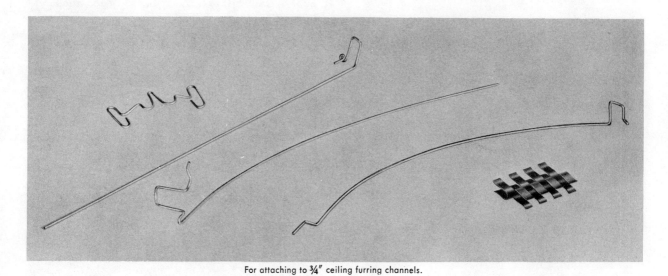

For attaching to ¾″ ceiling furring channels.

Fig. 19 – Clips for Attachment of Gypsum Lath

is available with standard flange (perforated), wide flange (2½″), and expanded flange. In addition, a small-nose type with a scalloped flange is manufactured.

Most corner beads are made from galvanized steel sheet, though some types are available in zinc. Beads of other non-ferrous metals may also be obtained on special order. Corner bead is manufactured in lengths of 7, 8, 9, 10 and 12 feet.

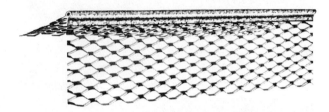

Fig. 20 — Expanded Wing Corner Bead

Arch corner bead (Fig. 21) are flexible corner beads which define a curved plastered edge or corner.

Metal arches (Fig. 22) are perforated assemblies of sheet metal with fixed curves, used to define unframed, arched openings.

Corner reinforcement [*"Cornerite"*] (Fig. 23) is an expanded metal reinforcement for interior angles or the juncture of two walls. It is available with 2″ or 3″ legs and is fabricated from expanded metal lath.

Expansion joint (Fig. 24) is a W-shaped cross section designed to absorb shrinkage and expansion in a large area of plaster.

Base screed or base bead (Fig. 25) is a terminal accessory that provides a straight dividing strip between a plastered wall and a baseboard of another material. Base screeds are usually manufactured from 26 ga. galvanized sheet steel in 10-foot lengths and are made with plain or expanded flanges. Curved point base screeds are also available. Base screeds generally provide ½″ plaster grounds but may be shimmed to provide ⅝″

grounds. A base bead used to separate plaster and a finish such as terrazzo, which is ground in place, must be fabricated from solid brass, white metal, plastic, or other approved material. This type of base bead may either be formed from a single piece of material or made by welding or riveting a solid projecting nose to a standard wall attachment member.

Casing beads (Fig. 26). These are terminal accessories that provide both screed and finish trim around openings. They can also be used as an edge divider or stop between a plaster surface and other materials such as wood panels, acoustical tiles, lighting fixtures, and similar objects. Available in quarter round, square or modified square section types, these accessories are normally produced in 7 and 10 foot lengths with ½″, ¾″ and ⅞″ grounds but are available in 1″, 1⅛″, and 1¼″ grounds to provide for special plaster thickness. They are usually manufactured from 24 gage galvanized sheet. The ½″ and ¾″ beads are available with short or expanded flanges; the ⅞″ bead is ordinarily available with a short flange only, while the 1″, 1⅛″ and 1¼″ beads are usually available with expanded flanges only.

Fig. 21 —
Arch Corner Bead

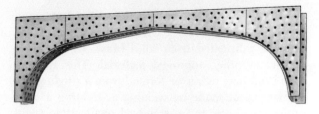

Fig. 22 — Metal Arch

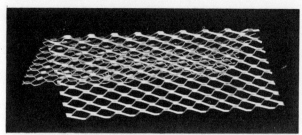

Fig. 23 — Corner Reinforcement

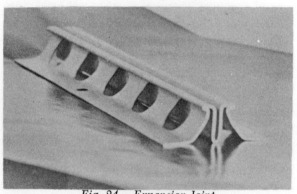

Fig. 24 — Expansion Joint

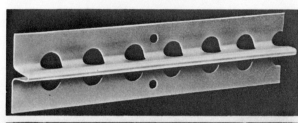

Fig. 25 — Base Screed

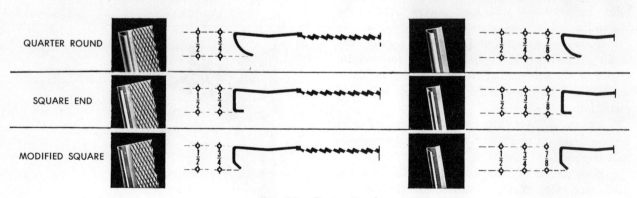

Fig. 26 — Casing Beads

Partition caps (Fig. 27) are used to terminate a 2″ solid partition and to provide a metal cap to define and protect the edge of the panel. They are also often used for special terminal conditions requiring extra strength and rigidity such as lighting troffer edges against which service ladders are placed, and similar conditions.

Concealed picture mold (Fig. 28). A metal picture mold is inserted flush with the plaster and serves as a ground as well as a means of supporting wall-hung objects. It is fabricated from 26 gage metal and produced in 10 foot lengths. Plaster ground of ½″ is provided, shimming being used to provide a ⅝″ ground.

Access Panels are produced by several manufacturers of metal lath and accessories in a variety of sizes, and are designed for various plaster thicknesses. Access panels equipped with automatic self closing devices and other fire protection features required for special conditions are also available.

BONDING AGENTS

Bonding agents are relatively new materials originally designed to bond plaster to concrete surfaces. They are all proprietary in nature, and most are water based emulsions. Manufactured in the form of liquids of about the same viscosity as oil paint, they function by producing adhesion between a base surface and subsequent plaster applications. These materials are not to be confused with the asphaltic or bituminous types of bonding materials

once used in plastering, but no longer recommended.

Bonding agents generaly provide bond strengths as great or greater than most plasters. They are not damaged by acids or alkalis, and will not emit toxic fumes if burned. They are not deteriorated by temperatures ranging from below zero to above 200° F.

The use of these materials in new construction has, to date, been principally confined to the application of a finish coat directly to monolithic concrete. Savings have been realized by using this method of finishing concrete rather than resorting to honing and spackling prior to painting exposed, formed concrete.

In remodeling work, gypsum, lime and portland cement plasters as well as certain acoustical materials may be bonded to brick, stone, block, plaster, wood, glass, metal, ceramics, and painted surfaces. The only limitation on their use is that the surfaces to which the material is applied must be structurally sound and rigid. In addition, bonding agents should not be applied over water base paint, glue, casein sizes or wallpaper, or other materials soluble in water.

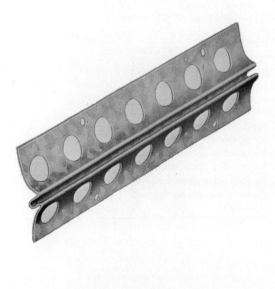

Fig. 27 – Partition Cap   *Fig. 28 – Concealed Picture Mould*

Table VI. Specification Designations for Plastering Materials

Materials	ASTM	Federal	Other
Gypsum Plasters			
1. Neat plaster	C28	SS-P-402 Type N	—
2. Ready-mixed	C28	—	—
3. Wood-fibered	C28	SS-P-402 Type W	—
4. Bond plaster	C28	—	—
5. Ready-mix finish plaster	—	—	—
6. Acoustical plaster	—	SS-A-111	—
7. Gauging plaster			
Regular	C28	SS-P-402 Type G	—
High strength	—	—	—
8. Keene's cement	C61	SS-C-00161	—
Lime (Structural)			
Quicklime (dolomitic)	C5	SS-Q-351	—
Quicklime (calcitic)	C5	SS-Q-351	—
Finishing Hydrate	—	—	—
Normal (Type N)	C6	—	—
Special (Type S)	C206	SS-L-351	—
Mason's Hydrate	C207	SS-L-351	—
Normal (Type N)			
Special (Type S)			
Portland Cement			
Regular (Types I-V)	C150	SS-C-192b	—
Air Entraining (Types I-A, II-A, III-A)	C175	SS-C-192b	—
Ready-mixed finish coats	—	—	ACI-C3-C-29T
Aggregates			
Sand (plastering)	C35	—	—
Aggregate for portland cement stucco	—	—	ASA A42.2, para. 4a.
Vermiculite (plastering-basecoat)	C35	—	—
Vermiculite (fines for finish coat)	—	—	ASA A42.1, para. 2.545
Perlite (plastering-basecoat)	C35	—	—
Perlite (fines for finish coat)	—	—	—
Wood fiber	C28	—	—
Pumice	—	—	—
Water	—	—	ASA A42.1, para. 2.60
Lath			
Metal			
Flat expanded	—	QQ-B-101C	Simplified practice recommendation R3-57 U.S. Dept. of Commerce

Materials	ASTM	Federal	Other
Rib laths	–	QQ-B-101C	Simplified practice recommendation R3-57 U.S. Dept. of Commerce
Sheet laths	–	QQ-B-101C	Simplified practice recommendation R3-57 U.S. Dept. of Commerce
Wire	–	QQ-B-101C	Ref. specs. California Lathing and Plastering Contractors Assoc., Inc. ASA A42.4, Para. 2.50, 2.55 and 2.60
Gypsum			
Plain	C37	SS-L-0030	–
Perforated	C37	SS-L-0030	–
Insulating	C37	SS-L-0030	–
Long Length	C37	SS-L-0030	–
Lathing Accessories			
Cold-rolled channels	–	–	Simplified practice recommendation R3-57
Corner beads	–	–	Simplified practice recommendation R3-57
Cornerite	–	–	Simplified practice recommendation R3-57
Strip lath (stripite)	–	–	Simplified practice recommendation R3-57
Base screeds	–	–	Simplified practice recommendation R3-57
Casing beads	–	–	Simplified practice recommendation R3-57
Concealed picture mold	–	–	Simplified practice recommendation R3-57
Tie and Hanger wire	–	–	Simplified practice recommendation R3-57
Prefabricated Metal Studs	–	–	Simplified practice recommendation R3-57
Metal Reinforcement for Stucco	–	QQ-B-101C	ASA A42.2 para. 4a. Ref. specs. California Lathing and Plastering Contractors Assoc., Inc.
Miscellaneous Plastering Materials			
Bonding agents	–	–	–
Hair or fiber (stucco)	–	–	ASA A42.2. para. 4a
Acoustical plaster or plastic	–	SS-A-111	–

CHAPTER 3

LATHING AND THE PREPARATION FOR PLASTERING

The versatility of lath and plaster as construction materials is demonstrated in Chapters 2 and 5 where the variety of opportunities available to the designer is discussed. Fullest realization of the capabilities inherent in lath and plaster construction, however, depends quite as much upon resourceful preparation and management at the construction site as on intelligent planning and design. This chapter, therefore, is devoted to the presentation of factors more or less preliminary to plaster preparation that affect the economy and quality of the finished work. Plaster preparation and application, as construction operations, are discussed in detail in Chapter 4.

For convenience of reference, this chapter is divided into three sections: 1. Basic Preparations, II. Lathing, III. Non-Lath Plaster Bases. The distinction between these and the relative importance of each is developed.

I. BASIC PREPARATIONS

As used here, *basic preparation* means the management of those conditions of work existing on the job and those building components normally already in place at the commencement of lathing and plastering. Traditionally, the lathers and plasterers are held responsible for the ultimate appearance of the building regardless of the presence of conditions beyond their normal influence. In self-protection against this popular misconception, these trades have, over the years, developed working customs which pertain to broader aspects of the construction job than their specialty would otherwise encompass.

When working conditions exist which are unfavorable to the best performance of the lather or the plasterer, correction or compensation becomes his concern, regardless of the cause or origin. For example, climatic conditions are among those over which he seeks control. It is obvious, however, that there are economic limits controlling the extent to which the lather's and plasterer's basic preparations may go in establishing favorable conditions; there are no economical measures he can take, for example, that will eliminate major construction faults or interference with his production schedule by other trades. Primary responsibility for such conditions falls on others even though recognition of the existence of the condition is the concern of lathing and plastering.

The over-all design of the building, and the supervision of its construction, control at least as many factors affecting the performance of plaster as do the lathers and the plasterers themselves.

Structure. One important condition closely related to plaster performance not primarily influenced by the quality of the plasterer's work is the building structure. As finish materials, lath and plaster cannot be expected to assist the structural frame in supporting its loads. But, if it is not properly designed and erected, the structure may transfer some of its loads to the plaster, invariably resulting in what are commonly known as structural cracks. The loads imposed by the building are not the only forces acting within the structural frame that can be transmitted to the finish material. Expansion and contraction of the structural materials, or uneven settlement of the foundations of the frame, can produce the same effect.

While it is recognized that not all stresses can be eliminated, the proper design and erection of the frame, along with proper construction of the plaster base with respect to the frame, can effectively reduce transferred loads to magnitudes within the stress range of lath and plaster. To accomplish this, movement of structural members due to the natural deformation of the frame acting under load must not be restrained by the plaster membrane. In general, complete detachment of the finish from the frame is desirable, and where this is not possible the structural elements involved should be designed for minimum deformation. In the case of contact plaster ceilings, for example, the joists must be so designed as to deflect less than the maximum that can be tolerated by the plaster acting in tension. In the case of differential expansion and contraction of the elements supporting the plaster base, as in discontinuity of framing materials, interruption of the plaster membrane by the use of control joints is necessary to avoid or control cracking.

A more detailed discussion of structural cracking in plasterwork is to be found in Chapter 6. A reasonably clear understanding of the causes of this defect, and measures for its prevention, is important to effective basic preparation work.

Temperature, humidity and ventilation. While temperature, humidity and ventilation, as they affect lathing and plastering, will be dealt with individually in this text, their relationship is such that one cannot be entirely separated from the others. It should also be remembered that the effect of these climatic factors is manifest in all materials of construction in varying degrees and, therefore, of importance to many aspects of construction other than plasterwork. For this reason, control of the climatic conditions of the job, particularly during the finishing stages, is usually a responsibility that must be shared by more than one trade. Notwithstanding a common interest in temperature and humidity, their control is essential to the plasterer during certain seasons of the year. This applies to most areas of the United States, inasmuch as the effect of extremes of temperature and humidity on the curing of plaster is severe.

The ambient climatic conditions under which plastering is done must be controlled within definite limits. In addition, since lathing and plastering is a laminous process, ideally the temperature and humidity conditions under which each layer of the construction is produced, from structure to finish, would vary little from one operation to another. Under the most favorable circumstances, lathing and plastering operations are conducted when temperature and humidity are uniformly maintained as closely as possible to the anticipated operating conditions of the area when in use. Although such ideal job conditions are seldom encountered, preceding laminations of materials should at least be allowed to adjust to the climatic conditions under which succeeding applications are to be made prior to the starting of such work. For example, it is generally accepted that areas to be plastered should be subjected to temperature and humidity control for at least a week prior to application. This allows for material adjustment to local climate, and this control should be maintained at least until all plaster coats are applied and allowed to dry.

Temperature. In acceptable practice, it is held that under no circumstances should temperature be maintained lower than 55 degrees F., a figure derived from numerous industry researches conducted on the effects of temperature fluctuation on plasterwork.

Studies have indicated that regardless of prevailing temperature, a sudden change can produce stresses, both within the plaster itself and in the materials to which it is attached, of such magnitude as to cause rupture of the membrane. In most areas of the United States, particularly during spring and fall, temperature differentials can be extreme between day and night. Damage to plaster due to *thermal shock,* as the effects of temperature variation are termed, is more severe with respect to the magnitude and rate of the variation when the plaster is not fully dry. Plaster is sensitive to thermal shock to some degree regardless of its age, however, and the shock can be induced by either sudden increases or decreases in temperature. Avoiding thermal shock is a consideration more critical to gypsum plasters than to those employing other cementitious materials. Ordinary precautions, under normal working conditions, eliminate much of the hazard.

Since twenty-four hour uniformity of temperature throughout the space being plastered is desirable, locations of temporary heating devices should be selected to necessitate minimum moving during application and hardening. Strong drafts of cold or hot air in the working space are to be avoided and large openings to the outdoors must be controlled during and after plastering. The minimum working temperature of 55 degrees F., recommended by ASA and other authorities, is thought to represent an average for most job conditions, although special cases will require individual consideration. Substantially higher, or lower, working temperatures are more difficult to maintain uniformly with temporary heating facilities in unfinished buildings. They are more susceptible to shock producing

changes caused by changes in weather, by moving of heating units, by opening doors, and similar conditions. Generally speaking, the more nearly completed the structure at the time of plastering, the more easily and safely can higher working temperatures be maintained.

Under no circumstances should plaster be applied in freezing temperatures, or while the temperature alternates between freezing and thawing. Such fluctuations interfere with the setting action and often results in flaking or spalling plaster, a defect for which the only remedy is replacement.

Sometimes, when it is convenient, the permanent heating system of the building is used to maintain temperature for plastering. This, of course, requires that the system be operational prior to starting plasterwork, and this is not always possible. Those heating systems having distribution devices mounted over the finished areas, such as surface type radiators, are not operable until after plastering is completed. However, systems employing other distribution methods, such as duct work or recessed convectors which must be in place before plastering begins, often can be operated early enough to eliminate the need for temporary facilities.

The major advantage in using the permanent system is obvious in the fact that temperature can more easily be controlled uniformly without interruption until the building is occupied. A major hazard in operating the permanent system during plastering lies in the likelihood of green plaster being in contact with high temperature sources, such as heat supply piping and ducts, which can produce dryouts and other defects in the finished work. Radiant panel heating systems having distribution piping embedded in plaster especially should not be operated until the slab is dry. (See Chapter 8).

In by far the most cases where heat is required, temporary facilities are employed. As mentioned previously, quality results demand that such facilities be maintained uniformly throughout the structure, continuously from a time prior to plastering operations until the permanent system is in operation. In such circumstances, the general contractor usually provides and maintains this equipment. However, when such facilities are not provided at the commencement of lathing and plastering, sometimes the plastering subcontractor will provide the temporary facilities for use during his plastering operations and until the plaster has dried.

Temporary heat for construction work can be supplied economically in a number of ways: Salamanders, infrared heaters, and portable blower units have all been used with varying degrees of success. Salamanders are the most common because of their simplicity and low first costs but latest industry recommendations discourage their use. Salamanders can be purchased or improvised for use with a number of fuels. Their advantage, besides low cost, lies in the fact that the total quantity of heat being supplied, as well as the temperature maintained, is controlled by the number and disposition of units which are quickly available and easily handled. The disadvantages of using salamanders are many, the most important being the large number of units required; inefficiency in use of fuel; working space occupied; localized heat concentration; production of fumes, even when vented; soot deposits; they are easily moved and, therefore, subject to dislocation and removal before the plaster has hardened sufficiently. Other highly portable heat sources have most of the disadvantages of the salamander; and some also have fewer advantages, including higher first cost.

Unvented gas heaters should never be used for heating spaces for the application and hardening of plaster, although there are many lightweight, self-contained, convenient units of this type available to the construction industry at moderate prices. The fuel conversion process involved in the burning of gas causes plaster stains and adds moisture directly to the air of the space being heated, thus increasing the relative humidity. With the temperature differentials and rates of heat loss common to construction job conditions, the rate at which the gas-heated air increases in moisture content often is greater than can be compensated for economically or conveniently, within the conditions of the

job, by ventilation. Thus, as the local atmosphere approaches saturation from other sources, the drying of plaster is slowed causing, at best, construction delays and, at worst, sweatouts. Sweatout, a serious plaster defect, is discussed in Chapter 6.

A method used more and more today with good results utilizes the principles of a permanent system: a central source of heat that is distributed in controlled quantities to remote areas. This type of system consists of a heating unit or units, capable of providing the quantity of heat necessary, strategically located out of the working area, and equipped with portable flexible ducts to deliver the heat where it is needed. Ducts can have damper-diffusers at the point of delivery to control the heating of individual spaces. This method has several obvious advantages, among the more important of which are more positive control of temperature and distribution, opportunity for positive ventilation, and set-up and maintenance of a single unit.

Humidity and ventilation. After application, water is removed from the plaster mortar by suction or evaporation, or both. While suction is discussed farther on in this chapter in the description of plaster bases, evaporation is the main concern here.

The amount of water that the air will absorb by evaporation depends upon two conditions: the quantity of moisture already being carried by the air (expressed as *absolute humidity*), and the temperature of the air. Air absorbs and retains moisture in direct relation to its temperature. The higher the temperature, the greater the quantity of water that can be absorbed by a given volume of air. A more detailed discussion of this principle is found in Chapter 8, in the section dealing with thermal characteristics of plasterwork.

In newly plastered spaces the air can become saturated with moisture thus inhibiting or completely stopping the drying process. This condition is most prevalent in hot, humid climates; where ventilation is neglected to conserve temporary heating costs; and, as observed above, where gas heaters or other moisture producing devices are employed. Particularly since the uniform and reasonably quick drying of plaster is advantageous from an economic as well as from a quality point of view, humidity conditions appear to be as important to plastering as temperature. Where outdoor temperatures are sufficiently low to require temporary heat inside the structure, and the heat source is not moisture producing, the relative humidity in the plastered areas can usually be controlled by moderate ventilation. The colder outdoor air introduced to replace air already saturated, when heated to the temperature of the space, will have a lower relative humidity, and therefore absorb additional moisture.

The rate at which a given atmosphere will absorb moisture also varies directly with the rate of air movement over the evaporating surfaces; hence, fans and other air circulation devices are used to accelerate drying under high moisture conditions. Such methods are employed when outdoor and indoor temperatures are similar, as during summer work. However, where both temperature and relative humidity are sufficiently high, and indoor conditions are similar to those outdoors, plaster drying cannot be facilitated by ventilation alone. Sometimes such conditions exist also in tightly enclosed, uncompleted buildings designed for total air conditioning. In such instances, mechanical or chemical dehumidification is required.

If the drying of gypsum plaster proceeds too slowly, a defective condition of the plaster, commonly known as *sweatout*, will be produced; and if it dries too swiftly, a *dryout* will occur. In sweatout the plaster either loses or never acquires its structural integrity and must be replaced with new mortar to be cured under proper conditions. Dryout is a state of partial set wherein less than complete crystalization of the gypsum has taken place due to the absence of sufficient water. A dryout is best repaired by applying water and alum. Alum accelerates the setting of the gypsum and assures the set before the plaster dries again. Although both dryout and sweatout can be serious, they are caused by extreme or abnormal conditions.

Control of evaporation is desirable, not only from the standpoint of avoiding sweatout and dry-out, but because the timetable of the whole finishing stage of the job depends upon plaster drying. Painting cannot begin until most of the moisture has gone from the slab. In addition, evaporation rates directly affect the quality and uniformity of color in certain pigmented plasters.

Humidity conditions are critical also in portland cement plasters where the continued presence of water is required over a longer period of time for proper curing. Here, due to the large surface area of the plaster slab, in proportion to its volume, evaporation tends to occur more quickly than in structural concrete and, therefore, generally prevents the full strength development usually associated with portland cement. Under conditions producing slow curing as in low temperatures, or during rapid evaporation, or in combinations of low humidity and high temperatures with moving air, special precautions must be taken to prevent the escape of necessary curing water. In exterior plastering work, water-soaked curtains are often hung over the curing slab to protect it against evaporation caused by sun and wind. Another method commonly used for both exterior and interior work involves the use of fog-spraying equipment to maintain a humid local atmosphere and prevent evaporation. Whereas the setting of gypsum plaster requires the presence of water, usually for less than eight hours, portland cement plasters must remain moist for several days.

Illumination. Since much of the visual quality of the finished plaster depends on how well the plasterer can see as he works, proper illumination is essential at the time of application. Where this cannot be provided naturally, artificial light is used, the most common method being a temporary installation of electric incandescent lights. Care should be taken as to the proper distribution and angle of light striking the working surface. If these are markedly different than the conditions under which the work will be ultimately viewed, surprising surface defects may appear. The visual performance of plaster is discussed in Chapter 6.

II. LATHING

Lathing as a job operation can be said to consist of the installation of a supporting structure specifically developed and erected to receive and hold the plaster. As such it is not limited merely to the application of the lath itself, but also often includes the construction of a complete framework that must support itself and the plaster applied to it as well. The purpose of this section is to discuss the contributions and responsibilities of the lather in the total context of construction, and describe the procedures and methods he employs in the erection of such supporting frameworks, in the application of lath, and in the attachment of accessories, so that maximum design utilization can be made of the skills and materials available.

The lather and his tools. The unique skills of the lather, which have developed throughout the history of building — from the matting of reeds to be daubed with mud to the construction of intricate metal frameworks supporting elaborate and independent structural forms, supply one of the keys to the construction versatility of lath and plaster. The talents demanded of the lather are diverse. Although he is considered a specialist in terms of the use made of his work, his art requires a wide knowledge of construction techniques.

The solution of many of the lather's problems require ingenuity beyond the scope of most building crafts. The architect commonly leaves to him the detail of his own structures, obliges him to devise his own connections and anchorage, and establish his own lines and levels. Yet, great demands on precision and speed are made of the lather without regard to these difficulties of his task.

The lather's apprenticeship involves a prescribed course of training and experience which includes the study of geometry, draftsmanship and other academic subjects in addition to the acquisition of basic skills. The development of surface shapes as in formed ceilings, the integration of electrical and mechanical equipment with furring structures, and the requirement for extreme precision of form present to the lather layout problems of an engineering order.

For all of the diversity of performance demanded by his job, the number of special tools the lather requires is surprisingly small. Many are common to most trades: ball peen hammer, steel square, monkey wrench, levels, screw drivers, plumb bob, rule, hacksaw, files, star drills, chisels and punches, are all familiar tools to most craftsmen. Following are descriptions and illustrations of those special tools commonly used by the lather:

End cutting nippers (Fig. 1) are used for tie wire twisting and cutting.

Todd's wire nippers (Fig. 2) are similar to the end cutting nippers, but have removable and replaceable jaws with which to cut and twist hanger and tie wires. These are available in lengths of 6, 8, or 10 inches, the width of the jaws vary from 1 inch to 1½ inches.

Fig. 1 — End Cutting Nippers

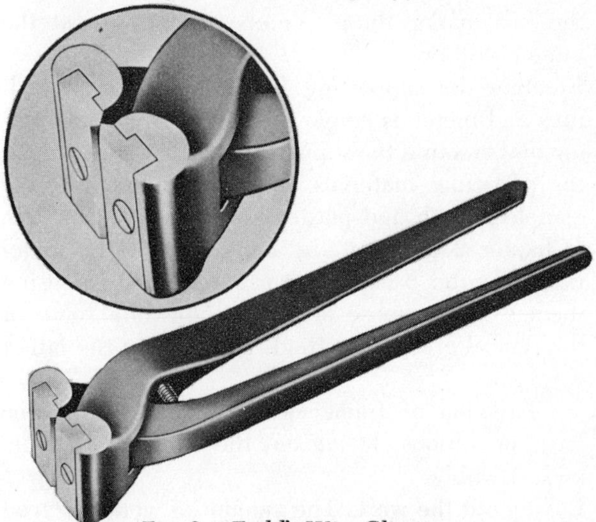

Fig. 2 — Todd's Wire Clippers

Pattern lath hatchet (Fig. 3). This is the lather's traditional hatchet used for nailing, trimming and cutting gypsum lath ("California" illustrated, 12½ inch handle, 2½ inch bit).

Wiss lather snips (Fig. 4) are standard sheet metal cutters used for trimming metal lath, cutting corner beads, and doing similar jobs.

Channel cutter (Fig. 5). This is used to cut cold rolled channels, steel studs, metal lath, base screeds and casings. It is 8½ inches long, and has tempered steel blades.

Hammer drive (Fig. 6) is used as a supporting guide to drive anchoring studs with a 2 to 3 pound hammer. It permits driving studs into concrete, steel or wood.

Magnetic nail holder (Fig. 7). Several types are available, with varying lengths and shapes. It is used primarily for driving short concrete stub nails.

Nail bag (Fig. 8). This is used to carry lathing nails.

Water level (Fig. 9). This level is used to transfer reference marks from one location to another. It consists of a long piece of flexible hose with glass tubes inserted at each end. To exclude air bubbles, the hose is filled with water by siphoning. When the tubes are placed together the level of the water is marked. Any time the water level coincides with the two marks, these reference points are at the same elevation.

Erecting the supporting framework. The procedures and methods employed by the lather in forming and erecting the supporting frame depend upon the particular materials he is using, and how the completed lath and plaster assembly will function. (Chapter 2 discusses the limitations of the materials; Chapter 5 explains current methods of using them.) The purpose here is to illustrate some of the typical erection methods and devices the lather employs.

Erection of framework is divided into three basic operations: laying out the work, fabrication, and assembly.

Laying out the work. The amount of work involved in this operation is, of course, directly related to the complexity of the shape required by the design. The primary tools the lather uses are simple, and include such things as steel square, plumb bob, rule, tape, marking crayons, chalk line, spirit level, and water level. He seldom has the benefit of the tripod level, transit, or other engineering instruments. The water level, while an elementary instrument, is versatile and accurate. The lather uses it to establish reference for elevations. With the water level he can relate two or more points even though the lines of sight between them are obstructed. For example, the ceilings of remote rooms can be established at identical elevations, or a ceiling in a single room can be leveled without sighting. Since lathing involves the installation of a supporting structure capable of receiving and holding the plaster, the lather is responsible for providing the structural integrity required. His understanding of the principles of structure, along with his experience and skill, are taken for granted in the construction industry. To the architect, this ability of the lather means, among other things, that the form of the finished enclosure can be separated, and be different from the form of the structure. This is significant not only for the circumvention of stress transfer to prevent cracking, but aesthetically as well; for because of this, the designer has more freedom of form when working in lath and plaster than in any other structural medium.

Chapter 4 discusses in detail the functions of plaster as applied to its backing, where it is pointed out that the thin coat of plaster cannot correct errors in alignment of the backing. While a true surface is a function of the plasterer, the accuracy of plumb, level and square are functions of the backing, and as such they are the responsibility of the lather. However, if he is applying lath over a frame installed by another trade, as often happens, then it follows that his responsibility is limited.

Attachment and forming devices. The lathing craft has developed a number of standard methods for solving common problems. Just as the primary use of the nail distinguishes the carpenter from the joiner, so the use of the various simple devices des-

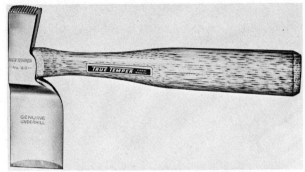

Fig. 3 — Pattern Lath Hatchet

Fig. 4 — Wiss Lather Snips

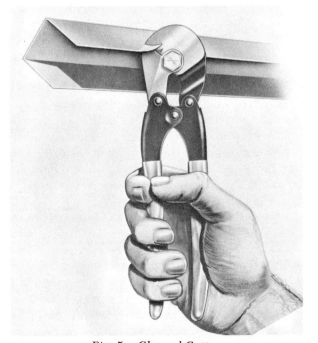

Fig. 5 — Channel Cutter

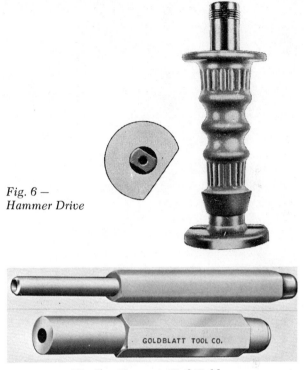

*Fig. 6 —
Hammer Drive*

Fig. 7 — Magnetic Nail Holders

cribed here distinguishes the metal lather from other erection trades. The list that follows includes only the more common things of this type and is intended to show the general extent to which lathing as a trade is characterized by the conditions of the job and the materials at hand. Various proprietary manufactured devices are also available to the lather that serve many of the same functions as these job-improvised items. The intent here is to illustrate the facility available to the designer through the skill of the lather in improvising connections and attachments in the field.

McClusky bend. Fig. 10 shows a method used on the job to bend channel irons at right angles that maintains intact more of the inherent strength of the channel that can be obtained by a joined angle. This bend is generally formed on the lather's bench with the vise and monkey wrench. Similar bends can be made in flat and band iron. The bend

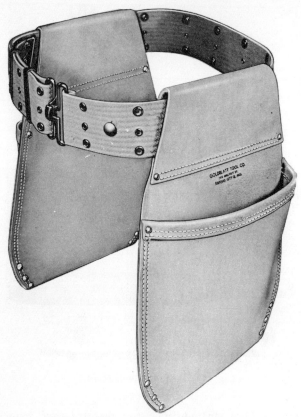

Fig. 8 — Lathers Nail Bag

Fig. 9 — Water Level

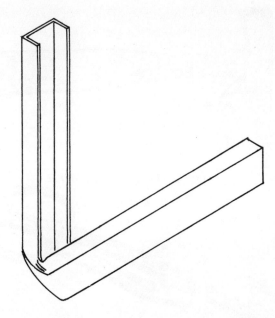

Fig. 10 — McClusky Bend

is useful in many furring conditions, particularly where continuity of the framework is required in changes of plane.

Beam and runner clip. Fig. 11 shows a devicc commonly used to attach runner channels to the flanges of structural steel beams. The clip is formed of round rod in two separate interlocking loops. One loop includes a cradle for the runner and is pre-formed to hook over the beam flange. The other loop fits as shown in the illustration, and is bent over the opposite flange in place, thus tightening the clamp. Fig. 12 shows a variation of the rod clip used as a runner hanger.

Furring slug and strut. Fig. 13 illustrates one of the devices used for attaching furring structures to masonry walls. A channel strut is held in position against the masonry by a wedge or slug driven between its flanges through a horizontal mortar joint. The strut serves as a spacer and an anchor between the plaster base and the masonry surface.

Hanger wire clip. Fig. 14 shows a method for attaching suspension wires to beam flanges. The clip is formed in two separate interlocking pieces. The open loop is made at the bench and forms one side of the clip; the other side is formed in place as an extention of the tie loop. The four point contact so provided develops the full strength of the hanger.

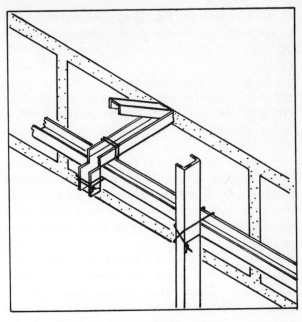

Fig. 13 — Furring Slug and Strut

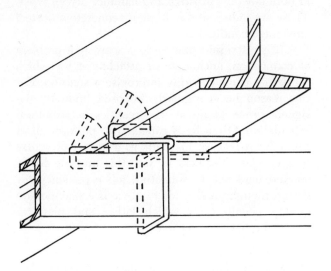

Fig. 11 — Beam and Runner Clip

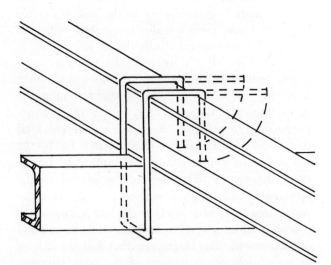

Fig. 12 — Rod Clip Hanger

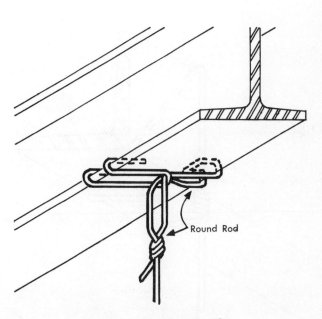

Round Rod

Fig. 14 — Hanger Wire Clip

Hanger wire tie. Fig. 15 shows a common wire tie applied to angle iron carriers that develops the full beam strength of the angle section by eliminating torque.

Saddle ties. Fig. 16 illustrates two ties for hanging or attaching furring and runner channels. The wrapping and crossing of the tie prevent rotation of the channels, and is accomplished with minimum twisting.

Channel splice. Fig. 17 shows the typical splice for furring and runner channels. The two types of members are spliced similarly except for the length of lap, as indicated. Notice that the two channels are engaged face to face, to provide a strong, compact joint.

Channel spacers and shims. Fig. 18 shows several methods of forming and attaching lath shims and channel spacers. These devices provide an air space in multiple lath armatures which might be desirable for a variety of reasons such as fire protection of small vertical shafts.

Figures 19 and 20 are examples of two typical assemblies utilizing the various devices described.

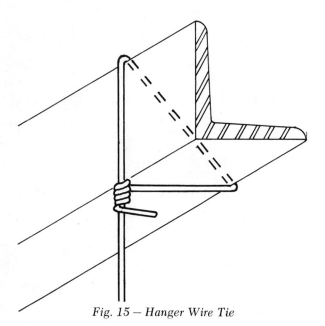

Fig. 15 — Hanger Wire Tie

Further discussion of assemblies and systems is to be found in Chapter 5.

In addition to the common devices illustrated, many other special methods for attachment and anchorage are known and used by lathers which are too numerous and too diversified for convenient reference. Among these are the various stud drivers, of both powder cartridge and hammer driven types. These are indispensable to many concrete and steel anchorage conditions.

It is often said that there is scarcely a problem of connection, anchorage or attachment for which the lather cannot readily improvise a solution. For this reason he is regularly imposed upon by designers prone to ignore the realities of structural articulation. Often he is expected to perform all of the difficult feats of his trade as a matter of course in every job. Needless to say, this attitude has a marked tendency to substitute job expediency for design thought, and leads to obvious economic and quality penalties for which lather and plasterer cannot be held responsible.

Erection of lath. Lath functions as the base, and often the reinforcement, for plaster. Because plaster must remain an inseparable part of the lath, whether the lath be metal or gypsum, so the lath must be bound to its support. In the case of flexible bases that are mechanically integrated with the plaster slab, structural continuity is important; in the case of metal lath, discontinuity tends to occur where individual sheets join, a structural problem overcome by lapping and securely fastening the sheets together. Gypsum lath, on the other hand, produces discontinuity effects of a different kind that in many instances are compensated for by the staggering of joints without attempting to bridge them structurally. The methods employed in the erection of lath depend on the type of lath, the supporting structure, whether the lath is applied to a horizontal or a vertical surface, and the method of attachment. The discussion that follows can be accepted only as an account of the more common conditions. It makes no attempt to describe all ac-

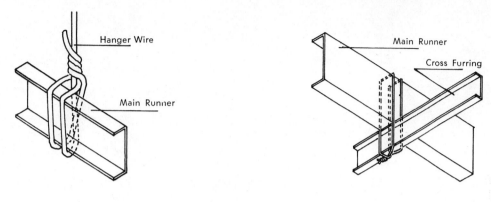

Fig. 16 — Saddle Ties

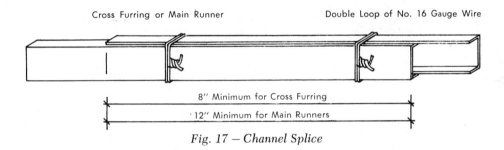

Fig. 17 — Channel Splice

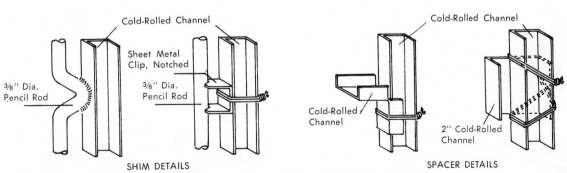

Fig. 18 — Channel Shims and Spacers

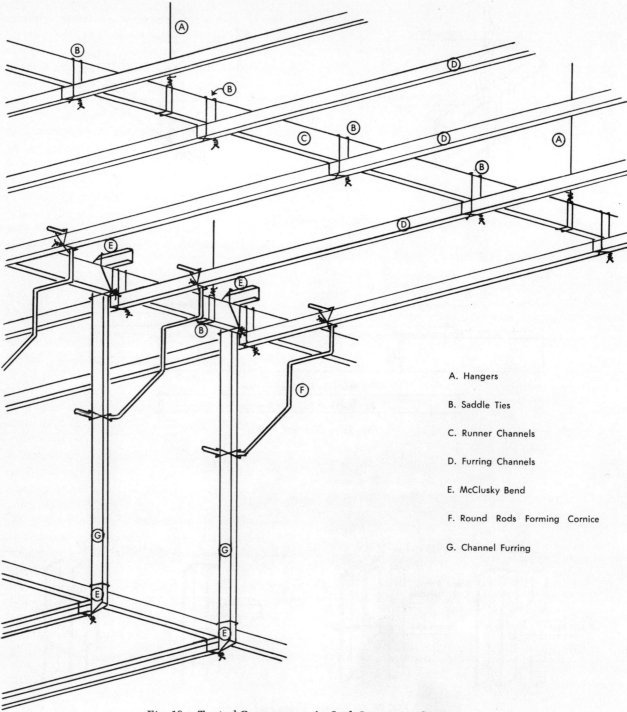

A. Hangers

B. Saddle Ties

C. Runner Channels

D. Furring Channels

E. McClusky Bend

F. Round Rods Forming Cornice

G. Channel Furring

Fig. 19 – Typical Components of a Lath Supporting Structure

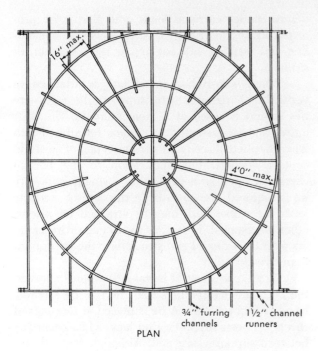

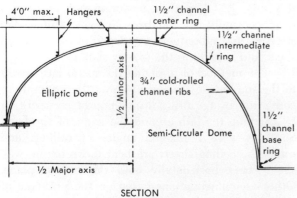

Fig. 20 — Typical Assembly for a Domed Ceiling

Some of the more important of these solutions which have become virtual rules follow:

Recommended procedures call for all lath to be applied with the long dimension of the sheet or board placed perpendicular to the supports. When applying lath to solid vertical surfaces, the long dimension should be placed horizontally. Studless solid partitions are constructed by utilizing long length laths, either metallic or gypsum, erected with the long dimension standing vertically between floor and ceiling.

Ribbed metal lath is placed with the ribs against the supports. Gypsum lath is usually manufactured with a special and easily recognized face side, which is placed to receive the plaster. Joining of lath has been the subject of recent consideration by the industry. Generally, metal laths and wire laths are lapped at the ends at least 1 inch, and ½ inch at the sides except in the case of ribbed laths, where outside ribs may be nested.

In general, gypsum lath should be butted on all sides with ends staggered and side joints aligned. End joints may be arranged in either of two ways: staggered on supports only, or staggered between supports with special clips used to secure the ends together. Some authorities recommend that all joints be covered with strip lath in quality construction.

Lath is attached in a number of ways, most of which are common; these methods include, however, a substantial variety of proprietary systems. Of course, the method employed in a particular case depends on the nature of both the lath and the supporting structure. The various standard attachment devices are illustrated and described in Chapter 2. Here we are concerned more with the methods and conditions of use. Detailed specification data are to be found in the published standards of the various manufacturing and trade associations, the literature of the individual manufacturers, and in the specifications of the American Standards Association.

Metal lath, wire lath and wire fabric are all secured to wooden supports by nails or staples. ASA specifications require that these materials be

ceptable methods, particularly the many proprietary systems available.

The installation of lath, like many other jobs, entails recurring problems which, once solved, are subject to classification for future reference. These solutions constitute the standard practice of the trade where these recognizable problems arise.

fastened at intervals not exceeding 6 inches for horizontal application with 1½ inch gauged, barbed roofing nails with $\frac{7}{16}$ inch heads, driven home. On vertical supports, bent 4d common nails, 1 inch roofing nails or 1 inch 4 gauge wire staples are permitted. Where ribbed lath, stiffened wire lath or sheet lath is installed, nails and staples must be ⅜ inch longer than non-ribbed expanded metal lath and the other laths mentioned. This rule holds except where fastening occurs through ribs, whereupon 1⅜ inch penetration for horizontal application and at least ¾ inch penetration in vertical supports is needed. When common nails are used to attach expanded metal lath, they must be bent across at least three strands.

The wire tie is the most common device for attaching metal lath to supports of unnailable materials and for fastening one sheet of lath to another. The wire for this purpose as well as for use in furring and suspension is specified by the ASA as: "Galvanized, soft annealed steel, or of a material and size having superior corrosion resistance and equivalent strength. . . ." The Metal Lath Manufacturers Association's "Specifications for Metal Lathing and Furring" call for tie wire to be Class 1, galvanized in accordance with Federal Specification "QQ-W-461e Wire, Steel, Carbon, (Round, Bare and Coated)," and further states that wire size shall be measured in U.S. Steel Wire Gage. [While the American Society for Testing Materials publishes no "standard specification" for tie wire to be used particularly for the attachment of lath or the fastening of furring, a specification (ASTM A112) for wire lengths used for tying telephone wires to insulators describes zinc coatings and metal performance in terms of ductility and strength for conditions in many ways similar to those encountered in lathing work. However, reference to these standards must be accompanied by a conversion in wire size units from U.S. Steel Wire Gage to British Wire Gage.] In general, the requirements for lather's tie wire are that it be of standard and consistent size and strength; soft enough to twist and draw sufficiently without rupture; elastic enough not to

deform under carrying loads; and that it be protected against corrosion in such a way that handling and forming will not impair the corrosion resistance.

Where non-ribbed metal lath is attached to vertical or horizontal metal supports, 18 gage wire ties should be used at 6 inch intervals. The ASA makes special fastening provisions for ribbed lath when applied directly to certain types of joists in contact ceilings. For application to the bottom chords of open web steel joists a single loop wire tie is required at every rib. In the case of concrete joists the ribbed lath may be attached by inserts, other mechanical devices, or by 10 gage wire hangers with the exposed end struck over the lath rather than twisted.

Where one sheet of metal lath adjoins another, the best practice requires that the two be securely laced or tied together. A tie is placed at side laps of sheets between supports. End laps, when occurring between supports, are tied. Although methods for this vary, it is important to obtain sufficient structural continuity of the base to avoid differential stressing and subsequent transferral of concentrated shear and tension to the plaster slab.

The method of applying the metal lath sheets to the supporting structure follows the principle of continuity by requiring installation of cornerite, or by carrying the lath around the angle of the base. Similarly with horizontal angles at ceilings and soffits the ceiling sheets are bent down or the wall sheets bent horizontally onto the ceiling plane. Other recommendations based on the principle of unrestrained angles call for the definite interruption of the plaster base at critical plane intersections. This principle is discussed in Chapter 6, under "Structural Cracking."

Gypsum lath attachment can involve many proprietary systems. These include patented clips for connecting abutting edges of sheets, attaching laths to unnailable supports, special ceiling and floor runners, and similar items. Specifications and directions for the use of such devices are published in all important cases by the manufacturers.

The ASA specifies standard nailing for gypsum lath on wooden supports, requiring 13 gage 1⅛ inch blued nails with ¹⁹⁄₆₄ inch flat heads for ⅜ inch lath, and a similar nail ⅛ inch longer for ½ inch lath. Gypsum lath 16 inches wide is secured by 4 nails per lath in each support, and 24 inch wide lath by 5 nails. Where special fire resistive construction is required, the rating desired should be checked to ascertain the type, size and spacing of nails. Nails are driven carefully in a line square with the face of the lath, flush but not drawn, so that the lath face is undamaged. No nail is driven closer than ⅜ inches to the edge of the lath.

For attachment with staples, the Gypsum Association recommends 16 U. S. gage flattened galvanized wire staples with a ⁷⁄₁₆ inch wide crown and ⅞ inch long legs for ⅜ inch thick lath, and 1 inch long legs for ½ inch lath. For ⅜ inch lath, staples are driven with the crown parallel to the long dimension of the framing member, using not less than 4 staples per 16 inch width of lath per framing member and not more than 5 inches on center; driven in such a manner that the crown bears tightly against the lath, but does not cut into the face paper. For ½ inch thick lath, the spacing is the same as that detailed above. However, in 24 inch spacings of supports, 5 staples should be spaced 4 inches on center per lath per support. For 24 inch wide lath, 6 staples per lath per support are recommended.

Lathers who specialize in the application of gypsum lath develop great speed and precision in handling, fitting and nailing the material. Various tools such as nail holders, special stapling machines, and other devices have been developed to aid the lather in this work and are in use in some areas.

Installation of accessories is the final operation performed by the lather. The various accessories serve several basic functions. Terminals of several types serve to define limits and protect the perimeter of the plaster plane, and are used at junctures of other materials, to frame openings, and for similar purposes. Grounds of various types, some designed to perform multiple functions, establish the thickness of plaster over the base, and the contour of surface. Other accessories define and reinforce corners, angles, provide for shrinkage and expansion, provide for the attachment of trim or appurtenances, and the like.

Most accessories are either partly visible in the finished plasterwork or affect in some way the visual character of the plaster. For these reasons considerable precision is often required in the installation. The line made by a corner bead must be true and plumb, as that made by a picture mould must be straight and level. Joints made in casings and trim must be clean and tight. The skill required for proper installation depends in part on the extent to which accessories must be formed, spliced and aligned; whether or not they are partially or fully exposed; and on the importance of the function served.

The forming of accessories, like many other lathing operations, presents many problems for which the craft has found practical solutions it has retained and repeated often enough to become standard practice. Some of these are described and illustrated farther on. Others, while less widely used and, therefore, not discussed here, are nonetheless ingenious or useful, and continue to exist in the repertory of tricks of the individual craftsman.

Fig. 21 illustrates a method of forming a corner bead at a re-entrant angle. The bead is cut and a splice wire inserted in the nose to regulate alignment. The bend is then made and the flanges are tied to lock the joint.

Fig. 22 shows how a moulded casing bead is formed at a reentrant angle by coping to produce a mitred appearance. A similar procedure may be followed with bull nose corner beads. This device allows faster, more convenient fitting than a mitred joint, at the same time providing for better fastening and a stronger joint.

Fig. 23 illustrates a base screed which has been cut through to the flange and bent 90 degrees to form a re-entrant angle. This provides continuity in the outstanding leg and reinforces the corner.

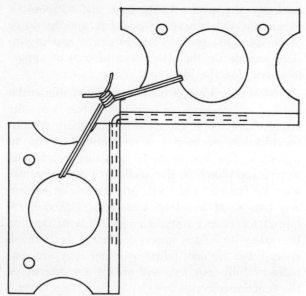

Fig. 21 — Forming Corner Bead Around Re-entrant Angle

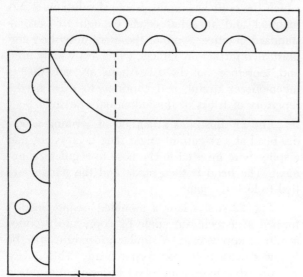

Fig. 22 — Forming Casing Bead at Re-entrant Angle

Fig. 24 illustrates the formation of a projecting angle with a base screed by cutting and bending.

Fig. 25 demonstrates a method of increasing grounds by cutting the wing of an expanded cor-

ner bead. Cuts are made and the bead is fastened in place. When the bead is secured, the lather pulls down on the nose of the bead, causing it to rotate outward. This method is often used in lathing columns where relatively thick grounds are required for fire protection.

Accessories used to define and trim curved openings in plaster are generally formed by means of wood or channel iron templates. The template is first formed according to the required contour. The flange or wing of the accessory is then cut at intervals sufficient to permit a smooth bend. The accessory is then attached to the template in such a way as to not hinder permanent fastening to the plaster base. After the accessory is secured in place, the template is removed.

Fig. 26 illustrates a method of splicing corner bead by inserting a wire in the nose and tying the two pieces through the flanges. The aligning wire is kinked slightly to prevent it from sliding past the joint. When two straight lengths of an accessory are joined together, a means of alignment must be provided if the joint is to be inconspicuous.

Fig. 27 shows an easily formed sleeve slip used to splice and align two pieces of concealed picture mould. Alignment is usually done with plumb bob and level in conjunction with control grounds attached to the lath only, and not anchored to the supporting structure. Depending on the type of accessory and plaster base, attachment may be stapling, wire-tying, or light nailing.

III. PREPARATION OF NON-LATH PLASTER BASES

When plaster is applied directly to masonry or concrete without lath or furring, special problems sometimes arise. Although usually the work of other trades, the surface condition of such bases is of concern to the plasterer, and often requires his attention prior to application of the plaster. Aside from preparatory steps that can be taken by the plasterer to assure successful work, there are certain basic requirements for non-lath bases. These requirements have to do with their inherent quality

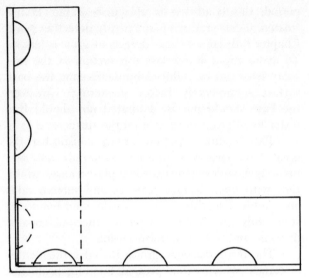

Fig. 23 – Forming Base Screed at Re-entrant Angle

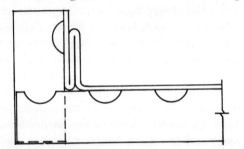

Fig. 24 – Forming Projecting Angle with Base Screed

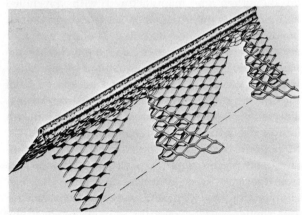

Courtesy Bostwick Steel Lath Co.

Fig. 25 – Cutting Expanded Wing of Corner Bead to Increase Grounds

over which normally the plasterer has no control. **Unit masonry** must present a sound, true face without sharp protrusions or depressions if the plaster slab is to be of relatively uniform thickness. Joints should be struck flush with the face and properly cured. The masonry over which a continuous surface of plaster is placed should be of the same material throughout and of uniform suction. Where the masonry material changes, the plaster plane should be interrupted by a control joint, or the juncture spanned by strip lath, the former method being the more positive. Where non-uniform moisture conditions exist in the masonry surface, over-all wetting immediately before plastering is required to equalize suction.

The surface must be free of dust, loose particles, grease, or other foreign material that might interfere with bonding. Loose dry material is removed by brushing, compressed air, or other methods.

Efflorescence is removed by washing with a 10 per cent solution of muriatic acid applied to a wetted surface and flushed clean. Oil and grease are removed by burning with the blow torch or by an acid bath.

Ordinarily, plaster should not be applied directly to the interior face of an exterior perimeter

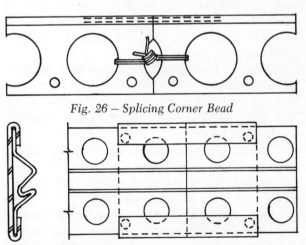

Fig. 26 – Splicing Corner Bead

Fig. 27 – Concealed Picture Mould Spliced with Formed Sleeve

wall. Unless the wall is effectively dampproofed and condensation conditions do not exist, the chances of water damage and staining are great. It is necessary to isolate the plaster slab from moisture within the wall in order to maintain an effective bond between the masonry and plaster in a direct application. Often this is accomplished by cavity wall construction. Most coatings that are used as moisture barriers over masonry also destroy the suction characteristics of the materials. When direct application of this type is unavoidable, the exterior surface of the masonry should be treated for moisture control. Recommended practice is to fur and lath the interior surface of all exterior walls that are to be plastered.

Masonry materials are classified as plaster bases according to suction characteristics, and divided into three categories: those materials providing high suction rates; those providing medium suction; and those of low suction. The first category includes soft common brick, soft or porous partition tile, gypsum partition tile, and lightweight concrete blocks. In the medium suction group are common concrete block, common face brick (medium hard), medium hard tile, and many types of stone. The third group includes hard-burnt brick, glazed tile and some types of stone such as granite. Most unit masonry materials available can be used as plaster bases for both gypsum and portland cement plasters — except, of course, gypsum tile, which requires gypsum plaster.

Masonry bases generally provide both mechanical and adhesive bond. Mechanical bond is strongest in rough surfaced porous materials. Many partition tiles are scored during manufacture to improve mechanical bond.

Masonry materials in the higher suction ranges have a tendency to withdraw the mixing water from the applied plaster at excessive rates. With gypsum plasters, if there is insufficient water left for the plaster to fully set, *dryout* may result. This can be remedied by subsequently spraying water on the slab. In portland cement plaster, which requires the presence of water for curing over a longer period, this condition is also undesirable. If untreated, it can produce permanently defective work. Chapter 6 discusses these defects at greater length. To avoid rapid water loss the suction of the masonry base can be reduced by dampening the base surface immediately before plastering. However, the base should not be saturated nor should free water be allowed to remain on the surface.

The medium suction group constitutes the greater proportion of masonry materials, and fortunately includes many excellent plaster bases. Materials with ideal surface textures and suction rates are readily available which provide good bond and sufficiently low suction to reduce the incidence of dryouts, and aid in uniform curing.

The third masonry group includes the denser materials, which often present bonding problems. In many cases these surfaces cannot be used as bases for the direct application of plaster without the interposition of a bonding agent. This is a thin coat of specially formulated material having transitive properties, and is discussed as a basic plastering material in Chapter 2. Another method of overcoming the lack of adhesive bond in hard materials is by deforming the surface to produce mechanical bond by keying. Some of the harder tiles, such as those used in walls where a plastered surface is desired on one side and a glazed ceramic surface on the other, are manufactured with dovetailed kerfing on the unfinished side for plaster or mortar bond. In the absence of either bonding agent or adequate keying, metal lath can be attached to the hard masonry surface to provide the necessary bond. In this event the lath must be spaced from the surface sufficiently to allow for plaster keying. This is accomplished by using self-furring lath, rib lath or flat lath with self-furring lathing nails.

Monolithic concrete. A sound bond between concrete and plaster requires primarily a surface free from loose particles, coatings, dust and other foreign matter. As with unit masonry, efflorescence and similar surface deposits can be removed by washing with a 10 per cent solution of muriatic acid properly flushed. Grease and oil film can be removed by an acid bath. Heavier deposits can be removed by burning. Dust and scale are removed by brushing.

Adequate bonding of plaster on monolithic concrete surfaces must depend on mechanical keying. For this reason the concrete surface must be suitably roughened regardless of location or the type of plaster used. The necessary bonding keys can be produced in the surface in several practical ways: the contact surfaces of the formwork can be specially treated prior to the pouring of concrete; the concrete surface can be treated before complete set; or the concrete surface can be treated after the material has set and cured. Different procedures are required in each method.

The texture of concrete surfaces can be controlled to some extent, by the selection of form materials. Unplaned lumber is sometimes used although such forms are often difficult to strip and tend to leave splinters and fibers attached to the concrete. A more satisfactory method is to spray contact surfaces with ammonia, which gives the lumber a coarse texture. Burlap or material of similar texture is sometimes used to line the forms. Specially corrugated linings also are used that provide a more positive key pattern in the concrete surface. Certain proprietary devices, such as the "Kif" which is a flared serrated disc of flexible material — can be attached to the form surface to produce regulated patterns of key cavities in the concrete surface.

To be most effective, corrugations must be ¼ inch deep and not more than 1½ inches wide. The disc forms should be spaced on centers not greater than 6 inches. Various other devices can be obtained or improvised for this purpose that can be equally effective if it is kept in mind that key cavities as a substitute for a roughened surface having a uniform texture usually require considerable deformation of the plane surface, and must be spaced in reasonable scale to the thickness of the applied plaster coat. The main consideration in sizing and spacing the pattern for the key type of mechanical bond is a structural one. It involves the sectional area of plaster available at key fillets and

other critical points to resist shearing stress concentrations and the span of the plaster slab between keys.

There are also several ways in which to produce a mechanical bonding surface on monolithic concrete after removal of the forms. If the forms are stripped before the surface is completely set, it can be roughened by wire brushing or scratching with a scoring tool. Treatment by this method can be aided by applying set-retarding compound to the contact surfaces of the forms before pouring. This is particularly helpful when it is inconvenient or impracticable to strip forms from concrete that is still green and relatively weak, as in structural concrete.

The treatment of concrete surfaces that have completely set requires heavy tooling or acid etching. A bonding texture can be produced by dressing the surface with a bush hammer, a common stonecutters' tool, or by spawling the surface with a hatchet. Stone dressing and cutting chisels either manually or mechanically driven can also be used. Pneumatic tools or other deep vibration producing equipment, however, should not be used on reinforced structural concrete before complete curing has taken place in order to avoid possible damage to the bond between concrete and reinforcement.

An etched bonding surface can be produced with repeated applications of a relatively strong solution of muriatic acid. The acid must be handled carefully and, for safety, it should not be used in proportions stronger than one part acid in six parts of water by volume. To confine the action of the acid to the surface, the natural suction of the concrete should be satisfied by a liberal application of clean water prior to application of the acid solution. When the desired texture has been developed, all traces of the acid must be removed by thoroughly washing the surface.

Still another acceptable method of preparing a monolithic concrete surface for plastering, which is in common use for certain conditions, is the application of a dash coat of a rich, low consistency mixture of portland cement, sand and water. This mixture is applied unevenly by forcible dashing, usually with a coarse brush. Although the material has some transitive characteristics and is in a sense a bond coat, it is not to be confused with patented bonding agents used over monolithic concrete for gypsum plastering. The dash coat of grout may be considered more a surface preparation, a method for roughening the monolithic surface, than as an intermediate plaster coat. It is not a substitute for the scratch coat in portland cement plastering and stucco work, nor is it a reliable bonding agent for gypsum plaster.

Bonding agents or bond plasters are used as a first coat for gypsum plaster over monolithic concrete and other low adhesion surfaces. These are discussed as basic materials in Chapter 2. A finish coat of plaster can be applied directly to the bond coat, eliminating the scratch and brown coats, if the intention is merely to give a smooth finish to the concrete. However, full plaster thickness is required if the surface is to be straightened. Bonding agents are useful in remodeling work where special conditions arise, as in the case where plaster must be bonded to discontinuous or unrelated materials. With many of these products safe bond can be secured under controlled conditions to masonry, tile, wood, glass, plasterwork, painted surfaces, and metal.

Foamed insulation board. Recently a non-moisture conducting foamed insulation board has been introduced commercially. Subsequently other materials of a similar nature have become available. Although at this writing it is too early to evaluate the total performance of these products, they are to be observed with some interest. As yet no industry standards have been set and the materials now available conform only to the standards of the individual producers. At least one of these products is sold as a lightweight board 10 inches or 12 inches wide, in lengths of 3 feet, 8 feet, and 9 feet. This board, 1 inch thick, is made of foamed polystyrene expanded to 40 times its original volume. The internal air cell structure is non-interconnecting, and the material being impervious to water, offers a relatively moisture proof, vapor resistant plaster base having insulating value.

These boards are attached to the masonry surface by a ¼ inch bonding coat of portland cement mortar applied first to the back of the board, or attached by adhesives as recommended by the manufacturer. They may be applied with the long dimension either horizontally or vertically, but in any case the edges are butted tightly. Manufacturers of these materials generally recommend that rich mixes of sanded plaster be applied in three coats.

CHAPTER 4

PLASTERING

The purpose of this chapter is to familiarize the reader with the methods, skills and equipment available for construction in the plastering trade, and to outline the important conditions and limitations affecting performance. It is not intended to be a manual for instruction in apprentice training, nor is it to be viewed as outlining the only acceptable procedures. Rather, it aims to help the reader recognize those factors in the trade that have led to the establishment of existing practices. By an awareness of the principles upon which methods of plaster application are based, and an understanding of inherent limitations, all persons sharing the responsibility for the construction of buildings will gain a foundation of basic knowledge that will enable them to contribute to the progressive development of better methods and higher standards.

For convenience of reference, this chapter is divided into three sections dealing with specific aspects of plastering: I. Skills, Tools and Equipment, II. Preparation of Material, III. Application of Plaster Coats.

Like many other building materials, plaster usually constitutes one lamination of a composite enclosure assembly. It is either the last, or next to last, component to be installed in a system made up of a number of parts and requiring several operations. It is selected because it possesses those characteristics which no other component of the assembly can provide by itself. Among its major functions, plaster serves as a refining element insofar as it can correct minor deviations in the alignment of other components of the system, conceal pipes, ducts, conduits and the like, and provide a base for decoration.

I. SKILLS, TOOLS AND EQUIPMENT

The plasterer's art has undergone many changes throughout the history of the craft. We have noted in Chapter 1 that in medieval England the skills required of him were akin to those of the artist, and he was obliged to produce his own designs for the ornamentation of buildings while he applied the plaster. During another period, casting and moulding were his major skills. In our time, the skills demanded of the plasterer are again in the process of change. The introduction of plastering

81

machines has required the development of a mechanical bent previously foreign to the craft. As always throughout the history of this versatile craft, this transition is being made effectively.

Naturally, the number of men working together as a team during plastering depends upon the size of the area being plastered, the completion schedule, whether the plaster is being applied by hand or by machine, and other factors. But the classification of skills found on any job will remain fairly constant. Descriptions follow of the three major categories of labor employed.

Journeyman. Of all members of the trade. the journeyman possesses the highest skill and bears the greatest responsibility. Often he works with helpers and is responsible for the work of every member of his crew. It is the job of the journeyman to set all levels and lines and to lay out the work. The journeyman in the plastering trades, like those in other construction crafts, often possesses certain skills that make him more valuable for particular phases of the operation. Some men do only finishing, while others may spend most of their time applying basecoat materials. In addition to these distinctions there is another group of journeymen who are skilled in casting, moulding and ornamental work. Their work is usually considered a separate craft within the plastering trade. A journeyman usually achieves his status in recognition of training experience and skills received or developed during an extended period of apprenticeship.

Helper or apprentice. Before he can become a journeyman plasterer, the mechanic must undergo on-the-job training and other instruction. Under the National Standards of Apprenticeship for the crafts of the plastering industry, established by the U. S. Department of Labor, a man desiring to become a journeyman plasterer must work not less than four years at the crafts of plastering, casting, artificial marble, and imitation stone work; and not less than five years at the crafts of modeling, sculpturing and model making.

In addition to on-the-job training, each apprentice must supplement his experience with 144 hours

of classroom instruction for each year of his apprentice training in subjects related to the trade.[1] On the job, the apprentice acts as an assistant to the journeyman in all straightening, filling-in and finishing operations after the journeyman has established the critical elements of the work.

Plasterer's tender. This class includes those men whose job it is to mix the plaster, deliver it to the journeyman, construct scaffolds, handle materials, perform the clean-up tasks and other jobs. They are the least skilled members of the plastering team.

Plastering crew for machine application. The application of plaster by machine has brought about a new organization of plastering crews. The greatest share of the total material handled is now applied by one person, the nozzle-man. The leveling operations are conducted by a crew of darby men who follow the nozzle-man as closely as possible. The plasterer's tender is responsible for keeping the plaster mixed, maintaining the continuous operation of the pumping machine, and moving the hoses for the nozzle-man.

The number of men in a plastering crew varies; the capacity of the machine will to a great extent determine the number required. Smaller pumps that can deliver 1 to 1½ cubic feet of mortar per minute might require a crew of one nozzle-man, two plasterers and two plasterer's tenders. Larger machines may require one nozzle-man, three or four plasterers, and three laborers. Many contractors have stated than an important consideration in job managment is to keep the machine in continuous operation. If there are many closets, breaks in the line of the wall or ceiling, intermediate partitions, and the like, a team requires more plasterers to level the surface than would be the case in a large open area. In highly subdivided buildings such as hotels and apartments, in order to keep up with the machine as many as six plasterers may be needed per nozzle-man.

When scratch coats are being applied, fewer plasterers are required per crew. One machine manufacturer states that to apply exterior scratch coat at the rate of 150 to 225 square yards per hour, a crew of one nozzle-man, one plasterer and two laborers are needed. For applying the brown coat two additional plasterers are required.[2]

When acoustical plaster is being applied, the crew may consist of only the nozzle-man and a laborer to keep him supplied with plaster. In the hands of a skilled workman certain sprayed finish coats can be placed to such a degree of uniformity and precision that straightening operations are not required.

Training programs for mechanical application. On-the-job training of crews in the use of plaster pumps has usually been provided by the manufacturers of the various machines. Training schools staffed by technical representatives are conducted throughout the United States. These courses teach a variety of subjects ranging from the use and maintenance of machines, to handling of the job, scaffolding requirements, and the mixing and proportioning of plaster. The length of time required to train a crew depends largely upon the individual natural abilities of the journeymen to acquire the feel of the machine and their readiness to accept the new method. In the final analysis, the ultimate training and practice in the effective use of plastering machines becomes the problem of each individual shop, and is solved accordingly, often with great ingenuity.

PLASTERING TOOLS

So far, the current trend of mechanization in plastering has had little effect on the assortment of hand tools needed by the plasterer. While use of the hawk and trowel has, to some degree, been supplanted for handling the bulk of the basecoat material, their use on any particular job appears to be required no less frequently. The use of straightening and finishing tools, that category which accounts for the greater share of the assortment, has been affected little, if at all, by the advent of machines. It is interesting to note that archaeological explorations in Egypt by Dr. Flinders Petrie unearthed plastering tools that were used about 2500 B.C.[3] Although somewhat smaller than the tools used today, they bear a strong resemblance to those found in a journeyman's kit. Perhaps the difference in size of the tools may serve as a commentary on the relative pressures of the two periods on labor productivity. Small hand tools are owned by the journeyman, while larger tools and equipment, such as those used jointly and those required for the mixing, delivery, storage and mechanical application of plaster, are usually the property of the plastering contractor.

Trowels are used to apply, spread, shape, and smooth plaster. They consist of a tempered or stainless steel blade with a handle. The blade must resist scratches and corrosion, and must not stain the plaster surface. The shape and size of the blade is determined by the purpose for which the tool is intended and the manner in which it is used. The four most common types are:

The *rectangular trowel* (Fig. 1) is approximately 4½ inches by 11 inches. It serves as the principal conveyor and manipulator of mortar.

The *pointing trowel* (Fig. 2) is smaller than the rectangular trowel and pointed. It is designed for use in places where larger trowels will not fit. A variation of this trowel is the pipe trowel, which, as the name implies, is used for working around and behind pipes. This tool is 2 inches wides and about 10 inches long. The nose, instead of coming to a sharp point, is rounded.

The *margin trowel* (Fig. 3) is similar to the pointing trowel in size, but has a square end, and is used where larger trowels are inconvenient. These trowels, because of the square end on the blade, work in small areas similar to the way rectangular trowels are used on larger areas.

The *angle trowel* (Fig. 4) is shaped like a V and sometimes as a U. This trowel is used for finishing interior corners (angles).

The hawk (Fig. 5) is a square lightweight platform with a centered vertical handle used for carrying mortar. The size of the hawk varies from 10 inches to 14 inches, and it is usually made of aluminum. During application it is used to carry the mortar from the mortar board to the wall or ceiling area where the plaster is to be applied. Plaster is removed from the hawk with the trowel, and then laid in place. Generally the hawk will carry from three to five trowelfuls of mortar.

The float, as the name implies, is used to glide over the surface of the plaster to fill voids and hollows, and to level bumps left during previous operations. It also densifies and compacts the material under the pressure applied by the plasterer. Another purpose of the float is to impart a texture to finish plaster. A variety of floats is available, each having a special size, shape or blade for a particular type of performance. These are the floats most commonly used:

The *wood float* (Fig. 6) is the oldest known plastering tool. Two floats, dating from 2500 B.C., are owned by University College in London. They

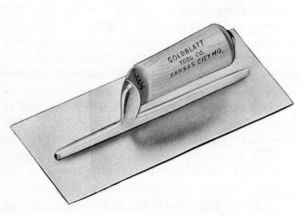

Fig. 1 — Rectangular Trowel

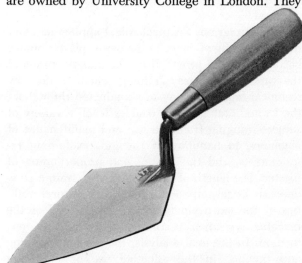

Fig. 2 — Pointing Trowel

Fig. 3 — Margin Trowel

Fig. 4 — Angle Trowel

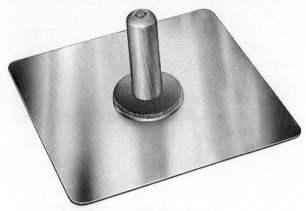

Fig. 5 — Hawk

Fig. 6 — Wood Float

were discovered at Kahun, Egypt. One is 3¾ inches long and 1⅛ inches wide, and is rounded at both ends. The other is slightly larger and appears to have been used for rough work.[4] Modern floats are usually 4 inches by 9 inches by ¾ inches and have a wood handle. The grain of the wood affects the degree to which the float will cut into the plaster surface. Cross-grained floats tend to cut more rapidly and are less prone to warping than those with longitudinal grain. The pride the plasterer takes in his tools is illustrated in the description of wood floats given by Millar in his work, *Plastering; Plain and Decorative,* written in 1887. In describing wood floats he states: "With the exception of panel and mastic floats which are made of hard wood, all other kinds are made of yellow pine and there are none so well made, or at least so suitable to the worker, as those made by himself."[5]

Panel and mastic floats, at least in Millar's time, were made of beech, pear or other hard light-colored woods. They were used during the floating of the finish coat. The woods from which these floats were made were selected because they would not stain the putty-coat.

The *angle float* (Fig. 7) is made of aluminum or stainless steel, and is box-shaped like a wide U; it is 9 inches to 10 inches long, 4 inches wide, and the side walls turn up ¾ inches. The aluminum

float is used for the least abrasive finish coats, since the sole (blade) is more likely to scratch than the stainless steel tool.

The *sponge float* (Fig. 8) is often used where a certain texture is to be imparted to the finish coat. The size of these floats varies according to the preferance of the plasterer. The soles (blades) of sponge floats consist of a flat metal plate 8 inches to 10 inches long and 4 inches to 5 inches wide, to which a layer of rubber or foam plastic is cemented.

Fig. 7 — Angle Float

Fig. 8 — Sponge Float

The density of the rubber or plastic will determine the degree of texture that the finished surface will have.

Cork and carpet floats (Fig. 9) are similar in performance to sponge floats except that the soles have a layer of cork or carpet attached to them. They are inclined to wear more rapidly than sponge floats.

The paddle (Fig. 10) is a wedge-shaped tool with a blade 2 inches to 3 inches wide, 3 inches long and tapered from ¾ inches to a fine edge. A handle approximately 5 inches long is attached to, or cast as, part of the blade. Paddles can be made of wood, hard rubber, light metal alloys or plastic. They are used to clean and smooth out the interior angles of a room. In some cases the use of this tool is substituted for trowelling of the angles as cleaning and straightening can be accomplished faster, and therefore with less expense. However, this method does not produce work of a quality comparable to that of a properly trowelled job. It is most frequently used in lower cost residential work or other building types where more emphasis is placed on economy than on achieving work of the highest quality.

The metal scratcher is a hand tool used to scarify the surface of scratch and brown coats to provide adequate mechanical bond with subsequent plaster applications. A piece of metal lath is often used effectively for this purpose.

Brushes. When a surface is being leveled, either during basecoat or finishing operations, the tools must move over the plaster smoothly. Too dry a plaster surface (that is, one from which too much of the original mixing water has been removed) will resist the trowel or float. Where necessary, therefore, small amounts of water are dashed onto the wall or ceiling to act as a lubricant between the tooling surface and the plaster. This water is applied by brush. During base-coat levelling operations if water is required it is dashed or flipped onto the surface, to avoid picking up particles of loose sand and plaster. The use of excessive amounts of water is to be avoided. During finishing, the water

Fig. 9 — Carpet Float

Fig. 10 — Paddle

is applied by lightly brushing the surface of the final coat. Excess plaster left on the finish coat when all trowelling is completed is removed or blended into the surface by a very light brushing. These small deposits are called *dribbles* or *fat*.

Brushes are also used to produce texture in the final coat. The variations possible in brushed textures is limited only by the ingenuity of the plasterer. Examples of brushed textures will be found illustrated later in this chapter. These are the brushes most commonly used, with descriptions of the important differences in their construction:

The browning brush (Fig. 11) is used during base-coat operations for dashing water onto the plaster. The chief requirement of this brush is that it hold a fairly large amount of water. The size of the brushes that can be used varies, but generally range from 6 inches long, 4 inches to 5 inches wide, and 2 inches thick.

Finishing brushes. Because these brushes must come in direct contact with the final coat, the quality of their bristles is important. Bristles should be soft and pliable enough not to scratch the finish coat but with sufficient spring to avoid drag. The size of brushes used is determined by the preference of the plasterer. They range in width from 1½ inches to 8 inches or 9 inches. The narrower brushes, often called tool brushes, are used for brushing out moldings, miters or other detail areas. A good paint brush makes an acceptable finishing brush.

Texture brushes (Fig. 12). The bristles of texture brushes are stiffer and should be able to scratch the surface of the plaster without being rapidly worn down. Whisk brooms, wire brushes and many other types are used, depending upon the texture desired.

As we have seen, the plasterer is not required to furnish all the tools or equipment he must use on the job. In addition to the larger equipment, many of the hand tools are owned by the contractor and are issued to the journeyman for particular jobs. Among these are:

The rod or straightedge (Fig. 13). The rod is the first tool used in leveling and straightening plaster that has been placed on the wall or ceiling. Rods are made of either wood or lightweight metal alloys such as magnesium. They vary in length from 4 feet to 8 feet, depending on the preference of the journeyman or the size of the room being plastered. Generally, longer rods require more effort to manipulate but produce truer surfaces. Wood rods are usually 1¼ inches thick and have a blade that is 6 inches wide at the center of the rod, tapering to about 1 inch at each end. A slot large enough to serve as a handle, is cut in the center of the blade. Metal straightedges are usually extruded and have a shaped handle running the full length of the blade.

The featheredge (Fig. 14) is a tool used to "cut-in" corners and provide sharp, straight lines at the intersection of planes. In many ways the featheredge resembles the rod; the main difference is that the blade tapers to a sharp edge. It is necessary to keep the edge of this tool dressed to a fine line. Metal featheredges weigh approximately 2 pounds and are between 4 feet and 6 feet long. Certain metal featheredges can be used as brown-

ing rods by attaching a larger wooden handle. Wooden featheredges are available generally in the same lengths as those made of metal, and are about 1 inch thick.

Fig. 11 — Browning Brush

Fig. 12 — Texture Brush

The darby (Fig. 15), in effect, is a very large float and is used for the preliminary smoothing and leveling of a surface. It is used for further straightening of the brown coat after the rodding operation is completed, to level plaster screeds, and to level the first coat of finish plaster. A serrated darby which has a fine, saw-tooth edge is used for roughening the surface of the brown coat to receive the finish coat. The darby is usually 3 feet 6 inches to 4 feet long, with a blade about 4 inches wide. Handles are attached near each end of the blade. The blade of the darby is held nearly flat against the plaster surface, and in such a way that the line of the edge is about 45 degrees to the direction of the stroke.

The slicker, a tool resembling a featheredge, is used for the same purpose as the darby: to level and smooth the brown coat to provide a true plane over which the finish coat can be applied. The slicker is made of either wood or lightweight metal

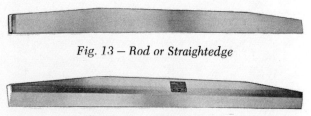

Fig. 13 — Rod or Straightedge

Fig. 14 — Featheredge

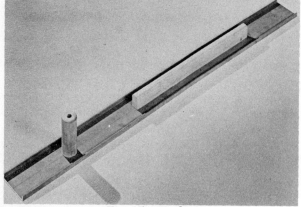

Fig. 15 — Darby

alloys. The length of the blade of this tool varies from 2 feet 6 inches to 4 feet. The blade is about 5 inches wide and tapers to an edge of $\frac{1}{16}$ inch. There are no handles or hand holes on this tool. Because of the flexibility of the blade it can be drawn across the surface with greater speed than the conventional darby. The slicker, like the paddle already described, is used where a good, but not necessarily excellent, quality of work is desired. Often a piece of beveled wood siding is used as a slicker.

In addition to the larger hand tools already described, large pieces of equipment such as mixers, scaffolds, and the like, are also furnished by the plaster contractor. Some of these are here described:

Scaffolding. Scaffolds are of two general types: the trestle type and the pole type. Trestles are made by connecting wood or metal "horses" together with wood ledgers. The trestles are arranged as supports for scaffold planks, usually 2 inches by 10 inches or 2 inches by 12 inches, which are laid from trestle to trestle to form a platform. Trestle scaffolds are used where the height of the platform need not exceed 8 feet.

The pole type of scaffold is used where the platform height exceeds 8 to 10 feet. The supporting elements of this scaffold are fabricated of steel tubing welded to form a boxlike structure consisting of metal trussed sides supported on steel pipe columns. The bases of the pipe legs are sometimes equipped with casters or wheels to allow the scaffold to be moved easily. These scaffolds are also designed to be folded and easily moved through doors or corridors without completely dismantling the frame. Heights from 18 inches to 10 feet can be obtained by easy adjustment. The platform sizes available are generally 5 feet by 10 feet, 10 feet by 10 feet and 10 feet by 20 feet. Some types are constructed in sections that can be assembled and braced as independent, high-stage structures permitting work in high spaces such as churches, auditoriums, gymnasiums, stairwells, and the like.

Another type of scaffold that is used primarily in the plastering of corridors consists of a rolling frame with an inclined platform. The inclined platform allows one plasterer to work on the upper portions while another works on the lower wall area. An advantage is the elimination of joinings in the corridor wall.

The scaffolds used by the plasterers are usually more sturdy than those used by the lathers, since the plasterer's scaffold must be able to support greater concentrated loads of men and wet mortar. **Power equipment** for use in plaster construction is manufactured to perform three basic functions: mixing, transportation, and application of mortar. Generally, such machines are specifically designed to perform one of these operations, although there are some models that can perform more than one function.

Plaster mixing machines consist primarily of a metal drum containing mixing blades and a motor housing, with transmission equipment mounted on a chassis usually equipped with wheels and designed for road towing. Mixing is accomplished either by rotation of the drum or by rotation of the agitator blades inside the drum. Most machines are built so that the mixing drum may be tilted for easy discharge into a wheelbarrow, mortar box, or pump hopper. Mixer capacities range from 3 to 12 cubic feet. The size of the job and methods of mortar handling and placement determine optimum capacity.

In addition to the machines for general use, already described, one type of machine has been designed and developed specifically for mixing lime putty and gauging material. This machine consists of a drum containing a motor-driven agitator which blends lime putty and gauging very rapidly, and with a degree of thoroughness not generally obtainable by conventional hand-mixing methods. The intense agitation beats the material into a creamy consistency that produces high yields and superior working qualities.

Plastering machines (Fig. 16) are now available that can be used for applying base-coat and finish coat plaster, and for transporting the mortar from one location in a building to another. There appear to be several advantages in mechanical application, among the most important of which is increased production per dollar of labor cost.

Two types of machines are used in the placement of mortar, each utilizing a different spraying principle. The first, the "wet mix pump," carries the mixed mortar from the mixing machine to the nozzle. Here compressed air is introduced to provide the spraying force. The second, or "dry mix" machine, uses compressed air to carry the ingredients to a special mixing nozzle where, water under pressure combines with the mix to form the mortar and provide the spraying force. The dry mix machine is the type used in structural concrete application. There is also a type of machine in which wet mix is forced from a tank through a hose to the nozzle by compressed air in the tank. It is used primarily for spraying rough concrete. Nearly all the machines being used by the plastering industry today are of the "wet mix" variety. These, in turn, are manufactured in three principal types: worm drive, piston pumps, and hand hopper machines.

Worm drive machines operate on a principle similar to that of a meat grinder. Mixed plaster is fed into a hopper and forced through the hose by the screw action of a rubber-lined rotor and stator assembly in the neck of the machine. The power for this type of unit can be supplied either by a gasoline engine or an electric motor connected through a reducing gear. There are many sizes available, some capable of handling both sanded and lightweight plasters, and others that move only the lighter materials. The hopper capacity of these machines ranges from 3 to 5 cubic feet and, depending upon the size of the pumping unit, can deliver from 0.5 to 2 cubic feet of mortar per minute.

Piston type pumps. The more powerful and versatile plastering machines on the market today use hydraulic, air actuated or mechanically driven pistons to supply the force for moving the wet plaster. Plaster is drawn from the hopper to the pump either by gravity flow or suction, depending upon the design of the machine. In general, piston type pumps are capable of handling sanded plasters, light-

Fig. 16 – Plastering Machine

weight aggregated plasters, and various acoustical and lime putty plasters. One of the most important features of these powerful machines is their ability to lift plaster vertically several stories, where it may be delivered to another unit which applies it. The continuous flow of material is advantageous in several respects. First, the plaster contractor's production is not dependent upon the convenience of the general contractor for the use of hoisting facilities and second, separate mixing plants at intermediate floors are eliminated. The necessity for mixing plaster far in advance of use, a practice that is harmful to quality, is also eliminated by the continuous flow feature.

Hand hopper machines (Fig. 17). As the name implies, this machine consists of a combination nozzle and hopper that is held in the hand during operation. They are used for applying finish plasters, and are particularly useful for applying finish plasters with integral color because the spraying makes it easier to attain an even textured, uniform colored surface than does hand application. The power for spraying the plaster is supplied by compressed air produced by either gasoline or electric powered portable compressors. Hopper capacities are generally in the range of $\frac{1}{10}$ cubic foot.

Hopper type sprayers may be used for sand blasting and sand texturing by attaching a special nozzle and filling the hopper with an abrasive material.

Mechanical trowels were developed for use in finishing operations, they are electrically operated, and resemble a six-bladed fan (Fig. 18). They are generally furnished with two sets of thin steel blades, one set more flexible than the other. The flexible blades are used for drawing-up the putty coat. They can be used to within 2 inches of the angles of a room, after which an angle float is used to finish the operation. The stiff set of blades is utilized in the final water troweling of the putty coat. These blades can be used to within ½ inch of the angles. Because of the power with which the blades are driven, it is possible to delay the troweling for a longer time than can be done when hand tools are to be used. This delay can be advantageous in that the plaster is given the ultimate opportunity to complete its volumetric change before the troweling begins.

Water required for mechanical troweling is supplied from a portable pressure tank, through a flexible tube to the hollow central drive-shaft of the machine. The power to move the blades is delivered by a small, 110-volt motor attached to the trowel. The appliance weighs approximately 6 pounds.

Many advantages have been claimed for the use of mechanical trowels. Among the benefits possible are greater and more uniform densification of the finish coat, more rapid finishing, less difficulty with hard troweling plasters, and less precision required in preliminary leveling as the finish plaster is being doubled-up.

A limitation of the power trowel is the necessity to hand trowel angles and abutments, thus producing areas of differing density. Also, there is the possibility of water being thrown by the trowel onto adjacent surfaces.

The power trowel has made possible several new uses of plaster that heretofore have not been available to the building industry. Among the more notable developments have been the use of plaster panels for exterior curtain wall construction and in-place construction of excellent chalkboards. Prior to the invention of the power trowel it was not economically feasible to produce by hand a plaster surface with the high degree of uniformity, hardness and density required for these building components. Construction details of these uses, with amplifying discussion, are in Chapter 5.

II. PREPARATION OF PLASTER

For the purpose of this discussion, the preparation of plaster is considered to end at the mixing box, finishing board or machine hopper. Prepara-

E-Z-On Corp.

Fig. 17 — Hand Hopper Machine

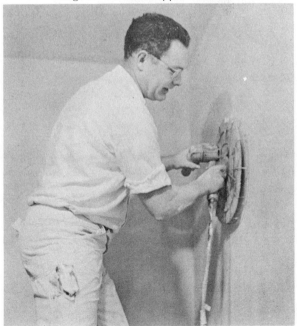

E-Z-On Corp.

Fig. 18 — Power Trowel

tion involves three distinct operations: selection of the component materials, proportioning, and finally mixing.

Selection of materials. As noted elsewhere, plaster is essentially a combination of water, cementitious material or binder, and an inert aggregate. Except for the relatively small amount required for hydration of the binder, water is necessary only to transform the binder aggregate mixture from its dry granular state, to a plastic form that facilitates application.

Selection of the component materials is therefore confined to choosing that cementitious material and that aggregate whose properties, when combined, most closely coincide with the properties required of the plaster. The basic selection of materials and formulation should be made by the designer, with responsibility for small on-the-spot mix adjustments left to the plasterer. These adjustments may be made on the basis of working characteristics, drying conditions, and other factors. Chapter 2 describes the various types of basic plastering materials and compares the characteristics and the properties that each is capable of imparting to the plaster.

Proportioning component materials. The proportions in which cementitious material, aggregate and water are combined can, in some instances, exert greater influence on the properties of a plaster than the type of cementitious material and aggregate used. Of the numerous successful plaster formulations that have been used over the years, a number have remained in continuous use and have evolved into the generally recognized standards now common in the trade. These proportions are stated as the recommended maximum aggregate proportions intended to produce generally satisfactory plaster under average conditions. They should not be construed as recommendations that establish the maximum degree of quality obtainable.

Tables I and II list the more widely recognized of the standard proportions for basecoats and finish coats. The proportions listed apply only to job-mixed plasters and not to ready-mixed materials which today account for a sizable share of the plaster manufactured. Furthermore, these proportions have been established primarily for hand application procedures, so that some modification may be necessary for machine application. At the present time, the optimum formulation of mortar for mechanical application varies from one particular machine to another, so that each manufacturer's instructions are to be consulted in every instance. The proportion standards listed in Tables I and II concern only the cementitious material and aggregate. The amount of mixing water — the third basic ingredient of plaster — is now generally left to the judgment of the individual plasterer, with the admonition that only a sufficient quantity be added to produce a mortar having necessary workability. As plaster tends to take on more functions as a building material a more precise control of the properties of the final product becomes desirable. The designer's interest in the water-cement ratio may be expected to increase to the point where it too will be specified.

Although sufficient evidence exists in experimental data and in common practice to indicate for most mortars a definite relationship between the physical properties of set plaster and the amount of water used in mixing, no engineering standards are available for the precise practical control of this factor.

Relationship of proportions to characteristics of plaster. To realize the maximum utility from plaster, the mix should be designed specifically to produce those properties required for the particular conditions encountered. In some instances, adherence to minimum proportion standards may not produce a plaster capable of meeting all these requirements.

A knowledge of the general effect on various plaster properties of the interaction of the three primary materials can permit adjustments in proportions to accentuate desirable characteristics. When mixed together, water and cementitious material combine to form a paste. When aggregate is added the particles become coated and subsequently are connected and bound rigidly together

Table I. Maximum Aggregate Proportions For Job-Mixed Basecoat Plasters Over Various Backings

Proportion Units	Gypsum	Lime		Lime-Portland Cement		Portland Cement
		Types of Plaster				Portland Cement
		Dry Mix	Putty Mix	Dry Mix	Putty Mix	
1 Part Cementitious Material =	100 lbs. gypsum	100 lbs. hydrated finishing lime (Type "S")	1 cu. ft. lime putty (Type "N")	100 lbs. hydrated finishing lime (Type "S") + 94 lbs. Portland Cement	Cu. ft. lime putty (Type "N") to 94 lb. Bags of Portland Cement	94 lbs. Portland Cement
1 Part Aggregate =	100 lbs. sand or 1 cu. ft. perlite or vermiculite	100 lbs. sand	100 lbs. sand	100 lbs. sand	100 lbs. sand	100 lbs. sand or 1 cu. ft. perlite or vermiculite
Plaster Bases	*One Coat Work*					
Any Sound and Rigid Surface	Bonding Agent	Bonding Agent		Bonding Agent		Bonding Agent
	Two Coat Work					
Gypsum laths	1:2.5					
Gypsum partition tile	1:3 or 1 wood fibered plaster: 1 sand	1:7.5	1:3.5	1:7.5	2:1:9	
High suction masonry						
Medium suction masonry						
Low suction masonry						
Concrete ceilings	Bond plaster					
	Three Coat Work					
Gypsum laths	1:2, 1:3 or Both 1:2.5	1:6.75, 1:9	1:3, 1:4	1:7.5, 1:9	1:1:6, 2:1:7	Both 1:3 to 1:5*
Metal Laths						
Gypsum partition tile	Both 1:3, or Both 1 wood fibered plaster: 1 sand					Both 1:3 to 1:5*
High suction masonry						
Medium suction masonry						
Low suction masonry						
Concrete walls and columns	Sc.-Bond plaster, Br.-1:3					
Concrete ceilings						

Note: Hair or fiber may be added to gypsum plaster scratch coats and should be added to lime, lime-portland cement and portland cement plasters as follows: (lbs. fiber per cu. yd. mortar):

	Scratch	Brown
Lime	7.5 lbs.	3.4 lbs.
Lime-Portland cem.	6 lbs.	3 lbs.
Portland cem.	4-5 lbs.	

* Up to 10% by weight of dry hydrated lime or up to 25% by volume of lime putty may be added for each part of portland cement as a plasticizer.

Table II.
Standard Proportions for Job-Mixed Finish Coat Plasters

TROWEL FINISHES

1. LIME PUTTY   : GYPSUM GAUGING PLASTER

   (a)   3   :   1 by volume

Equivalents

200 lbs. dry hydrate	: 100 lbs. gauging plaster
5 cu. ft. putty	: 100 lbs. gauging plaster
40 gal. putty	: 100 lbs. gauging plaster

   †(b)   4   :   1 by volume

Equivalents

300 lbs. dry hydrate	: 100 lbs. gauging plaster
7.5 cu. ft. putty	: 100 lbs. gauging plaster
60 gal. putty	: 100 lbs. gauging plaster

† Specifications of the Finishing Lime Association of Ohio.

2. LIME PUTTY   : KEENE'S CEMENT

   (a)   MEDIUM-HARD FINISH

     50 lbs. dry hydrate   :   100 lbs.

Equivalents

not more than 100 lbs. putty :	100 lbs. Keene's Cement
not more than 1¼ cu. ft. putty :	100 lbs. Keene's Cement
not more than 9 gal. putty	: 100 lbs. Keene's Cement

   (b)   HARD FINISH

     25 lbs. dry hydrate   :   100 lbs.

Equivalents

not more than 50 lbs. putty	: 100 lbs. Keene's Cement
not more than ⅝ cu. ft. putty	: 100 lbs. Keene's Cement
not more than 4¾ gal. putty	: 100 lbs. Keene's Cement

3. LIME PUTTY   :   PORTLAND CEMENT

   200 lbs. dry hydrate   :   94 lbs. (bag)

Equivalents

   5 cu. ft. putty   :   94 lbs.

4. PORTLAND CEMENT   :   SAND*

   94 lbs. (1 bag)   :   300 lbs. **

* Finish may be troweled or floated.

** Lime may be added as a plasticizer in amounts up to 10% by weight of portland cement if dry hydrate or 25% by volume of portland cement if putty.

5. GYPSUM GAUGING
OR NEAT PLASTER   :   VERMICULITE FINES

   100 lbs.   :   1 cu. ft.

FLOAT FINISHES

1. — LIME PUTTY   :   KEENE'S CEMENT   :   SAND

   2   :   1½   : 4½ by volume

**2. — LIME PUTTY : **
GYPSUM GAUGING PLASTER   :   SAND

   1 dry hydrate   :   1½   : 2.3 by weight

3. — LIME PUTTY   :   PORTLAND CEMENT : SAND

   2 dry hydrate :   1   : 2.5 by weight

4. — LIME PUTTY   :   SAND

   1   :   3   by volume

5. — GYPSUM NEAT PLASTER   :   SAND

   1   :   2   by weight

NOTE 1. Lime finishes may be applied over lime, gypsum & portland cement basecoats, other finishes should be applied only to basecoats containing the same cementitious material.

NOTE 2. A gypsum-vermiculite fines finish should be applied only to gypsum-vermiculite basecoats.

NOTE 3. Lime equivalents based on Type "N" hydrated lime.

as the paste changes from the plastic to the rigid state. While the water and cement paste is thought of primarily as a binder, during the plastic state it must also possess sufficient fluidity to serve as a lubricant between aggregate particles, and have sufficient plasticity to readily assume the form imposed upon it during application.

Strength. The relationship of strength to plaster performance is discussed in Chapter 6. The inherent strength properties of the various cementitious materials and aggregates are described in Chapter 2. Here we will show the effect on plaster strength of various quantitative relationships of binder, aggregate, and water. Both calcined gypsum and portland cement require a specific amount of water for hydration. During mixing and application, this water combines chemically with both materials to form crystals. The process of crystallization is the basis for the *set* phenomenon, and for the ultimate strength of hardened plaster.

While hydrated lime will not combine chemically with water, it does require the presence of a small quantity to permit combination with atmospheric carbon dioxide, the process by which surface hardness is produced in lime plaster.

The quantity of water required for crystallization of any of the cementitious materials is a relatively small part of the total amount of water added to a dry mix; the remainder is necessary only to bring the mortar to a workable consistency. After set or hardening has occurred, water is removed by evaporation. Though the excess water soon leaves the plaster, it plays a large part in determining the permanent character of the plaster, especially its strength. Water, which occupies a certain part of the total volume of the mortar, upon its departure after set leaves a network of tiny voids which by displacing binder material serves to reduce plaster strength.

In the case of calcined gypsum, the quantity of water necessary to produce a binder paste of a certain consistency will vary somewhat with different gypsums. This characteristic is expressed in pounds of water required to bring 100 pounds of

calcined gypsum to a standard and measurable state of fluidity which is called *normal consistency*. The high-strength or "alpha gypsums" described in Chapter 2 are *low consistency* materials (that is, less water is required to produce a given state of fluidity than in the case of regular calcined gypsums), resulting in a denser material having considerably greater strength.

The type, quantity and gradation of aggregate added to the binder-water paste also affects the strength of the plaster to a considerable degree. In general, as the proportion of aggregate is increased in a mix, the amount of mixing water necessary to produce a workable mortar consistency also increases, resulting in lower strength. Likewise, if aggregate is added in proportions exceeding those generally recommended, the correspondingly reduced proportion of binder material may not be sufficient to completely surround each particle, resulting also in lower strength.

Analysis of job and experimental data derived from several sources indicates a relationship between the type and proportion of aggregate, the quantity of mixing water, and the compressive strength of gypsum plaster.

It should be noted that there is a rather wide spread between comparable data obtained from different sources. This indicates the influence of factors other than those considered.

Fig. 19 illustrates this relationship. The three lines represent median values for the three aggregates: sand, perlite, and vermiculite. The quantities of mixing water indicated are those that will generally produce a workable mortar.

Workability. While having only a small and indirect effect on the properties of in-place plaster, the workability of plaster mortar influences the cost of placing and finishing it. As already stated, the purpose of the greater part of the water added during mixing is to provide the degree of fluidity necessary for application. Table III indicates average amounts of water required per 100 pounds of calcined gypsum for various quantities of the three aggregates:

Table III.

Gypsum Basecoat Plasters: Average Water Requirements

(Lbs. Water per 100 lbs. Gypsum Plaster)

	Gypsum Plaster: Aggregate Proportions		
Aggregates	1 : 2	1 : 2½	1 : 3
Sand	57	62	68
Perlite	64	71	76
Vermiculite	75	84	95

As stated, these are average figures. The actual amounts of water required vary somewhat with the particular materials used and the job conditions.

Where machine application is to be used, the machine manufacturer's recommendations should be followed. Often this requires a somewhat higher mortar consistency than is necessary for hand application. For this reason some manufacturers recommend the use of a low consistency gypsum to produce proper mortar consistency with the same amount of water the mechanic is accustomed to adding, and at the same time not adversely affecting strength.

Yield, or the volume of plaster mortar resulting from the combination of a certain amount of binder, water, and aggregate, is also of economic importance, since it determines how much coverage can be obtained for a certain material cost. Yield data are also needed in making material quantity estimates.

There can be a difference in yield between a given mortar applied by hand and the same mortar applied by machine. The volume of a mortar as it leaves the mixer is made up, in part, of air entrained during the mixing process. The amount of this entrained air removed by manipulation of the mix during hand application is indeterminate, although usually it is considered to be relatively small. However, it is known that with certain types of spray equipment, a large percentage of the en-

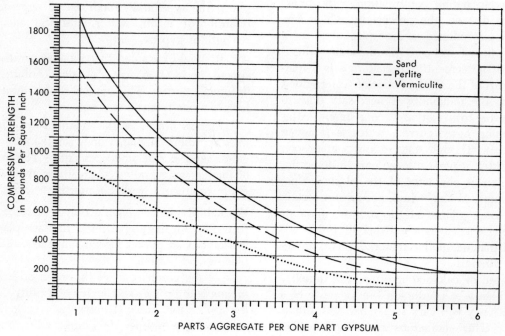

Fig. 19 — Approximate Compressive Strengths for Gypsum Basecoat Plasters

trained air is removed at the nozzle, reducing yield but resulting in a denser, stronger plaster than could have been obtained if the entrained air had been retained. Fig. 20 lists yields for various proportions of gypsum and the three aggregates applied by machine. Table IV lists average basecoat yields that might be expected with various sanded plasters.

To compute the approximate dry volume and yield (wet volume) of a mixture of cementitious material, sand, and water, the absolute volumes of each component material are added together. To obtain the absolute volume of a material, it is necessary to know the volume and weight of a solid cube (that is, with no voids present) of the material or its specific gravity.

Water weighs 62.4 pounds per cubic foot, and each cubic foot contains 7.48 gallons. To find the absolute volumes of cementitious materials and sand, divide the weight of the loose material by the weight of a cubic foot of the solid material (specific gravity by 62.4). To find the volume of mortar, the absolute volumes of binder and aggregate are added to the volume of water (.13 cubic foot per gallon). It is extremely difficult to determine the absolute volumes of lightweight aggregates due to the indeterminate amount of air within each particle of the aggregate.

Often it is convenient to represent yield figures in terms of coverage, or the amount of surface area that will be covered by a given volume of plaster mortar. In computing coverage, such factors must be considered as type of plaster base, method of application, thickness, and methods of working. Table VI provides average coverage figures for gypsum plaster based on minimum plaster thicknesses recommended over various bases. The figures represent basecoats only and do not include ⅛ inch thickness of finish coat.

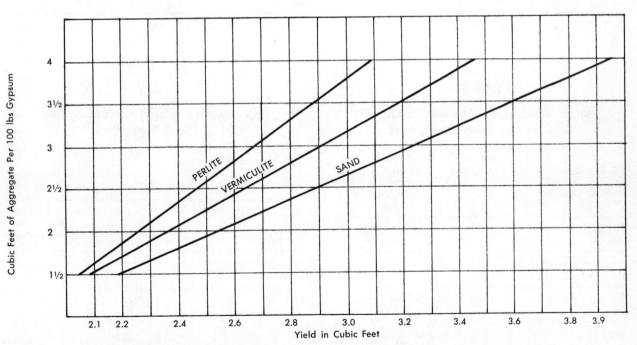

Fig. 20 — Yields for Mechanically Applied Gypsum Basecoat Plasters (Cubic Feet Per Cubic Foot Aggregate)

Table IV.

Yields for Various Job-Mixed Basecoat Plasters

Materials and Mix Proportions (See Table 1)	Equivalent Proportions by Weight of Dry Materials	Approximate Yield (Based on Quantities in Column 2, plus 8 gal. Water per 100 lbs. Cementitious Material)
Gypsum Plaster : Sand		
1 : 2	100 lbs. : 200 lbs.	2.97 cu. ft.
1 : 2½	100 lbs. : 250 lbs.	3.28 cu. ft.
1 : 3	100 lbs. : 300 lbs.	3.50 cu. ft.
Lime : Sand		
1 cu. ft. putty : 3 cu. ft. sand	100 lbs. : 675 lbs.	5.80 cu. ft.
1 cu. ft. putty : 3.5 cu. ft. sand	100 lbs. : 750 lbs.	6.48 cu. ft.
1 cu. ft. putty : 4 cu. ft. sand	100 lbs. : 900 lbs.	7.17 cu. ft.
Lime : Portland Cement : Sand		
1 cu. ft. putty : 1 bag : 6 cu. ft. sand	40 lbs. : 94 lbs. : 750 lbs.	5.80 cu. ft.
2 cu. ft. putty : 1 bag : 9 cu. ft. sand	80 lbs. : 94 lbs. : 900 lbs.	8.32 cu. ft.
Portland Cement : Sand		
1 : 4	94 lbs. : 400 lbs.	3.97 cu. ft.
1 : 5	94 lbs. : 500 lbs.	4.28 cu. ft.

NOTE: Yields may be adjusted for varying quantities of mixing water by adding or subtracting 0.13 cu. ft. for each gallon added or eliminated.

Table V.

Specific Gravities and Absolute Volumes of Cementitious Materials and Sand

Material	Specific Gravity	Absolute Volume of Proportion Units
Portland Cement	3.1	94 lbs. (dry) — .49 cu. ft.
Gypsum	2.28 – 2.33	100 lbs. (dry) — .69 cu. ft.
Hydrated Finishing Lime – Type "N"	2.73	1 cu. ft. putty — .26 cu. ft.
Type "S"	2.50	100 lbs. (dry) — .64 cu. ft.
Sand	2.65	100 lbs. (dry) — .61 cu. ft.

Water: .13 cu. ft. per gallon

Table VI.

Approximate Basecoat Mortar Coverage (Hand Applied)

1 Cubic Foot of Mortar:

⅜" thick over plain gypsum lath	covers 3.2 sq. yds.
½" thick over unit masonry	cover 2.3 sq. yds.
½" thick over gypsum tile	covers 2.1 sq. yds.
⅝" thick over metal lath*	covers 1.4 sq. yds.

*Measured from back plane of metal lath

Hardness in a plaster is usually directly proportional to strength. Generally, as the proportion of aggregate and water to cementitious material is increased, hardness of the resulting plaster is decreased. A discussion of the relationship of hardness to the various functions of plaster is included in Chapter 6. Fig. 21 shows the effect on hardness of increasing the proportion of sand in gypsum-sand plaster.

Hardness in finish coats, particularly those containing lime, is related to some extent to troweling procedures. Nevertheless, as in basecoats, the cementitious material used has the greatest effect. Table VII was developed by one manufacturer to indicate relative properties of some finish plasters. Where indicated (*) generic terms have been substituted for the proprietary names included in his original tabulation.

Tendency to shrink or expand is expressed in terms of the coefficient of linear expansion, and is discussed in relation to plaster performance in Chapter 6. *Rich* plaster mixes (mixtures containing

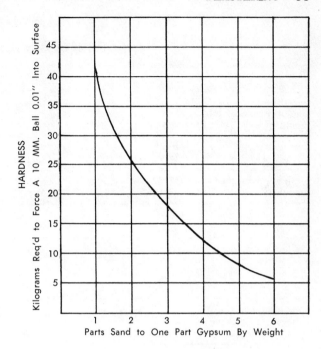

Fig. 21 — Effect of Sand on Plaster Hardness

Table VII.

Comparison of Properties of Some Finish Plasters

	Mix (by Weight Dry Material)	Color	Finish Texture	Hardness in Kilograms (Note A.)	Workability Factor
Gauging Plaster to Lime	1 : 2	White	Smooth	34	1
High Strength* Gauging Plaster to Lime					
Medium Hard	1 : 2	White	Smooth	56	1
Hard	1 : 1	White	Smooth	108	2
Quick Setting* Keene's to Lime					
Medium Hard	2 : 1	White	Smooth	50	4
Hard	4 : 1	White	Smooth	70	7
Gypsum Trowel Finish	Neat	White	Smooth	55	3
Ready-mixed Colored Finish	Neat	7	Float	(B)	5

(A)   Kilograms required to force a 10mm ball 0.01″ into plaster face.
(B)   Hard finishes but the aggregate in the surface does not permit an indication with this test.

Table VIII.

Properties of Gypsum Job-Mixed Basecoat Plasters

Property	Sand		Perlite		Vermiculite		Wood Fibered to Sand	
	1 : 2	1 : 3	1 : 2	1 : 3	1 : 2	1 : 3	1 : 0	1 : 1
Compressive Strength Pounds per sq. in.	775-1050	525-700	600-800	450-600	400-525	250-325	1750-2350	
Tensile Strength Pounds per sq. in.	150-200	100-150	165-170	90-150	130-160	70-100	280-400	240-250
Modulus of Elasticity Pounds per sq. in. x 10^6	1.0	1.15-1.20	0.21-0.33			0.028	0.65-0.75	
Density In-Place Pounds per cu. ft.	104-120	104-120	50-56	41-45	50-55	42-45	79-82	
Coefficient of Linear Expansion inches/inch/degree F x 10^{-6}	6.50	6.75	7.35	7.30	8.35	8.60	9.30	
Thermal Conductivity BTU/sq. ft./hour/°F/ inch thickness	5.51	5.60	1.64	1.31	1.74	1.42	3.15	

Source: Gypsum Association.

a relatively high percentage of cementitious material) are generally subject to greater initial shrinkage upon drying than are *lean* mixes. It is generally recommended that mixes tending toward the lean side be used for exterior plaster, due to the materials used and the presence of environmental conditions producing movement. Along with this are the more severe consequences of possible cracking resulting from movement than would be the case in interior applications.

Summary tabulations of some of the properties of gypsum plasters are in Tables VIII and IX.

MIXING THE MATERIALS

Mixing consists primarily of two operations: first, measuring the components according to the required proportions and adding them to the mixing box or machine; second, combining the components into a homogeneous mixture while adding

Table IX.

Calculated Tensile Strains at Failure for Various Gypsum Plasters[6]

Plaster Proportions	Tensile Strength Lbs./sq. in.	Modulus of Elasticity Lbs./sq. in.	Computed Tensile Strain at Failure Microinches/ in./in.
Wood-Fibered Gypsum Plaster	290	753,000	386
1 : 4 Vermiculite Brown Coat	80	175,000	457
Lime-Gauging Finish Coat	70	111,000	631
1 : 2 Sand Scratch Coat	310	985,000	315
1 : 3 Sand Brown Coat	210	730,000	280

sufficient water to bring the mortar to the necessary consistency.

Plastering materials may be measured either by weight or by volume. While measurement by weight is more accurate, the process is often economically impracticable for job use so that volume measurement is by far more common. Except for sand, all plastering materials are sold in bags containing a specified weight or volume. This facilitates measurement since in many instances proportioning is done in the units in which the materials are packaged.

Two widely used volumetric means of measuring bulk material at the job are the measuring box (usually built to hold one cubic foot of material), and the standard No. 2 shovel. The shovel is most convenient and is widely used but it is accurate only to a very low degree. This is because the lack of unit volume control created by the custom of accepting a "shovelful" as being more than level full, and the tendency of sand to bulk when damp.

These proportioning units are in common use for the materials listed, their equivalents being given for convenience:

WEIGHT MEASUREMENTS

1. Gypsum — 100 lbs. = 1 bag
2. Portland Cement — 94 lbs. = 1 bag
3. Hydrated Lime — 100 lbs. = 2 bags
4. Sand — 100* lbs. = 7 No. 2 shovelfuls

VOLUME MEASUREMENT

1. Gypsum — 1 cu. ft. = 60* lbs. (volume not used in proportioning)
2. Lime — (All types) 1 cu. ft. of putty = 40 lbs. of dry materials + water
3. Portland Cement — 1 cu. ft. = 1 bag = 94 lbs.
4. Sand — 1 cu. ft. = 100* lbs. = 7 No. 2 shovelfuls
5. Perlite — 1 cu. ft. = 7.5-15 lbs.
6. Vermiculite — 1 cu. ft. = 6-10 lbs.
7. Water — 1 cu. ft. = 7.48 gal. = 62.5 lbs.

* Average weight

During recent years, the use of ready-mixed plasters has become more and more widespread. Ready-mixed conventional plasters formulated by the manufacturer contain calcined gypsum and an aggregate. Only the addition of mixing water is required on the job. The different types of ready-mixed materials are described in Chapter 2. In addition to the ready-mixed "hard-wall" materials, many proprietary "acoustical" materials are produced which, like the former, require only the addition of water at the job.

Mixing by hand. Traditionally, plasterers have mixed materials with hoe and mixing box. With this method experienced mechanics and tenders are able to recognize the proper application consistency by the "feel" of the mortar as it is being mixed. While still being used today on small jobs, hand mixing is being increasingly replaced by machine mixing which, with its savings in time and effort, results in savings in costs. In addition, a more homogeneous mix, having a highly uniform consistency, is easier to produce by machine.

The equipment required for hand mixing of basecoat plasters consists of a mixing box and a hoe — usually one with a perforated blade. First, the dry cementitious material and aggregate are thoroughly mixed until a uniform color is obtained; then the dry mixture is hoed into the required amount of water until all the materials are thoroughly blended and the required consistency is obtained. Mixing time should be limited to 10 to 15 minutes after the materials have been thoroughly blended. Excessive mixing or agitation should be avoided because the rate of solution of the cementitious material may be hastened and thus result in accelerated set. After mixing, the mortar is transported with minimum additional agitation from the mixing box to the mortar board for application.

Hand mixing is still the method generally used to produce finish coat mortar containing lime. The method employed is to form lime putty into a ring on a 5 foot square, smooth-top, board called a *finishing board*. Water is then poured into the ring and the gauging material sifted into it to avoid lumping. Gauging may be gypsum gauging plaster, Keene's cement, or portland cement added to provide early strength and increased hardness. After all the gauging has been added, the mixture is allowed to stand for one minute to permit saturation. Then it is thoroughly blended with the lime putty. Sand, if it is to be incorporated, may be either added to the lime prior to making lime putty or mixed into the gauged lime putty following the mixing procedure described. After mixing is complete, the finish material is applied without delay.

Lime putty may be produced in one of several ways. According to some beliefs, the oldest, the most expensive, and the best method is to slake quicklime and age it thoroughly, (for a minimum of two weeks). The resulting putty is both plastic and free of oxides. The recommended method of slaking quicklime may be found in the appendix to the Standard Specification for Quicklime for Structural Purposes, ASTM C5-26. The introduction of hydrated lime eliminated the need for on-the-job slaking. Putty is produced from normal hydrate by soaking it in an equal amount of water for a minimum of 16 hours so as to develop maximum plasticity. More recently, the development of special hydrate has also eliminated the soaking period required for the normal type. Special hydrate produces a putty with the necessary plasticity for ordinary use shortly after being mixed with water. It can therefore be added dry to other plaster components at the time of mixing. Before using, lime putty may be forced through a piece of wire mesh to remove lumps and to increase plasticity. Chapter 2 includes a more detailed description of the characteristics of the various types of lime.

Mixing by machine. On large jobs mixing of basecoat mortars and supply operations may follow either one of two basic patterns: several small capacity mixers may be located conveniently throughout the working area; or one large machine may be located centrally, delivering mortar through pumps and hoses or conveyors to the plastering crews. Some contractors particularly recommend the decentralized method because they feel higher yields

and better quality plasters are realized when the time period and agitation between mixing and application are minimized. However, many others think mechanical delivery of mortar to the board has a decided economic advantage. Machines used for transporting and placing mortar are described in section I of this chapter. The mixing machine operates continuously during the preparation of a batch, beginning as materials are added and ending as the mortar is dumped. The ASA specification for gypsum plastering calls for this sequence of operations: [7]

Job mixed gypsum plasters

1. Put in the approximate amount of water.
2. If sand is used, add approximately one half the amount of aggregate. If vermiculite or perlite is used, add all the aggregate.
3. Add all the cementitious material.
4. Add the remainder of the sand aggregate.
5. Mix to the required consistency, adding water if necessary.
6. Dump the entire batch and use.

Ready-mixed gypsum plasters

1. Put in the approximate amount of water.
2. Add the plaster.
3. Mix to the required consistency, adding water if necessary.
4. Dump the entire batch and use.

It is strongly recommended that approximately 10 per cent of the estimated quantity of mixing water be withheld from the mortar until mixing is almost complete, and then added as needed to produce the necessary consistency. This precludes the necessity of adding more dry material to correct a mortar which has become too fluid — a practice generally resulting in mortar which does not contain the prescribed quantities of materials.

It has sometimes been noted, in the case of plaster containing lightweight aggregates, that mortar in the mixer will appear too dry even though water in sufficient quantity has already been added. If mixing is continued without adding more water, the mix will, at a certain point, suddenly become more fluid. This phenomenon has been attributed to surface tension on individual aggregate particles which is maintained up to a point and then suddenly destroyed, releasing the water thus held to the mix. It is generally recommended that the mixer be allowed to run no longer than three minutes after all materials have been added.

The procedure recommended by the ASA for mixing portland cement plaster is somewhat different from that for mixing gypsum plasters. Portland cement and aggregate are mixed dry until a uniform color is attained, and then the necessary water is added.

To produce plaster of uniform quality, it is most important that all equipment used in its preparation be kept clean. Very small quantities of calcined gypsum which have set in the mixer, mixing box or on tools, can produce acceleration of the set if allowed to become mixed in with subsequent batches. If any considerable lapse occurs between mixing of mortar batches, it is recommended that water be placed in mixing machines and the machines left in operation.

III. APPLICATION OF PLASTER COATS

Plaster, being a thin composite mass of concrete material, depends for integrity of form on the monolithic character of its structure. The structural performance of the material itself, aside from any structure provided by the base to which it is applied, is thought to bear a relationship with the homogeneity — or at least the uniformity — of the slab. Uniformity or the lack of it, in thickness and density affects the structural performance of a concrete slab of any thickness, but it becomes more critical in thin slabs. This is due in part to the increasing difficulty of controlling the percentage of variation from a mean thickness as this mean decreases. A deviation in surface flatness of ⅛ inch in plasterwork averaging 1 inch thick is obviously less

important than the same variation in plaster ½ inch thick. Most plastering materials are subject to densification under the pressure of the tools of application, some being more compressible than others. It is believed that the uniformity of this change in density is more easily controlled by application of thin layers.

In addition, there is a minimum thickness that a monolithic slab of any given composition must have if it is to maintain its structural integrity. This varies with the elastic properties of the set material and the base over which it is applied. Minimum acceptable limitations, based on years of performance experience, have been established for the thickness of plasterwork. These are listed farther on in this section.

It is generally felt that practical control of thickness and density as the work progresses, particularly when the application is by hand, is facilitated by building up the total thickness in layers by more than one successive operation. For at least the last hundred years, plaster in the Western world has been applied in either two or three coats. In the book by Vitruvius on architecture, written about 16 B.C., in which he bemoaned the frantic haste of his time, there is a specification based upon earlier Greek work that had come to his attention. In this specification Vitruvius describes and recommends the use of seven separate coats of plaster. Unfortunately there is no way by which the merits of his instructions can be judged, for the fire attributed to Nero destroyed the greater part of Rome. The only authenticated plasterwork of that time is a bas-relief of the siege of Troy, now a museum piece.[8]

The material undoubtedly used in the time of Vitruvius was lime plaster, which must be subjected to considerable compaction. His advice is therefore not to be taken without qualification in our time when gypsum and portland cement, which generally produce less compressible mortars, are more often used as basecoat materials. The application of plaster in modern times by mechanical means, whereby uniform densification occurs more automatically, also reduces the control value of multi-basecoat work. However, it is still generally held that thickness and flatness of surface are most precisely controlled by application of three coats, regardless of the method used.

There is another important reason besides dimensional and density control for applying plaster in separate coats. That is, where all parts of the slab section are not of the same material or do not have the same physical properties. For example, where a first coat is used to stiffen a flexible base, usually it is mixed for greater strength than the remainder of the basecoat and, to perform its function, must be applied separately. Similarly, plaster finishes which are compounded of different materials than the base plaster necessarily must be applied in a separate operation.

The term *basecoat* applies to all plaster applied prior to the finish coat. It can be a single operation, (*lay-on* method), two operations, as in most two-coat work *(double-up)*, or a scratch and brown coat with drying between each coat, as in three-coat work. The basecoat provides the greater part of the mass of the plaster slab.

Except for acoustical plaster, the finish coat is a very thin layer which provides texture, intrinsic color, a sanitary and clean appearance, and serves as a base over which paint and other coverings can be applied.

General procedures. The methods by which plaster is applied are subject to many considerations. For example, often the size of the job determines whether plaster will be applied by hand or will be placed by machine; sometimes the base over which plaster is to be installed determines the methods by which the first coats of plaster will be installed; the degree to which a space is subdivided or the order in which it is made ready for the plasterer will prescribe the type and amount of scaffolding required, thus influencing the manner in which the work is scheduled. However, here are some requirements common to all installations:

(1) The plaster must conform to the planes and curves required by the specified architectural form. These lines must be established and held.

(2) Control procedures must be employed in the work that will guarantee the specified thickness in order to produce the required strength, fire resistance, impact resistance, acoustical, thermal, and other properties.

(3) Bond must be obtained between the plaster and the plaster base, and between the several coats in order to produce a slab possessing homogeneous characteristics.

(4) The surface of the plaster must be uniform and of a texture which satisfies the visual requirements that have been established, or it must be so prepared as to allow further applications or treatments (paint, wall covering).

The sequence of operations in the application of the base and finish coats is subject to several variables. The ceiling is always finished last if there is any possibility of its being damaged during the application of plaster to the walls; for instance, when the ceiling is to receive acoustical or ornamental treatment. Where removable partitions are to be installed in a large space it is usually desirable to plaster the entire ceiling before subdividing the area. The plaster contractor also tries to minimize duplication of scaffolding between lathing and plastering, if both operations are part of his contract.

This outline describes one method used to plaster a space in which the lath and plaster are installed by one contractor:

(1) Apply the lath to the wall surfaces.

(2) Apply the basecoat plaster as high as possible on the wall without the use of scaffolding.

(3) Erect scaffolds and apply the lath to the ceiling.

(4) Apply the basecoat plaster to the ceiling and complete basecoat plastering of walls.

(5) Apply the finish plaster to the ceiling and to the upper portions of walls.

(6) Remove the scaffolding and apply the finish to the lower portions of the walls.

Mechanical application procedures. The nozzle of the plastering machine is held 18 inches to 24 inches from the plaster base and is moved constantly and with a rhythm similar to that used for spraying paint. The pattern of the spray and the size of the plaster particles are controlled by the nozzle-man. The orifice of the spray gun can be adjusted to produce either a wide angle or a concentrated pattern. The nozzle-man can regulate the fineness of the spray by varying the air pressure. If no air pressure is introduced at the nozzle, the plaster will come out in a heavy stream, and as pressure is introduced and increased, the spray becomes finer. The mix proportions and the volume delivery of the machine determine the amount of pressure required for any given operation. Browning operations use air pressures ranging from 8 to 10 pounds, while finish coats by the same machine are applied at 12 to 15 pounds air pressure.

While section II of this chapter discusses in detail the mixing of plaster for mechanical application, several of these factors that relate closely to the placement of the material must be noted briefly here. Among the most important is the amount of water required in the mix.

As a general rule, sprayed plaster requires more mixing water than does hand applied plaster, in order to obtain a mix of a proper handling consistency. It is difficult to state the exact amount of additional water needed, because conditions vary with the type of plaster being used, the characteristics of the particular machine, the amount and type of aggregate, the length and size of hose, the working qualities desired by the plastering crew, and weather conditions. Every effort should be made to keep a minimum amount of water in the mix, because the strength of the plaster will decrease as the amount of water increases. A great deal of experimentation has been conducted to determine the feasibility of using air-entraining agents in the mix to reduce viscosity of the plaster without increasing the ratio of water to cementitious material. At the present time no industry standards exist for this practice.

The application of plaster by a machine in the hands of a skilled operator does not present problems in cleanliness greater than those encountered on the job when the plaster is applied by hand.

However, there are many places where precautions must be taken to avoid damaging those surfaces adjacent to the area being sprayed. Masking machines have been developed that not only solve problems such as the protection of walls, but also allow jambs, frames, lighting fixtures, heating outlets, and other pre-finished surfaces to be kept clean during the spraying of plaster.

Control procedures. *Flatness.* In nearly all plaster work it is necessary to have a surface that is free of waves and appearing to be flat. "Flatness" is a relative term, because it is difficult, if not impossible, to obtain a perfectly flat surface with any material. The main considerations are: (1) Is the surface flat enough to meet visual requirements? (Does it look flat enough?) (2) Is the surface flat enough to receive other materials that might be applied to the surface? (In this case, the application of wood or metal trim and casings would be as important as the application of paint or wall coverings.)

The degree to which a surface appears to be flat is determined largely by the conditions under which it is viewed. A glossy paint over a smooth surface will show deviations in a plane more readily than will a flat paint over a textured surface, as will acute angles of vision or illumination. Unfortunately, in plastering practice at this time there is no ranking order of finishes with regard to visual flatness against which to measure the acceptability of work.

There are standards that specify the amount that a plaster surface can deviate from a straight line. The "Reference Specifications" of the California Lathing and Plastering Contractors Association recommend that the plaster be finished "true and even, within ⅛" tolerance in 10 feet, without waves, cracks, or imperfections."[9] American Standard Specifications for Gypsum Plastering and Interior Lathing and Furring (ASA A42.1-.4) require that the plaster be brought "to a true surface." The standard of ⅛ inch appears to be the closest practical tolerance to which a plasterer can work by the methods in common use.

In dealing with a similar problem — the flatness of stainless steel sheets — the School of Architecture of Princeton University ascertained that "The significant factor in the definition of visual flatness would appear to be not the height nor the number of waves, but the steepness of the slope."[10] This work also concludes that there is a direct relationship between the allowable slope and the brightness or texture of the surface.

With plaster, the problem becomes of greater importance because the gradient of surface deviations must be low enough to allow the wood or metal trim applied over it to conform acceptably to the contour of the surface. While at the present time there are no precise definitions of acceptable flatness for plastering other than maximum allowable deviation from a straight line, it is entirely possible that standards could be developed similar to those established for stainless steel curtain walls.

In order to help him obtain acceptably flat surfaces and at the same time to insure that the plaster has been applied to the required thickness, the plasterer employs devices called *grounds* and *screeds*.

Grounds are narrow strips of wood or metal that are placed around, and parallel to, the edges of surfaces and openings within the plastered area. Usually they are attached directly to the plastering base, except in the case of gypsum lath. Grounds are designed to be used as guides for the straightedge when the final basecoat is brought to the required thickness and line. In addition to serving as a guide, many metal grounds are formed in such a manner that they can be used also as terminals, picture molds, casing beads, and base screeds. Different types of metal grounds, along with other accessories, are illustrated in Chapter 2.

Door and window frames are often used to form the grounds for plasterwork. It is not advisable, however, to plaster directly to a wood frame. Contact between the dimensionally unstable wood and the relatively stable plaster produces continuous differential movement that may cause damage to the plaster. The shock involved in the opening and closing of doors is another factor that favors separation of frames and plaster. If metal casings are not used at such locations the plaster should be struck away from the adjacent wood surface after the surface has been leveled. A further disadvantage is the likelihood that the grounds provided by the millwork will not provide for sufficient plaster thickness. Where hollow metal door frames are used, the plaster should not terminate against the frame unless special provisions have been made to dampen the vibration during door operation. Special anchorage, or grouting, or both, are used for this purpose. In any case, lath and plaster should recess into or behind the frame.

Plaster screeds are a special type of ground, often employed to establish surface lines for large ceiling areas, and where walls are too large for effective rodding between grounds. Formed of narrow strips or bands of plaster 4 to 6 inches wide, screeds are built up along the wall or ceiling to the desired plaster depth.

Plaster screeds are established by first placing *dots*, or small dabs, of quick-setting plaster — on the scratch in three-coat work, or on the plaster base in two-coat work. Usually they are placed 5 to 8 feet apart, depending upon the length of the rod to be used. Although not always used, thin strips of wood pressed into the face of the mortar dots also provide a firm base for the rod to bear upon during the straightening process.

In establishing screeds for walls, a plaster dot is placed at one side of the panel about 12 inches from the ceiling. This dot is plumbed up from the base ground by using either a spirit level or a plumb bob. The base ground sets the line of the wall and is the foundation point for establishing all grounds. Other dots are aligned with the first dot at intervals around the room, and are then connected with bands of plaster to form the screeds. After the screed has been built up it is rodded with a long straightedge to the plaster thickness specified, and then darbied to a smooth surface. The final basecoat is laid on between the screeds after they have become hard enough to allow the basecoat to be rodded.

The establishment of screeds for ceilings involves a process similar to that described for walls, except that where level lines are to be established independently of the plaster base, a water level is used to mark out a reference line on the side wall near the ceiling. To establish the dots, this datum is then transferred to the ceiling at intervals by various methods, including the use of improvised wood gauges.

Alignment. Where the plane of the ceiling is interrupted by dropped beams, ducts, coves, changes in ceiling height, and other factors, several methods are used to establish straight and level lines. One of the best, and most often used, is the application of corner beads. It is possible to obtain plumb, level, and straight planes by controlling the location and alignment of accessories, which at the same time serve to reinforce the exterior corners of the surface.

Another method, used particularly in conjunction with ornamental work and which is equally precise, is "lining and stripping." This procedure requires many more separate operations than does the use of corner beads. Sticks of wood are attached to the bottom of the beam with small dabs of fast setting plaster projecting to the established line of the finished face of the beam. Next, dots are placed on one side of the beam and are plumbed and filled in to form screeds. In order to obtain a beam of uniform width, a wooden gauge is used to transfer the line of screeds from one face to the other. When all screeds have been established, the sides of the beam are filled in with the base coat.

A ground is then placed that will establish a level soffit of the proper thickness. For this a horizontal 1 inch by 2 inch strip of wood is attached to the sides of the beam with spots of fast setting plaster. The bottom edge of the strip is leveled and serves as the ground. The basecoat and finish coat are then applied to the soffit, after which the strip is removed and the finish coat applied to the sides of the beam.

Although currently considered too expensive for ordinary work, this method of plastering makes it possible to control lines, levels, and angles independently of the plaster base, with great precision. Where precast ornamental work is used, this degree of precision is usually necessary to assure proper fitting and adjustment.

A less exacting method can be used to solve the aforementioned problems that will produce a fair appearance. The final results depend to a large extent upon the ability of the plasterer. In this case no screeds are placed on the sides of the beam, and no gauges are used to maintain uniform beam width. Dabs of fast setting plaster are placed at 2 foot intervals. Horizontal beam strips are pressed into them, after which the strip is leveled by eye, line, or spirit level. The soffit then receives a base and finish coat, and the strips are removed. Base and finish coats are now placed on the side of the beam, using the plaster edge of the soffit for a screed.

Thickness of plaster. The importance of adhering to the recommended minimum thickness for plaster cannot be overstressed. A detailed discussion of the functions that the thickness plays in the quality of plasterwork is included in Chapter 6. Crack resistance, for example, is considerably affected by thickness. A report issued by the Armour Research Foundation describing a number of tests conducted on plasterwork, states: "Plaster walls become more rigid as the thickness of plaster is increased. The deflection of plaster walls, employing either metal or gypsum lath, subjected to a 1200-pound racking load, decreases with an increase in plaster thickness."[11] The tests conducted by this organization also indicate that cracks due to racking forces and damage caused by impact loads also decrease as the thickness of plaster is increased.[12]

In a series of proprietary tests published in 1955 in which a sanded gypsum basecoat in the proportions of 2 to 1 and 3 to 1 and a lime putty coat ⅛ inch thick were applied over various plaster bases, it was noted that the resistance of a plaster diaphragm to cracking decreased by 60 per cent when the thickness was reduced from ½ inch to ⅜ inch. When the thickness was reduced from ½ inch to ¼ inch, the ability of the plaster to resist cracking decreased 82 per cent.[13]

The table that follows lists the minimum plaster thicknesses published by the American Standards Association in its document A42.1-.4 (1955), "American Standard Specifications for Gypsum Plastering and Interior Lathing and Furring." This tabulation is similar to the thickness requirements established by the model codes of the United States and Canada.

Table X.

Recommended Minimum Thicknesses of Gypsum Plaster Over Various Backings[14]

Plaster Base	Thickness of Plaster Including Finish Coat (inches)
Lath	
Metal Lath*	⅝″ Minimum
Wire Lath	⅝″ Minimum
Wire Fabric	⅝″ Minimum
All Other Types	½″ Minimum
Masonry	⅝″ Minimum
Monolithic Concrete Walls**	⅝″ Maximum
Monolithic Concrete Ceilings**	⅜″ Maximum

* Plaster thickness when measured from the back plane of metal lath, exclusive of ribs, shall be ¾″ minimum.

** If monolithic concrete ceilings or wall surfaces require more than ⅜″ or ⅝″ respectively of plaster to produce required lines or surfaces, metal lath or wire lath bonding for the plaster shall be attached to the concrete before application of plaster. Where the concrete ceiling or wall surfaces are such as to require the application of an excessive thickness of plaster to produce required lines or surfaces, lath shall be applied over metal furring secured to the concrete.

The ASA Specification further states that the finish coat should be a minimum thickness of 1/16″ and a maximum of ⅛″.

Bond. The physical integration of plaster with its base, and of one coat of plaster with another, is referred to as *bond,* a characteristic subject to some quality variation measured in terms of the force required to separate the lamination. Plaster bond is obtained either through adhesion or cohesion, depending upon the material to which plaster is applied.

Adhesion means the ability of plaster to adhere or cement itself to another material. Cohesion means the ability of plaster to hold itself together and remain in a mass, as would be required of plaster keys in metal lath.

The bond of plaster to metal lath is accomplished by the formation of keys that lock around the back of the open metal. The bond of gypsum plaster to gypsum lath is obtained when the plastic material crystallizes after being drawn into the paper backing by capillary attraction forming a bond with the paper fibers. A similar process occurs when plaster is applied to masonry, concrete, or other porous surfaces. The adhesive value that can be attributed to the roughness of the surface of the backing material is still a matter of controversy. A Bureau of Standards report on "Adhesion of Gypsum Plaster to Various Backings" reprinted in *The American Architect* for September 9, 1925, states that "in all cases it was found that the side of the brick wall or tile that was rough, or offered the better mechanical key, gave the greater adhesion."[15] In similar tests conducted at Virginia Polytechnic Institute it was stated that "Statistical analysis disclosed there was not a significant difference [in adhesion] between a scored surface tile and a smooth surfaced tile."[16] The adhesion of plaster to various bases is further discussed in Chapter 6.

APPLICATION OF BASE COATS

In addition to providing the mass of the plaster membrane, the basecoat serves to provide a true surface of uniform suction over which a finely controlled finish coat can be applied. Problems such as check cracking and surface discoloration are among those encountered when the finish coat is applied over a base that is not consistently dense and porous. Detailed discussion of the quality of the basecoat is included in Chapter 6.

Gypsum basecoats. The basecoats may be applied in one continuous operation as in the plastering method called *two-coat* or *double-up*. Or it may be applied in two separate operations, allowing time between for the plaster to set, as in the *three-coat* method. Two-coat work consists of a single base-coat and a finish coat. Three-coat work consists of two basecoats, the first called the *scratch coat*, the second the *brown coat*, plus a finish coat.

Three-coat work. This is the sequence of operations involved in three-coat gypsum plastering:

(1) Install the plaster base (lath, masonry, or the like).

(2) Attach the grounds.

(3) Apply the scratch coat approximately 3/16 inch thick, measured from face of base material.

(4) Before the scratch coat sets, rake and cross rake.

(5) Allow the scratch coat to set firm and hard.

(6) Apply the plaster screeds, if required.

(7) Apply the brown coat to the depth of screeds.

(8) Using the screeds for a guide, straighten the surface with a rod (straightedge).

(9) Fill in any hollows or voids and rod surface again.

(10) Level and compact the surface with a darby. Rake and cross rake to receive the finish coat.

(11) The angles (corners) are now sharply defined and the plaster is trimmed back around the grounds (corner beads, casing beads, etc.) to allow the finish coat to be applied flush with the face of the ground.

(12) Allow the brown coat to set hard and firm. The finish coat to be applied in the next operation can be placed over a partially dry brown coat or one that is allowed to dry thoroughly and then wetted evenly by brushing or spraying.

The scratch coat. A scratch coat is the first coat and is always applied over plaster bases such as metal lath. The scratch coat is 3/16 inch to 1/4 inch thick and its purpose is to stiffen the base, provide suction for the brown coat (which constitutes the bulk of the basecoat material), and to provide a positive mechanical bonding key with the base. For greater strength over these bases, scratch coats usually are applied with richer mortars than brown coats. The formulation of mortar is discussed in section II of this chapter.

In manual application the scratch coat should be applied with sufficient pressure and the mortar should be plastic enough to curl the keys around the back of the metal lath, wire lath, or perforated gypsum lath. Gypsum plasters for scratch coats applied to metal lath usually contain fiber to minimize the wastage due to material dropping through the lath.

The application of the scratch coat by machine presents no unusual problems when the plaster is being placed on solid backings such as gypsum lath or masonry. Where a plaster base is open, as with metal lath, adjustments are made in the operation of the machine to prevent the waste of plaster by being blown through the backing. A larger orifice and reduced air pressure produce the desired pattern. For some machines special nozzles for scratch coating are available. Generally one plasterer is required to follow the machine in order to make sure the surface is uniform and to inscribe the bond scratches.

The scratch coat is inclined to be sticky because of the richness of the mixture, and is therefore more difficult to straighten. However, for this application a perfectly straight surface is not a prime requisite. After it is applied, the operation is performed from which this coat derives its name. The coat is scratched and cross scratched to provide a rough surface for bonding the next coat. This scratching is done with a tool that leaves furrows approximately 1/8 inch deep, 1/8 inch wide, and 1/2 inch to 3/4 inches apart. It is apparent that the surface area of exposed plaster is increased by the presence of scratch marks — in fact, by as much as 50 per cent. Scratching is required in all of the model codes, and manufacturers' recommendations, thus indicating general agreement within the plastering industry on the value of the procedure.

Controversy with regard to this recommendation has developed since the Armour Foundation reported these findings: "Scratch marks have negligible effect on the strength of bond between scratch and brown coats as determined by direct short-time tension tests. Scratch marks appear to constitute a region of weakness in the scratch coat, which originate from the roots of these marks, both during the curing period of the scratch coat and upon structural deformation of the finished, cured construction. Cracks developing in the under coat from these weak regions may be transmitted to the brown and finish coats."[17] Both the Gypsum Association and the Finishing Lime Association of Ohio disagree with these findings. They contend that the short term tests are not substantiated by observations of actual construction. Further evidence of these conflicting data can be ascertained from the reports previously mentioned that dealt with the adhesion of plaster to various plaster backings.

Where a scratch coat is applied over unit masonry, similar procedures are used except that the mortar mix need not be as rich as that over lathing bases. Sufficient pressure should be exerted with the trowel to assure good contact with the base.

The brown coat (or second coat) of plaster applied in the three-coat process provides the major portion of the total plaster thickness. Usually it is mixed somewhat leaner than the scratch coat used over open bases. However, since this coat virtually constitutes the membrane, its strength will have an important effect on the strength of the total slab. Therefore the mix must be carefully formulated.

The brown coat is applied only after the scratch coat has set firm and hard. The plaster thickness should be brought out to grounds and screeds, straightened with rod, darbied, and scratched or raked to receive the finish coat. If a finish coat is not required, it is possible to darby and float the brown coat to a surface having the appearance of a heavily textured aggregate finish.

The working characteristics of the brown coat mortar are highly important. Since most of the total material used is handled in this operation, the ease with which the mortar is manipulated, particularly in hand application, affects both the quality and the economy of the job. Mortars of high plasticity

and properly controlled consistency permit longer trowel strokes without tearing, and are easier to straighten.

When the plastering machine is used the brown coat can be applied either in a single application or by spraying on successive coats to build up the thickness. In the hands of a skilled mechanic the plaster can be placed to lines as true as those normally found in hand applied plaster, and as proficiency is acquired the amount of straightening required can be reduced substantially.

Two-coat work. The two-coat method is used over gypsum lath or masonry bases. This is the sequence of operations employed in *double-up,* two-coat plastering:

(1) Install the plaster base.

(2) Attach the grounds and apply screeds.

(3) Apply the first thickness and double back immediately with a second thickness to the depth of the screeds.

(4) The remaining steps are similar to steps (8) through (12) in the outline for applying three-coat work.

In hand work the first coat of plaster should be applied with sufficient pressure and enough material to make good contact with the base and to cover it well. Before this application has set, and without cross raking, mortar of the same type is doubled back to bring the plaster out to grounds. The plaster is then struck to a true surface with rod and darby and left rough to receive the finish coat.

One-coat work. A third method known as *lay-on* or *single-coat* is an application of the entire thickness of plaster in one coat. Although not a widely acceptable practice at the present time, some sources insist that this application is very satisfactory. The data developed by field experience and laboratory tests, however, are too incomplete to justify a detailed description here.

Monolithic concrete bases. The application of plaster directly to monolithic concrete bases presents two distinct problems. The first arises from the difference in the coefficients of expansion of gypsum plaster and concrete. The second is bonding characteristics of the surface of the concrete. The problems and methods involved in direct plaster application are discussed in Chapter 3.

Bond plaster. Gypsum bond plaster is a specially formulated gypsum basecoat plaster having a coefficient of expansion closely approximating that of concrete. Ordinary gypsum plasters and wood fiber plasters show less shrinkage upon drying than concrete. For this reason they do not perform satisfactorily when applied directly to concrete surfaces. The surface of the concrete must be rough enough to insure mechanical key for the bond plaster. Bond plaster is prepared by the manufacturer so that at the job it requires only the addition of water.

The American Standards Association recommend this sequence of operations for plastering on monolithic concrete.[18]

Walls and columns

(1) Prepare the concrete surface so that it is sufficiently rough to provide mechanical bond.

(2) Apply the scratch coat of bond plaster.

(3) Apply the brown coat and trowel it into the scratch coat before the scratch coat has set.

(4) Bring the brown coat to the depth of grounds, using the double-back method of application, if required, to maximum thickness of ⅝ inch.

(5) Rod and darby the brown coat, straighten all angles, and leave the surface rough enough to provide bond for the finish coat.

Ceilings

(1) Apply the scratch coat of bond plaster.

(2) Scratch thoroughly and double back with an additional coat of bond plaster to a true surface, using the rod and darby for straightening.

NOTE: *"If monolithic concrete ceiling surfaces require more than ⅜" of plaster to produce required lines or surfaces, metal lath or wire lath bonding for the plaster shall be attached to the concrete before application of plaster. Where concrete ceiling surfaces are such as to require the application of an excessive thickness of plaster to produce required lines or surfaces, lath shall be applied over metal furring secured to the concrete."*[19]

(3) Leave the surface rough enough to receive the finish coat, if required. The minimum thickness of the plaster is ⅛ inch, the maximum ⅜ inch.

Bonding agents. Several manufacturers now produce materials which can be applied directly to concrete and other surfaces to act as bonding agents between the concrete and the applied plaster. The composition of these materials is of a proprietary nature and the manufacturer's instructions must always be consulted in order to establish surface preparation and method of application. Usually, bonding agents are liquid and can be applied by either brush or spray. They differ from bond plaster in that an adhesive bond is provided as well as compensation for differential expansion. Additional information on the properties of these materials is included in Chapter 2.

Basecoat application on solid partitions. There are several types of partitions in common use that have lath and plaster as basic components. Among these are solid plaster partitions using both metal and gypsum lath cores. In addition, there are a number of other lath and plaster partition types that employ wood, fabricated metal open web and channel studs. The advantages, limitations and characteristics of all these partitions are described in Chapter 5.

The sequence of steps in plastering solid partitions is somewhat different from that of other wall plastering. These methods are now in common practice:

Channel stud solid plaster partitions (Fig. 22).

Plaster is applied in five or more coats: scratch, back-up, brown, and a finish coat on each side.[20]

(1) Apply the scratch coat to the lath with enough pressure to form good keys on the back of the lath.

(2) Allow the scratch coat to set firm and hard, after which temporary bracing, if used, can be removed.

(3) Apply the back-up coat on the channel side of the partition. This coat is applied in two operations. The first coat should be thick enough

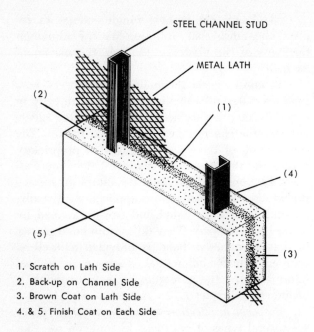

1. Scratch on Lath Side
2. Back-up on Channel Side
3. Brown Coat on Lath Side
4. & 5. Finish Coat on Each Side

Fig. 22 — Sequence of Plaster Application — Channel Stud Solid Plaster Partition (*Temporary bracing not shown.*)

to cover the keys on the back of the lath and should form a good mechanical bond with these keys. The second coat is doubled back and applied thick enough to bring the plaster to the grounds. The surface is then rodded, darbied, cut back and left rough to receive the finish coat.

(4) Allow the back-up coat to set and apply the brown coat on the lath side of the partition over the previously applied scratch coat.

(5) Rod and darby the brown coat and rake or scratch to receive the finish coat.

The plaster must extend to the floor in all cases, and the spaces between grounds must be filled. Where hollow metal door frames are used they must be filled solid to reduce damage due to vibration from door operation and to eliminate passages for fire or sound.

Studless metal lath solid partition (Fig. 23).

The number of coats and the sequence of operations in applying the plaster to this partition

system is similar to that outlined for solid plaster systems with channel studs. The ASA specifications allow these alternates in the sequence of application of the brown coat and back-up coats:

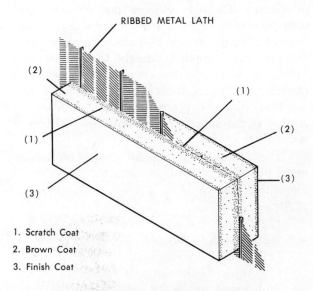

1. Scratch Coat
2. Brown Coat
3. Finish Coat

Fig. 23 — Sequence of Plaster Application — Studless Metal Lath Solid Partition

(1) "Brown coat shall be applied over face of the scratch coat, then back-up coat shall be applied on reverse side of the partition" or

(2) "Back-up coat shall be applied on the rib side of metal lath, or on the back side of the scratch coat, and shall be followed by the brown coat applied over the face of the scratch coat,"[21]

Gypsum lath solid partitions (Fig. 24).

In this partition either a single layer or multi-layer gypsum lath is employed as the plaster base. Temporary bracing may not be required in multi-layer partitions, but it is always needed in the single-layer system. In either system the plaster has a scratch, brown and finish coat, with a minimum of ½ inch of plaster on both sides of the lath.

These are the steps involved in plastering these partitions:

(1) Apply ⅜ inch scratch coat to each side of the lath, simultaneously if possible, or within three hours.

(2) Scratch lightly but only in a horizontal direction.

(3) Allow the scratch coat to set firmly and partially dry (not less than 16 hours).

(4) Apply the brown coat, rod and darby it to a true surface, allowing space for the finish coat to be applied flush with the grounds. The surface should be raked or scratched to receive the finish coat.[22]

Proprietary specifications should be consulted for variations in thickness of coats and sequence of plastering with these systems.[23]

Lime basecoats. Lime plaster depends entirely upon mechanical bond between coats and to the plaster base. It has been successfully applied over wood, metal lath, masonry walls, concrete, gypsum

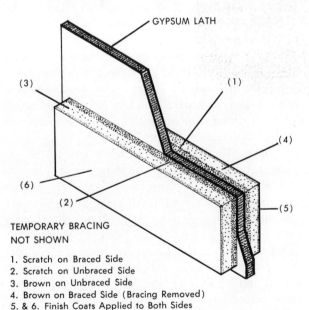

GYPSUM LATH

(3) (1) (4) (6) (2) (5)

TEMPORARY BRACING
NOT SHOWN

1. Scratch on Braced Side
2. Scratch on Unbraced Side
3. Brown on Unbraced Side
4. Brown on Braced Side (Bracing Removed)
5. & 6. Finish Coats Applied to Both Sides

Fig. 24 — Sequence of Plaster Application — Gypsum Lath Solid Partition   (Temporary bracing not shown.)

block and perforated gypsum lath, although the use of the last three bases is not generally recommended. Unlike gypsum, lime plaster does not set as a result of hydration. It derives its initial hardness through the stiffening that accompanies loss of water due to evaporation. While this process is occurring the surface absorbs carbon dioxide from the air. This combines with the lime to form crystalline calcium carbonate and magnesium carbonate. This process is called *recarbonation* and is described in Chapter 2.

Lime plaster requires a longer time between coats than is generally needed for other common plasters. The exact time required depends upon the temperature and amount of moisture in the room being plastered.

With one exception, the sequence of operations and the methods used to apply lime plaster basecoats are similar to those outlined for gypsum plaster. An additional floating is required the day after the brown coat has been applied. This floating is needed to increase the density of the plaster slab and to fill in all cracks that may have developed due to shrinkage of the plaster. A wood float, with a nail projecting approximately ⅛ inch through the sole, is used for this operation. The surface is compacted and scratched at the same time to provide keying for the finish coat. The float used for this procedure is called a "devil's float."

This is the sequence of steps for lime plaster over various plaster bases:
Three-coat work

(1) Apply the scratch coat with sufficient plaster and pressure to evenly cover the plaster base and provide positive keying.

(2) Allow the scratch coat to become hard, but not dry, and scratch with a metal scratching tool.

(3) Apply plaster screeds. Grounds and screeds are established to provide for ⅞ inch of plaster from the face of the plaster base.

(4) Allow the scratch coat to dry and then apply the brown coat to the depth of the grounds.

(5) Rod and darby the surface to a true plane and straighten all angles. Cut the brown coat back $\frac{1}{16}$ inch at grounds to allow the finish coat to be plastered flush with the grounds.

(6) Allow the brown coat to dry for 24 hours and float the surface with a devil's float, leaving the plaster rough to receive the finish coat.[24]

Two-coat work on masonry

(1) Apply grounds and screeds so that the total thickness of plaster will be at least $\frac{5}{8}$ inch from the face of the plaster base.

(2) Apply a thin coat of plaster to evenly cover and form good bond with the plaster base.

(3) Using the mortar of the same mix, double back and bring the plaster out to the grounds.

(4) Rod and darby the surface, straighten angles and cut the plaster back at grounds to allow for the finish coat.

(5) When the surface is firm, but not dry, float with a devil's float. Approximately 24 hours are allowed between the application of the brown coat and this operation.

Lime basecoat plasters, because they can be re-tempered, allow all clean (that is, no sawdust and other foreign matter) plaster droppings to be mixed into the fresh mortar and reused, thus effecting possible savings in material.

Exterior lime plaster (stucco). The methods for applying lime plaster to the exterior of a building are essentially the same as those previously described for interior lime plaster. The primary differences are in the curing procedures and the thickness of grounds recommended. After the scratch coat has been applied and has become firm, but not dry, it is scratched with a metal scratcher to insure firm bond with the brown coat. It is *moist cured* for not less than 48 hours.

The brown coat is scratched or raked and allowed to cure for approximately 7 days, after which the finish coat may be applied. The finish coat, like the scratch coat, is moist cured for two days after application.

Portland cement basecoats. Portland cement plas-

Table XI.

Recommended Minimum Thickness Of Lime Plaster Over Various Backings[25]

Plaster Base	Minimum Thickness of Plaster Including Finish Coat*	
	Interior Plaster	Exterior Plaster
Metal Lath 3 coats required	$\frac{7}{8}''$	$1''$
Masonry	$\frac{5}{8}''$	$\frac{3}{4}''$
Concrete Ceilings	$\frac{1}{16}''$ to $\frac{1}{8}''$	—
Walls	$\frac{5}{8}''$	$\frac{3}{4}''$

* Finish coats of interior plaster are $\frac{1}{16}''$ minimum and $\frac{1}{8}''$ maximum thickness.

Finish coats of exterior plaster are of sufficient thickness to secure the texture specified, but in no case are less than $\frac{1}{8}''$ thick.

ters offer relatively great resistance to moisture and abrasion, and are most frequently used where excessively damp conditions are encountered. These plasters should be considered as thin concrete slabs, and they are subject to the same controls normally exercised in concrete work. The term *portland cement stucco* generally refers to exterior work, while *portland cement plaster* is used to designate interior application of the material.

Bases. Portland cement plaster and stucco depend entirely upon mechanical bond for adhesion to plaster bases. They can be applied over concrete masonry, hard or medium burned bricks, or clay tile, metal lath (expanded, ribbed and sheet), wire lath, and paper-backed wire fabric.[26] Portland cement stucco can also be applied over old masonry and portland cement stucco, if the old material is sound and firmly attached. Where the face of masonry units have become soft, or cannot be thoroughly cleaned (as with painted brick), metal reinforcement is applied to the surface. Deteriorated stucco should be removed entirely and new stucco applied to the plaster base.

Portland cement plaster and stucco should not be used over the following plaster bases because of the possibility of bond failure due to chemical action, wide variations on coefficients of expansion, or the lack of opportunity for mechanical bond between the surfaces:

Portland cement plaster should not be placed over gypsum lath, wood lath, or fiber insulation lath.

Portland cement stucco should not be placed over lime, gypsum, or magnesite stucco.

Coats and thickness. Portland cement plaster and stucco are generally applied in three operations: scratch, brown and finish coats. These have been previously described for gypsum and lime plasters. Among the authorities that recommend three-coat application, regardless of the plaster base are:

American Standards Association
A42.2-1946
A42.3-1946

Department of Commerce, Bureau of Standards
Circular No. 311

Portland Cement Association
Bulletin No. P 160B-2

Bureau of Reclamation Specifications

Preparation of plaster bases is described in Chapter 3.

Certain specifications require that two-coat work be applied over properly prepared monolithic concrete bases. In this specification the first coat is portland cement grout, dashed onto the surface; the second, or finish coat, is ⅜ inch thick.[27]

These are the minimum thicknesses of the various coats for portland cement plaster (interior and exterior) recommended by the American Standards Association:[28]

Scratch coat	⅜ inch
Brown coat	⅜ inch
Finish coat	⅛ inch

The recommendations of the ASA are the same as those of the Bureau of Reclamation, the Portland Cement Association, and other major authorities.

Curing of portland cement plaster and stucco. An important consideration in the use of portland cement as the cementitious material for plaster relates to the high shrinkage coefficient experienced in the curing of the mortar. As has been said, most of the objectionable cracking in portland cement plaster is caused by volume change due to shrinkage of the plaster as it dries. The degree of cracking that will result is related to the ratio of shrinkage stress to tensile strength occuring in the particular slab. In order to obtain full strength and uniform shrinkage, it is important that the plaster slab dry slowly and uniformly.[29] The best method for accomplishing this has recently aroused considerable interest in the industry.

The method of curing portland cement plaster and stucco specified by the ASA and widely accepted as the proper procedure, is to moist cure the scratch coat (fog spray or a similar method) for 48 hours. After this period the brown coat can be applied. It, too, is moist cured for 48 hours, after which it is allowed to dry. The finish coat is not applied for at least 7 days after the brown coat, and is given a 48-hour moist curing treatment similar to the scratch and brown coats.

Another method for curing that has been used frequently in the past few years, with reported excellent results, follows these curing procedures:

The scratch coat is applied and allowed to dry slowly for 24 hours. The brown coat is placed to the required thickness and plane, and it, too, is allowed to dry slowly for 24 hours, after which the finish coat is applied. The finish coat receives four applications of fog spray during curing. The first spray is applied 12 hours after the finishing operations are completed. The three subsequent sprayings take place at 12-hour intervals. This method of curing has been used by the Bureau of Reclamation on several large projects and the results obtained have been reported as excellent. This method is now also recommended by a number of contractors.

The point of view upon which this method is based is set forth in a circular on "Stucco Investigations at the Bureau of Standards (with recommendations for portland cement stucco construction)" which states: "While there are many advocates of allowing the first two coats to cure several days before applying the finish coat, it has been noted at the Bureau of Standards that shrinkage cracks which developed in the scratch coat later appeared in the brown coat, and finally these same cracks showed through the finish coat. Therefore, it would seem more logical to apply all three coats one day apart, building up a fairly heavy thickness of mortar and keeping this uniformly wet for several days than to expect a finish coat of one-fourth inch to permanently seal cracks which had already worked through the first two coats."[30]

It is also maintained that the bond produced between portland cement plasters applied to a set but uncured preceding coat is considerably stronger than that produced when the base coat has been cured. In addition to providing resistance to delamination, this condition is thought to produce more complete structural integration and, therefore, a stronger slab.

When this was written, authoritative groups were investigating the relative merits of the two procedures. If the "green application" method is found to be more satisfactory than the present "standard" method, economic advantages will be realized as a result of more rapid completion of work.

FINISH COAT APPLICATION

The function of the finish coat is to provide an acceptable visible surface and to act as a base over which paint and other coverings can be applied. In contrast to the base coats, it is not used as a filler but as a thin veneer that will conform to the surfaces previously applied.

The finish coat plaster, to a greater degree than the basecoats, must be of a consistency to permit smooth spreading. The consistency of all plasters depends greatly on the amount of mixing water used, which is related to the change in volume of the material that occurs during the drying of the plaster. This is more particularly true in lime putty and portland cement plaster finishes than in gypsum finishes.

Interior plaster finishes are generally finished by one of three methods; troweling, floating or spraying of several basic combinations of materials. There are many variations of these methods that produce different appearances and performances. Examples of typical finishes are discussed farther on in this section. Before large areas are finished, it is customary for the plasterer to prepare samples of all textured finishes for approval. If more than one plasterer is applying the same material and there is no common sample that can be used for reference, unwanted variations in texture can occur.

While the problem of *joinings* (visible lines where finishing operations were not continuous) is more critical with some plasters than with others, it is important that when possible, the work be scheduled so that finishing can terminate at a natural line, such as an expansion joint, a break in the plane of the surface, or the intersection of adjacent planes.

Trowel finishes (non-acoustical) are used where a flat, smooth surface is required. Although they are not restricted to this use, generally they form the base over which wall coverings are placed. Trowel finishes tend to be relatively non-porous and can be polished to a mirrorlike finish. As such they are sometimes useful as reflecting surfaces in the control of light and sound, and for other special purposes. Samples of troweled surfaces were uncovered during excavations at Pompeii that closely resembled the reflective and abrasion-resistant qualities of highly polished marbles.

These are the steps for applying finishing coat plasters, where troweled surfaces are required:

Lime putty-gypsum finish. Consisting of gypsum gauging plaster and finishing lime, this plaster constitutes the most widely used material for smooth finish coats, and is called either *white coat* or *putty coat*. The gauging material used in this plaster is compounded for a range of setting times. High strength gauging plasters are available which provide very hard surfaces.

The putty coat is nearly always applied by a team of two or more men. These steps outline the application procedures required to place and finish the white coat. (A more detailed discussion of these and other methods are in the book *Plastering Skill and Practice,* by Van Den Branden and Knowles, © 1953, American Technical Society.)

(1) The plaster is applied by one mechanic, first to the angles over a partially dry base coat.

(2) A second plasterer follows, immediately straightening the angle with a rod or featheredge.

(3) The surface between the angles is filled with a "skim" coat of plaster. Pressure on the trowel must be sufficient to force the material into the rough surface of the base coat in order to provide contact for bond.

(4) The surface is immediately doubled-back with sufficient material to bring the finish coat to final thickness.

(5) The next operation is to float the angles. It may be necessary to apply a small additional amount of plaster during the floating to fill minor voids that appear in the surface.

(6) The remainder of the wall or ceiling surface is then floated and all depressions in the plane filled. This operation is called "drawing-up" and the hollows being filled are commonly called "cat faces."

(7) The surface is now allowed to "draw" for a few minutes. As the gypsum begins to set, the glaze caused by the presence of water on the surface begins to disappear and the surface becomes dull. At this time final troweling commences.

(8) The plasterer lightly brushes the surface with water. The brush is held in one hand and the trowel in the other so that troweling can follow immediately after the water is applied. It is essential that the plasterer apply all possible pressure to the trowel in order to compact the finish coat.

(9) The entire surface is rapidly troweled without interruption after which the troweling operation is repeated and continued until the plaster has set. Any shrinkage cracks that appear must be troweled in before the setting action takes place.[31]

The importance of proper troweling is stressed in this excerpt from a Building Materials and Structures Report issued by the Department of Commerce: "As the finish-coat mix is composed (in 'white coat' plaster) of lime putty, there is a decided tendency for this coat to shrink. This tendency can be overcome in two ways — by making the coat as thin as possible and by troweling it at exactly the proper time. A thin coat contains less volume than a thick coat and permits troweling with greater facility. With a thin coat the cracks can be closed, or rather prevented, by troweling just as the cementitious material is setting and hardening. If it is troweled before set has occured, the plaster will continue to shrink (and crack) after the troweling. It cannot be troweled after set has occurred, for the material is then too rigid to yield to the trowel."[32]

Gypsum trowel finish. This plaster is supplied ready mixed and requires the addition of water only. It is important that the manufacturer's directions be followed in the mixing and application. The workability of a gypsum trowel finish does not equal that of "white coat" plaster but requires less troweling and, when properly placed, presents a harder surface than a normal gypsum-lime putty plaster. See Table VII for a comparison of the properties of this plaster with other finishing materials. Gypsum prepared trowel finish is preferably applied to a partially dried basecoat. If the basecoat has dried, it should be wetted lightly and uniformly in order to reduce suction. The finish is applied in three operations. The first application should be as thin as possible but covering the base completely and pressed well into it. The second application is doubled back immediately, leveled out, and allowed to draw. The surface is then troweled smooth and imperfections repaired. Excessive use of water on the surface during troweling is to be avoided. Walls are worked top and bottom together to avoid joinings.

Keene's cement-lime putty finish. Keene's cement mixed in various ratios with lime will produce finishes substantially harder than gypsum gauged lime putty finishes. It is available both in a quick setting type or as regular Keene's cement. Regular Keene's cement hardens slowly and requires troweling for a longer period of time. The quick-setting material hardens faster, thus will not need the same amount of troweling as the regular material; it also may be troweled sooner.

The standard procedure for applying this plaster is to first lay on a thin coat of the material, forcing it with sufficient pressure to assure positive contact with the basecoat. The surface is immediately doubled-backed and the plaster brought out to the finish grounds. It is then allowed to draw for a few minutes, after which it is troweled with water. Troweling continues until the plaster has set.

Another method that has been used in England to obtain a particularly hard Keene's cement finish consists of three very thin coats of the material. Time is allowed between each coat for the surface to draw. The final coat is water-troweled until the plaster has set. The amount of water used in the troweling is kept to the minimum necessary to obtain slip. To produce a surface with a glasslike sheen the plaster can be polished with moleskin the next day.

Gypsum-aggregate trowel finishes. In order to obtain a texture that is neither as smooth as a troweled lime putty or gypsum finish, nor as coarse as a float finish, either sand or lightweight aggregate is added to the mix. The mix is troweled in a manner similar to that described for smooth finishes. The surface should be troweled with sufficient pressure to embed all the aggregate so that no loose particles remain on the surface after the plaster has set. The aggregate used in finish coats is usually finer than that for basecoats.

Portland cement-sand finish. Where a troweled finish is desired in portland cement plaster, the material is laid on over a partially dry portland cement plaster base to a depth of at least ⅛ inch. Preliminary finishing is accomplished with a wood float, after which the surface is troweled to force the particles of sand into the plaster and to compact the final coat. In order to prevent excess fines from being drawn to the surface, troweling should be delayed as long as possible. For the same reason, care must be taken to prevent the surface from being over-troweled. The finish coat should then be moist cured as described earlier in this section.

Float finishes are used where a surface texture is desired. The coarseness (or scale) of the texture depends upon the aggregate, the mix proportions, and the type of float used. The various proportions are described in section II, and some typical floats are illustrated in section I of this chapter.

Finish plasters used for float finishes usually contain aggregate; texture is imparted primarily by the action of aggregate particles disturbed by the moving float surface. It is important that the basecoat over which the plaster is applied be uniformly damp. When the basecoat is wetter in one spot than in another, the finish is likely to be coarser because of the tendency of aggregate to come to the surface under trowel action when excess water is present.

The procedure for applying a floated finish coat, with few exceptions, is similar to that previously described for lime putty trowel finishes. Floating is started as the glaze disappears from the surface. If floated prior to this time the plaster will stick to the tool, making leveling difficult. The plasterer, with brush in one hand, applies water to the surface while the float in his other hand moves in a circular motion immediately behind the brush. A surface is usually floated twice; a rough floating with a wooden float is followed immediately by a final working with a rubber float.

These plasters are commonly used for float finishes:
- Gypsum-sand (ready-mixed or job-mixed);
- Lime-Keene's-sand;
- Gypsum-lightweight aggregate fines;
- Colored Plaster (ready-mixed and job-mixed);
- Portland cement-sand.

Spray finishes. The latitude of the textures available in machine-applied plaster is broad, ranging from large globules to very fine granules. The degree of coarseness is regulated by the air pressure at the nozzle, the orifice size, the distance the nozzle is held from the surface being plastered, and the formulation of the plaster mix.

Although nearly all the larger plaster pumps available at the present time can be used for finishes, common practice in the industry is to employ smaller, more mobile machines. Both small worm drive pumps and the hand hopper machine described in section I are used in finish coat work.

The application of colored plasters by spraying has been particularly successful since it is comparatively easy to place colored finishes uniformly by machine. Most of the difficulties inherent in hand application of this material which affect the quality of color, such as uniform trowel pressure or amount of floating, are eliminated.

Spray finishes are generally applied in two thin applications. After the first coat has been placed, all depressions, holes or irregularities must be touched up by hand in order to prevent their showing in the final coat. It will be found, particularly with acoustical plasters, that some products are designed especially for machine use, others are formulated only for hand application, and many can be handled in either way.

For specific procedures, the recommendations of the manufacturer of the machine and those of the plaster producer should be consulted.

Acoustical plasters designed for mechanical application are generally applied in two or more coats. It may be necessary, before the final thickness is sprayed, to straighten the angles of the surface by hand, but the amount of this work can be minimized by careful spraying. The plastering machine usually has an orifice ¼ inch to ⅜ inch in diameter which is held 2 or 3 feet from the plaster base. Approximately 10 to 15 pounds of air pressure produce a fine spray pattern.

The hand application of acoustical plaster is usually accomplished by placing two or more coats that have a combined thickness of at least ½ inch.

The first coat is laid on firmly to a depth of ¼ inch and then straightened. New tools are generally used in applying acoustical plasters, because old tools are more likely to drag. The second coat is applied after the first has dried. Troweling should be done only to the extent necessary to provide a bond between the coats. The plaster should not be compacted because the sound-absorbing properties of the finished plaster depend to a large degree on the porosity of the set material.

The final operation in hand application of acoustical plaster, which varies considerably with different materials, is done shortly after the final coat is applied. With certain materials, the acoustical surface is produced by rapidly floating with a rubber or cork float. When this is done it is important that the operation continue without interruption, and that it be carried to a natural stopping point so that joinings will not be visible when floating is resumed. If a perforated finish is required, the surface can be developed by sand spray or a perforating tool. The sand spray method is accomplished by filling the hopper of a spray machine with dry sand and directing it into the wet final coat. This method is used for perforating the softer varieties of acoustical plaster. Random perforations of uniform pattern can be produced very quickly by sand spraying. The nail perforator, as the name implies, is a platform in which a number of sharp spikes are embedded. The use of a perforated texture tends to blend joinings that could not be avoided during the application of the final coat. The day after the surface has been perforated in this way, a trowel can be run lightly over the plaster to remove sharp ridges caused by the retraction of the perforator.

Textures of interior finishes. As stated previously, there are three types of finishes available in interior plasterwork; troweled, floated and sprayed. Many textures can be produced by further manipulation of the basic types.

The methods for obtaining the textures shown in Fig. 25 *A, B, C, D,* and *E,* have already been de-

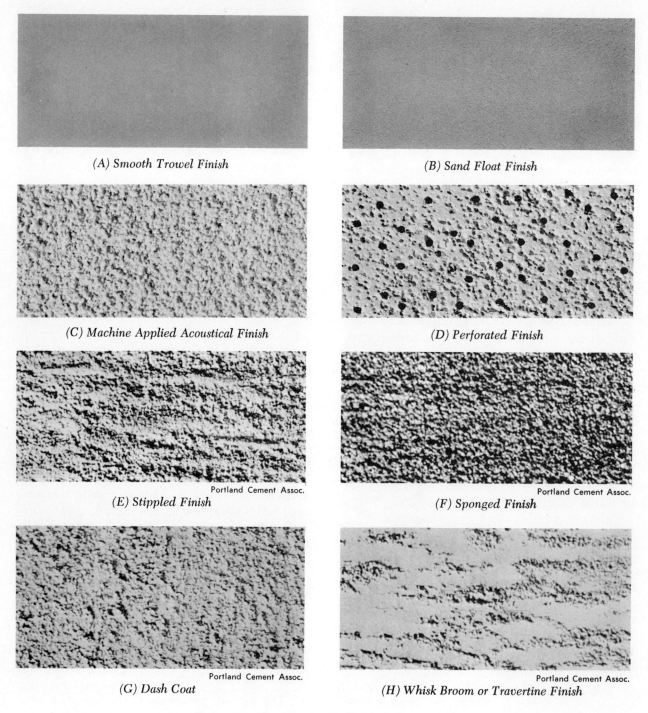

(A) Smooth Trowel Finish

(B) Sand Float Finish

(C) Machine Applied Acoustical Finish

(D) Perforated Finish

Portland Cement Assoc.

(E) Stippled Finish

Portland Cement Assoc.

(F) Sponged Finish

Portland Cement Assoc.

(G) Dash Coat

Portland Cement Assoc.

(H) Whisk Broom or Travertine Finish

Fig. 25 — Interior Finish Textures

cribed; here, briefly stated, are the methods used to produce the other textures illustrated:

Stippled finish. After the putty coat has been applied, additional plaster is daubed over the surface with a stippling brush. If the texture appears to be too harsh, it can be softened by brushing with water just as the plaster starts to set. A variation of this finish can be obtained by using a circular stippling brush and revolving it, while the plaster is being applied.

Sponge finish. By pressing a sponge against the surface of the putty coat a very soft, irregular texture can be obtained. If a coarser finish is desired, the sponge can be used with additional plaster and daubed onto the surface as described for stippled finish.

Dash coat finish. This texture is obtained by throwing plaster onto the surface with a brush. This method produces a fairly coarse finish which can be modified by brushing the plaster with water before it sets.

Travertine finish. The plaster is laid on thickly and is jabbed at random with a whisk broom, wire brush, or other tool that will form a dimpled surface. As the plaster begins to set, the surface is troweled intermittently to form a pattern of alternating rough and smooth areas.

Exterior plaster finishes. As a rule, the finishes used on the exteriors of buildings are more highly textured than those found in the interior. They are also thicker and more highly aggregated. Recommendations are made in Chapter 6 that will aid in the selection, beyond aesthetic considerations, of suitable exterior finishes. Generally, it will be found that with the heavier (coarser) textures, fewer problems will be encountered from staining, noticeable shrinkage, cracking, and dirt accumulation. Smooth troweled finishes are seldom used outdoors, except on areas like mechanically troweled curtain walls where surface quality is uniform and precisely controlled. When this method is used, particular care must be taken in the architectural detailing to provide adequate drips on overhangs in order to reduce water streaking.

Float finish (Fig. 26) is made with a rubber or carpet float, moved over the surface in circular strokes.

Wet-dash coat (Fig. 27), sometimes called "rough cast" or "Scottish harling," is a final coat, applied by dashing, and contains fairly coarse aggregate. The coarseness of the texture depends mainly on the type and size of the aggregate used and the consistency of the mix.

Machine applied finish (Fig. 28). In addition to plaster pumps, small hand-powered machines are used to flip finish plaster onto the surface. The effect is similar to a wet dash coat.

Scraped or American texture (Fig. 29). Several hours after the final coat of plaster has been applied and begun to set, a wood block, a steel straightedge, or some other tool that will tear the finish is passed over the surface in uniform strokes. The tool is worked upwards from the bottom of a wall.

Fan texture (Fig. 30). The finish illustrated here is one of the many possibilities for obtaining a textured finish by using the trowel held at an angle to the surface. The full range of textures available by this method is relatively unlimited. Because the character of such finishes tends to vary with the individual mechanic, standardization of sample is necessary to maintain uniformity in the appearance of the building.

English cottage texture (Fig. 31). This leaflike finish is produced by applying small amounts of mortar with a trowel which is twisted as it makes contact with the surface. The coarseness of the texture can be varied with the amount of material applied and the pressure put on the trowel. This finish is also subject to variation among individual plasterers.

Pebble dash (Fig. 32). This rough finish is obtained by throwing small pebbles or crushed stone against a newly plastered surface. Often a trowel is used to lightly press the stones into plaster. Like the two preceding examples, this finish also reflects differences in work by different persons.

Colored finishes. Many prepared commercial plasters are available for exterior use that contain integral color. These materials can be used in combination with any of the textures listed above. Many of them are proprietary and the manufacturer's instructions should be followed regarding their use and methods of application.

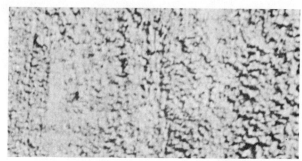

Portland Cement Assoc.

Fig. 29 — Scraped Texture

Portland Cement Assoc.

Fig. 26 — Float Finish

Fig. 30 — Fan Texture

Portland Cement Assoc.

Fig. 27 — Wet Dash Coat

Portland Cement Assoc.

Fig. 31 — English Cottage Texture

Courtesy Gypsum, Lime and Alabastine, Canada, Ltd.

Fig. 28 — Machine Applied Finish — (A) Coarse Texture (B) Medium Texture

Fig. 32 — Pebble Dash Finish

CHAPTER 5

LATH AND PLASTER SYSTEMS AND ASSEMBLIES

Lath, plaster and the various supplemental devices and accessories comprise the components with which a number of basic systems can be constructed. The number of individual variations possible in these systems is virtually unlimited. This chapter will describe those basic systems in general use today, and suggest some of the variations possible as they relate to certain specific construction requirements.

While the lath and plaster systems enumerated here generally cover the field of contemporary use, they by no means describe the total capabilities of the materials. Armed with a working knowledge of the basic components, a designer can often devise modifications of existing systems that better suit his particular needs, or he may create entirely new systems. Chapter 1 suggests some directions which these new uses may take.

For the purpose of description, lath and plastering systems in current use may be divided into these categories:

Interior uses
>Partitions and walls;
>Ceilings;
>Miscellaneous lath and plaster systems.

Exterior uses
>Wall surfacing;
>Load bearing walls;
>Curtain walls.

Whenever possible, components and systems will be described in generic terms and illustrated in this chapter. Many lathing and plastering materials manufacturers and contractors have developed proprietary modifications of the basic systems which utilize patented components. These are generally well illustrated in the literature published by the industry.

INTERIOR USES

Partitions and walls. There are three basic types of plaster partitions: solid plaster partitions which are monolithic plaster panels with a lath core; hollow plaster partitions consisting of two separate membranes supported by metal or wood studs; and masonry partitions consisting of a core of concrete block, clay tile, gypsum tile, or the like, with plaster applied to one or both sides.

Solid plaster partitions are usually considered non-bearing. Hollow and masonry partitions are classed as bearing or non-bearing, depending on usage, type of studs, or other structural characteristics.

While all partition systems perform the same general function — that of subdividing space — each has certain capabilities which makes it especially suited to certain specific requirements. The criteria used in selecting a partition type generally include:

Installation cost;
Fire resistance;
Weight;
Floor area occupied;
Sound transmission loss;
Accommodation of concealed mechanical and electrical equipment;
Allowable height;
Allowable length to height ratio;
Flexibility in planning.

Table I compares the efficiency of various partition systems with regard to some of these criteria.

Solid plaster partitions may be constructed with or without channel studs. The studless type consists of plaster applied to both sides of metal or gypsum lath which is attached to floor and ceiling runners with the long dimension of the lath sheets vertical. The channel stud type is applicable only to metal lath and as the name implies, relies upon channel studs anchored at floor and ceiling for support. When this is done, metal lath is attached with the long dimension of the sheet perpendicular to the studs.

Table I.

A Comparative Analysis of Partition Systems for Initial Selection of Partition Type

Partition Type	Weight Lbs. per Lin. Ft. Based on 8'-0" Ht.			Floor Area Occupied Sq. Ft. per Lin. Ft.			Fire Protection Fire-Resistance Rating (Hours)			Sound Transmission Loss Decibel Drop			Cost Index No Units		
	High	Low	Av'g.	High	Low	Av'g.	High	Low	Av'g.	High	Low	Av'g.	High	Low	Av'g.
1. Unit Masonry (Plastered)	337	169	232	.97	.25	.53	4.0*	0.5	2.92	58	37	44	1 Sample L.W. Conc.142		
2. Solid Plaster	203	70	135	.25	.13	.19	2.5	.42	1.19	47	33	38.7	126	100	113
3. Hollow (Metal Studs) Plastered Both Sides	214	65	130	.83	.21	.42	2.5	0.5	1.33	55	30	44.9	137	114	125
4. Hollow (Wood Studs) Plastered Both Sides	160	77	122	.61	.22	.45	2.0	.42	.89	55	33	43.1	135	110	120

* 7.0 Maximum

NOTE: For specific data on these types of partitions, consult other sections of this manual.

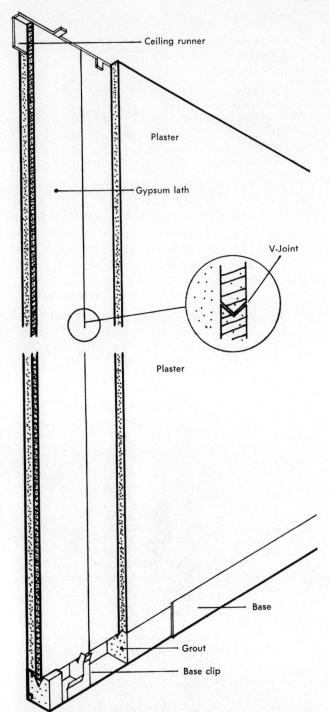

Ceiling runner

Plaster

Gypsum lath

V-Joint

Plaster

Base

Grout

Base clip

Fig. 1 — Studless Solid Plaster Partition — Gypsum Lath

The minimum thickness for solid plaster partitions (recommended by ASA) is 2 inches. The heights to which solid partitions may be carried depends upon thickness and structural rigidity. Maximum permissible lengths are determined by height and thickness.

Among the advantages of solid plaster partitions are economy of installation, increase in available floor space, relatively high crack resistance and durability, and simplification of scheduling and coordination of work, since only two closely allied trades are involved.

The main limitation on the use of solid partitions lies in the restrictions imposed on the incorporation of mechanical equipment by partition thickness. Conduits in all solid partitions should be limited to a size that will permit full plaster grounds on both sides of the partition. Water-carrying pipes should not be incorporated because of thermal and condensation problems.

Several factors determine the selection of a studless or channel stud solid partition; the studless partition is more economical, the channel stud type more versatile. Channel stud partitions may be constructed to a height of 24 feet or more. The studless type is limited to 12 feet with gypsum lath and 10 feet* with metal lath. The channel stud type is generally more applicable when there are a number of breaks or openings, when partition height varies considerably, or when greater than normal loads are to be hung on the partition. In general, accessories and grounds are more readily attached where channel studs are used.

Construction of gypsum lath studless partition. The components required are ceiling runner, floor runner or base clips, long-length gypsum lath, and plaster (basecoat and finish coat) (Figs. 1 and 2).

ASA specifications for interior lathing and furring include provisions which permit use of either ⅜ inch or ½ inch gypsum lath in single or mul-

---

* Nominal height is 8'-4" when using standard metal lath sheets; for greater ceiling heights, longer sheets are available on request.

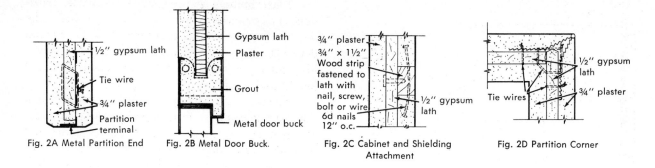

Fig. 2A Metal Partition End

Fig. 2B Metal Door Buck.

Fig. 2C Cabinet and Shielding Attachment

Fig. 2D Partition Corner

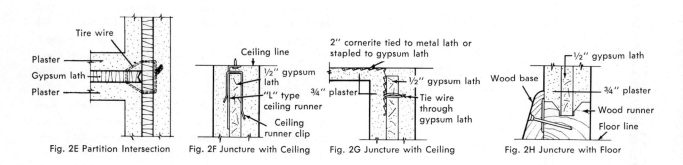

Fig. 2E Partition Intersection

Fig. 2F Juncture with Ceiling

Fig. 2G Juncture with Ceiling

Fig. 2H Juncture with Floor

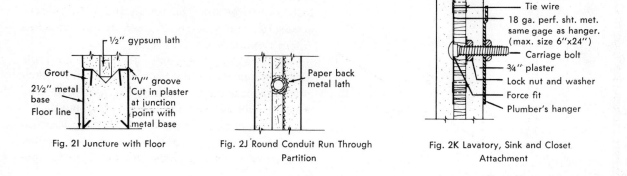

Fig. 2I Juncture with Floor

Fig. 2J Round Conduit Run Through Partition

Fig. 2K Lavatory, Sink and Closet Attachment

Fig. 2 — Gypsum Lath Solid Partition Details

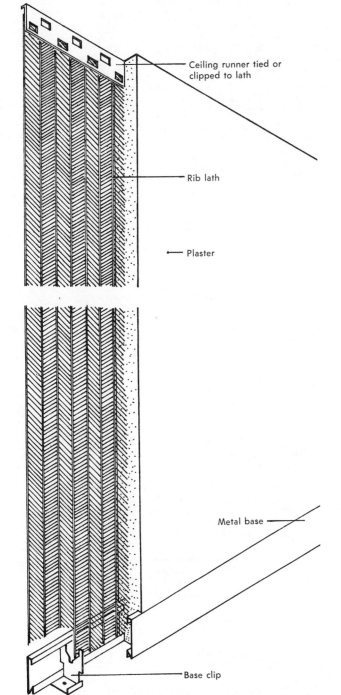

Ceiling runner tied or clipped to lath

Rib lath

Plaster

Metal base

Base clip

Fig. 3 — Studless Solid Plaster Partition — Metal Lath

tiple thicknesses. The ½ inch lath in a single thickness is most widely used.

Temporary bracing is used during erection of most studless partitions to hold the lath securely in alignment until the scratch coat has been applied to both sides and set and the brown coat has been applied and set on the unbraced side. The bracing is then removed and the brown coat applied to the previously braced face. Chapter 4 includes a more detailed description of plaster application to all types of solid partitions.

Construction of the metal lath studless partition. The components required are: ceiling runner; floor runner or base clips; metal lath; tie wire; plaster (basecoat and finish coat) (Figs. 3 and 4).

The types of metal lath used in studless partitions are: diamond mesh weighing not less than 3.4 pounds per square yard; flat rib lath of not less than 2.75 pounds per square yard; ⅜ inch rib of not less than 3.4 pounds per square yard; and sheet lath. Of these types the ⅜ inch rib lath is most widely used since less temporary bracing is required.

Construction of the channel stud solid partition. The essential components of this partition are: channel studs; metal lath; tie wire; plaster (basecoat and finish coat) (Tables II and III).

Optional components are ceiling runners and floor runners or base clips (Figs. 5 and 6).

Hollow plaster partitions are of three types, classified according to structure: the prefabricated metal stud; the wood stud; and the channel stud. Within each of these general types variations are possible for increasing sound-transmission loss or for accommodating unusually large mechanical or electrical components.

The over-all thickness of hollow partitions varies usually from a minimum of 3⅛ inches for the prefabricated metal stud type to virtually any required dimension in the channel stud type. Heights obtainable with hollow partitions run to 26 feet, depending on the type of partition, its length and usage. (See Tables IV, V and VII.)

The prefabricated metal stud and wood stud are most widely used as the structure of the hollow

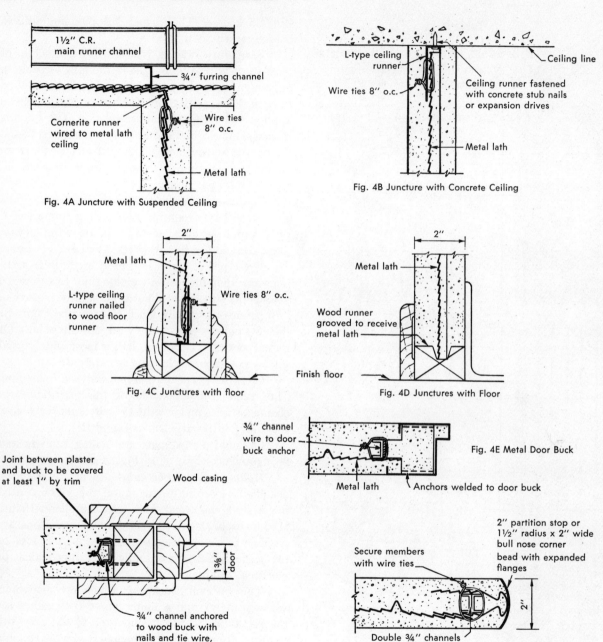

Fig. 4A Juncture with Suspended Ceiling

Fig. 4B Juncture with Concrete Ceiling

Fig. 4C Junctures with floor

Fig. 4D Junctures with Floor

Fig. 4E Metal Door Buck

Fig. 4F Wood Door Buck

Fig. 4G Metal Partition End

Fig. 4 — Metal Lath Studless Solid Partition — Details

Table II.

Sizes of Cold-Rolled Channel Studs and Thickness of Partitions for Various Heights of Metal Lath Solid Partions

Height Not to Exceed	Thickness of Partition	Size and Weight of Cold-Rolled Channels (Per 1000 ft.)
12 ft.	2″	¾″ 300 lbs.
14 ft.	2¼″	¾″ 300 lbs.
16 ft.	2½″	¾″ 300 lbs.
18 ft.	2¾″	1½″ 475 lbs.
20 ft.	3″	1½″ 475 lbs.
24 ft.*	3¼″	1½″ 475 lbs.

* For heights over 20′ furnish horizontal cold-rolled channels or rod stiffeners on channel side of partition every 6′ (placed horizontally). Heights over 24′ must be proportionately thicker.

NOTE: No limitations on length of these partitions for heights under 10′. Length, between columns, walls, or other vertical structural members, should not be greater than two times partition height when latter is 10′ or more, nor greater than 1½ times height when latter exceeds 14′; nor greater than the height when it is 20′ or more. For lengths exceeding these, thicknesses are increased 20 percent.

Table III.

Spacing of Channel Studs for Attachment of Metal Lath

Type of Metal Lath	Min. Weight* (Lbs. per Sq. Yd.)	Spacing of Supports (Inches)
Diamond Mesh	2.5	12
(Flat Expanded)	3.4	16
Flat Rib	2.75	16
Flat Rib	3.4	24**

* Weights given are exclusive of paper, fiber, or other backing.

** This spacing permissible for solid partitions not exceeding 16′ in height. For greater heights, permanent horizontal stiffener channels or rods should be provided on channel side of partitions, every 6′ vertically, or else these spacings should be reduced 25%.

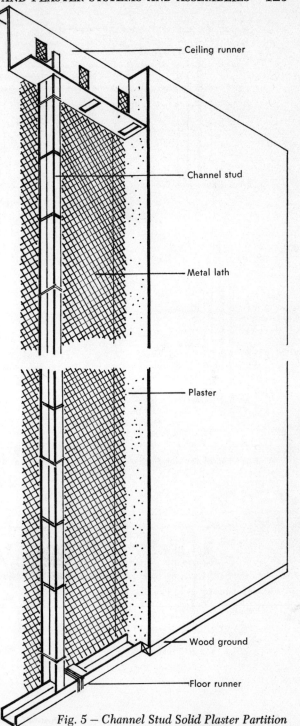

Fig. 5 – Channel Stud Solid Plaster Partition

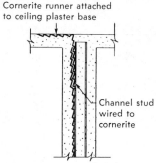

Cornerite runner attached to ceiling plaster base

Channel stud wired to cornerite

Fig. 6A Junctures with Ceiling

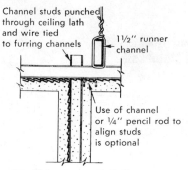

Channel studs punched through ceiling lath and wire tied to furring channels

1½" runner channel

Use of channel or ¼" pencil rod to align studs is optional

Fig. 6B Junctures with Ceiling

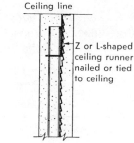

Ceiling line

Z or L-shaped ceiling runner nailed or tied to ceiling

Fig. 6C Junctures with Ceiling

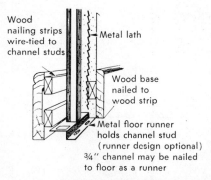

Wood nailing strips wire-tied to channel studs

Metal lath

Wood base nailed to wood strip

Metal floor runner holds channel stud (runner design optional) ¾" channel may be nailed to floor as a runner

Fig. 6D Junctures with Floor

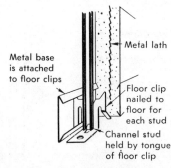

Metal lath

Metal base is attached to floor clips

Floor clip nailed to floor for each stud

Channel stud held by tongue of floor clip

Fig. 6E Junctures with Floor

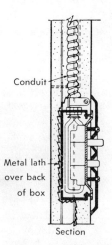

Conduit

Metal lath over back of box

Section

SWITCH BOX

Standard shallow outlets and switch boxes can be conveniently installed on either the lath or channel side of the partition. The boxes are only 1½".

Fig. 6F Switch Box

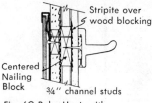

Stripite over wood blocking

Centered Nailing Block

¾" channel studs

Fig. 6G Robe Hook with Concealed Mounting and Wall Hung Mirror

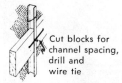

Cut blocks for channel spacing, drill and wire tie

Fig. 6H Centered Nailing Block

Fig. 6 — Channel Stud Solid Partition — Details

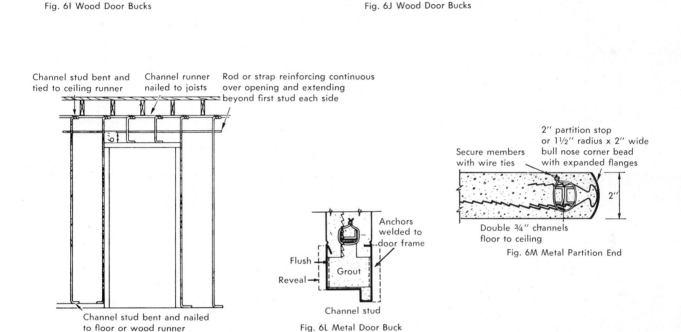

Casing laps plaster at least 1"

1⅜" door

Channel stud wired to 8d nails
Fig. 6I Wood Door Bucks

Washer spacer to permit tying of lath

Channel stud

1⅜" door

Casing laps plaster at least 1"

1" wood screws

Fig. 6J Wood Door Bucks

Channel stud bent and tied to ceiling runner

Channel runner nailed to joists

Rod or strap reinforcing continuous over opening and extending beyond first stud each side

Channel stud bent and nailed to floor or wood runner

Fig. 6K Elevation of Studs at Door Frame

Anchors welded to door frame

Flush

Reveal

Grout

Channel stud

Fig. 6L Metal Door Buck

2" partition stop or 1½" radius x 2" wide bull nose corner bead with expanded flanges

Secure members with wire ties

2"

Double ¾" channels floor to ceiling

Fig. 6M Metal Partition End

Fig. 6 — Channel Stud Solid Partition — Details

partition. However, the maximum degree of flexibility afforded by the channel stud structure makes its use desirable where unusually great partition widths are required, where ceiling heights vary, and in other special conditions. Metal studs have certain advantages over wood studs. Among these are incombustibility; horizontal runs of pipe, etc. can be placed without cutting or notching; a variety of wall widths are available; and all construction can be accomplished within the lathing trade, thus simplifying scheduling and coordination.

Construction of prefabricated metal stud partition. The necessary components are: floor runner track; ceiling runner track; prefabricated metal studs; metal or gypsum lath; clips or tie wires; basecoat and finish coat plaster; stud shoes (optional) (Figs. 7 and 8).

Partitions more than 10 feet long or 10 feet high should be stiffened with horizontal ¾ inch channels wired at 6-foot intervals on the inside of the partition. If the unsupported partition height exceeds 20 feet, 1½ inch channels should be used.

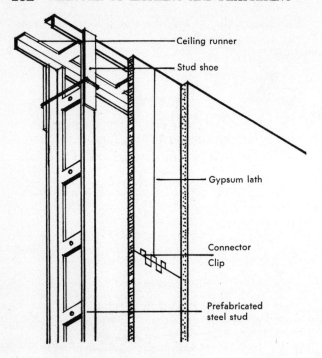

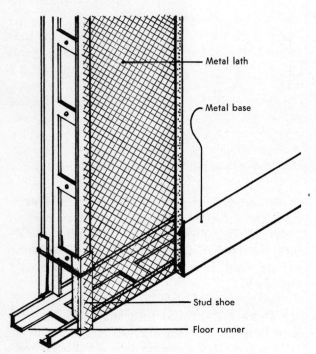

Fig. 7 — Prefabricated Metal Stud Partition

Table IV.

Minimum Requirements for Size and Spacing of Non-Bearing Prefabricated Metal Studs with Metal and Gypsum Lath

Width of Stud	Face-to-Face[a] Partition Thickness (in inches)	Maximum Heights[b] C-to-C Spacing of Studs		
		24"[c]	19"	16"
1⅝"	3⅛"	—	—	9'
2"	3½"	—	9'	10'
2½"	4"	9'	14'	15'
3¼"	4¾"	13'	18'	21'
4"	5½"	16'	20'	22'
6"	7½"	20'	24'	26'

[a] Plaster thickness: ¾" from stud face or ⅝" from face of metal lath; for ⅜" rib metal lath, with ribs against studs, thickness increases ½"; for ⅜" gypsum lath with ½" plaster, add ¼".

[b] For lengths not exceeding 1½ times height. For lengths exceeding this, reduce height 20%.

[c] For ⅜" rib, sheet, and ½" gypsum lath only.

Construction of channel stud partition. The essential components are: Floor runners or base clips; Channel studs; Stiffeners and spacers; Metal lath; Tie wires; Basecoat and finish coat plaster; Ceiling runner (optional) (see Figs. 9 and 10).

Table V.

Maximum Height of Channel Stud Hollow Partitions

Type of Partition	Face-to-Face Partition Thickness[a]	Maximum Height (C-to-C Spacing of Studs 16")[b]
Double row of ¾"	3"	14'
Channels Braced	4"	16'
Horizontally	5"	20'

[a] Plaster thickness: ¾" from stud face or ⅝" from face of metal lath; for ⅜" rib metal lath, with ribs against studs, thickness increases ½"; for ⅜" gypsum lath, with ½" plaster, add ¼".

[b] For lengths not exceeding 1½ times height. For lengths exceeding this, height should be reduced 20%.

NOTE: 4'0" is the maximum vertical distance between cross ties for ¾" channel studs.

When it is necessary either to obtain the maximum sound-transmission loss from a channel stud partition or to house a complex assortment of mechanical equipment, the cross ties which normally tie the two plaster membranes together may be omitted. This structure is termed a double channel stud partition. (See Fig. 9b.)

Table VI.

Maximum Recommended Height of Unbraced or Sound Insulating Channel Stud Partitions (based on 16″ stud spacing)

Stud Size	Height
¾″ Channel	8′-0″
1½″ Channel	10′-0″
2″ Channel	11′-0″

Table VII.

Maximum Spacing for All Types of Steel Studs in Hollow Partitions

Type of Lath	Weight of Lath (Lbs. per sq. yd.)	Maximum Recommended Spacing of Steel Studs for Hollow Partitions
Diamond Mesh	2.5	12″
(Flat Expanded)	3.4	16″
Flat Rib	2.75	16″
	3.4	19″
⅜″ Rib	3.4	24″
	4.0	24″
Sheet Lath	4.5	24″
⅜″ Gypsum	—	16″
½″ Gypsum	—	24″

Construction of wood stud partition. The components of a wood stud partition are the studs themselves, metal or gypsum lath, nails, staples or other fastening devices, and basecoat and finish coat plaster (Fig. 11).

Since the structure of a wood stud partition falls under the jurisdiction of the carpentry trade, the responsibility of the lather and plasterer is confined to attachment and application of the lath and plaster membrane.

Table VIII.

Maximum Spacing of Wood Stud Supports for Metal and Gypsum Lath

Type of Lath	Weight of Lath (Lbs. per sq. yd.)	Spacing of Wood Stud Supports
Diamond Mesh	2.5	16″
(Flat Expanded)	3.4	16″
Flat Rib	2.75	16″
	3.4	19″
⅜″ Rib	3.4	24″
	4.0	24″
Sheet Lath	4.5	24″
⅜″ Gypsum Lath	—	16″
½″ Gypsum Lath	—	24″

Specialized hollow partitions. To increase the effectiveness of prefabricated metal or wood stud partitions in reducing sound transmission, studs may be doubled (that is, placed in two parallel rows), or staggered, as shown in Fig. 12.

While this system may be dictated by certain conditions, similar or superior acoustical properties may be obtained with a hollow partition which utilizes resilient clip connections between lath and stud structure. These resilient devices are produced by several manufacturers, and are designed for use in ceilings as well as in partitions. In addition to the acoustical characteristics of resilient construction, stress transfer to the plaster from the structure is inhibited, thus providing increased crack resistance. (See Chapter 6.)

Plastered masonry partitions. The principal advantage of plastered masonry partitions is the degree of fire protection that may be obtained. However, this protection is generally gained at a sacrifice in adaptability and efficiency with regard to weight, and floor area occupied.

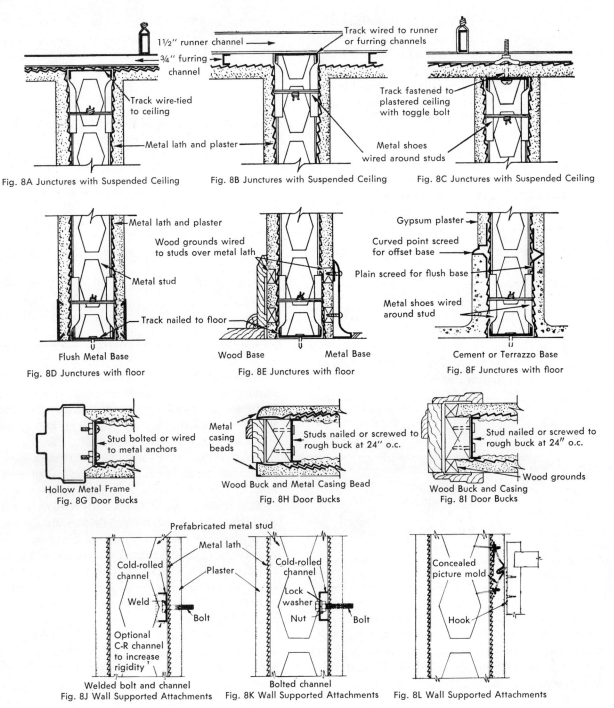

1½" runner channel

¾" furring channel

Track wire-tied to ceiling

Metal lath and plaster

Fig. 8A Junctures with Suspended Ceiling

Track wired to runner or furring channels

Fig. 8B Junctures with Suspended Ceiling

Track fastened to plastered ceiling with toggle bolt

Metal shoes wired around studs

Fig. 8C Junctures with Suspended Ceiling

Metal lath and plaster

Metal stud

Track nailed to floor

Flush Metal Base

Fig. 8D Junctures with floor

Wood grounds wired to studs over metal lath

Wood Base   Metal Base

Fig. 8E Junctures with floor

Gypsum plaster

Curved point screed for offset base

Plain screed for flush base

Metal shoes wired around stud

Cement or Terrazzo Base

Fig. 8F Junctures with floor

Stud bolted or wired to metal anchors

Hollow Metal Frame
Fig. 8G Door Bucks

Metal casing beads

Studs nailed or screwed to rough buck at 24" o.c.

Wood Buck and Metal Casing Bead
Fig. 8H Door Bucks

Stud nailed or screwed to rough buck at 24" o.c.

Wood grounds

Wood Buck and Casing
Fig. 8I Door Bucks

Prefabricated metal stud

Metal lath

Cold-rolled channel

Plaster

Weld

Bolt

Optional C-R channel to increase rigidity

Welded bolt and channel
Fig. 8J Wall Supported Attachments

Cold-rolled channel

Lock washer

Nut   Bolt

Bolted channel
Fig. 8K Wall Supported Attachments

Concealed picture mold

Hook

Fig. 8L Wall Supported Attachments

Fig. 8 — Prefabricated Metal Stud Partition — Details

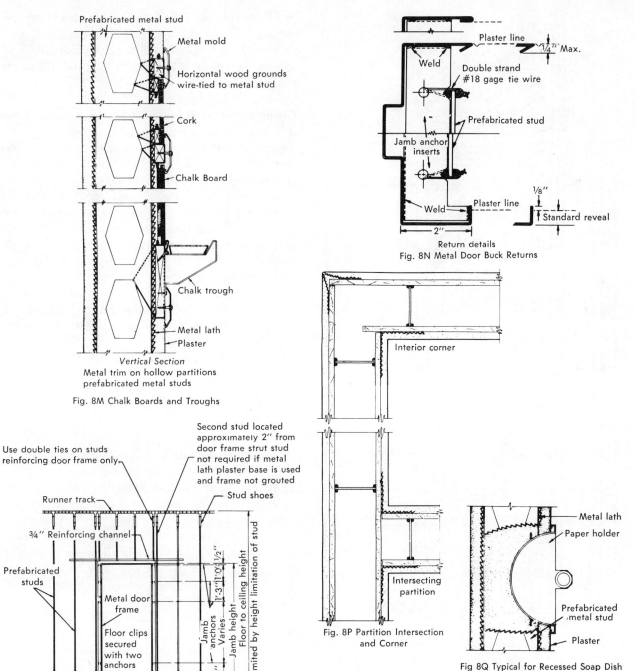

Prefabricated metal stud

Metal mold

Horizontal wood grounds wire-tied to metal stud

Cork

Chalk Board

Chalk trough

Metal lath

Plaster

Vertical Section
Metal trim on hollow partitions prefabricated metal studs

Fig. 8M Chalk Boards and Troughs

Plaster line

1/4" Max.

Weld

Double strand #18 gage tie wire

Prefabricated stud

Jamb anchor inserts

Weld

Plaster line

1/8"

Standard reveal

2"

Return details
Fig. 8N Metal Door Buck Returns

Interior corner

Intersecting partition

Fig. 8P Partition Intersection and Corner

Use double ties on studs reinforcing door frame only

Second stud located approximately 2" from door frame strut stud not required if metal lath plaster base is used and frame not grouted

Stud shoes

Runner track

3/4" Reinforcing channel

Prefabricated studs

Metal door frame

Floor clips secured with two anchors to floor

1'-3" 1'-0" 1'-1/2"

Jamb anchors Varies

1'-6"

Jamb height

Floor to ceiling height

Limited by height limitation of stud

Fig. 8O Elevation of Studs at Door Frame

Metal lath

Paper holder

Prefabricated metal stud

Plaster

Fig 8Q Typical for Recessed Soap Dish or Paper Holder

Fig. 8 — Prefabricated Metal Stud Partition — Details

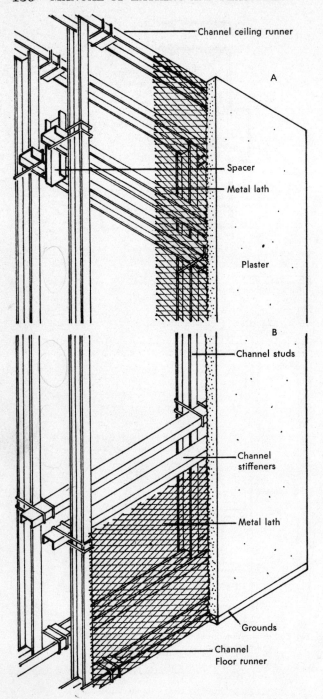

Channel ceiling runner

A

Spacer

Metal lath

Plaster

B

Channel studs

Channel stiffeners

Metal lath

Grounds

Channel Floor runner

Fig. 9 — Channel Stud Hollow Partition. (A) Typical Partition. (B) Sound Insulating Double Partition

Construction of the masonry core is usually the responsibility of trades outside the lathing and plastering industry. Application of plaster may be direct or over furred metal or gypsum lath, depending on the suitability of the masonry surface. This subject is discussed in Chapter 3.

Ceilings. For purposes of description, lath and plaster ceiling systems may be divided into three categories: *contact ceilings* which consist of a lath and plaster membrane attached directly to the structure above; *furred ceilings* which are separated from the structure by furring channels, rods or other devices; and *suspended ceilings* in which lath and plaster membranes combined with an integral supporting framework are suspended below the main structure by hangers. A fourth type of plaster ceiling, consisting of plaster applied directly to the underside of a floor or roof deck, is also in general use. Included in this type are direct application of plaster to concrete (either bond plaster or a bonding agent and a finish coat) and application of a special fireproofing or acoustical material to the underside of steel or concrete decks. For the purpose of classification, the discussion of this type of construction will be included in the section devoted to contact ceilings.

Lath and plaster ceilings, regardless of type, have certain characteristics which make them compare favorably with non-plaster ceiling systems. Plaster ceilings provide maximum flexibility because they are non-modular and can conform precisely to spaces of any shape, and are virtually unlimited in possible texture and color treatment. Where reduction of the noise level in a space is desirable, an acoustical plaster may be substituted for the conventional hard surfaced material. A plaster ceiling is an extremely effective fire barrier. It can prevent failures of combustible or heat susceptible structural elements for periods greatly exceeding those obtainable with other commonly used ceiling systems.

Contact, furred and suspended lath and plaster ceilings differ fundamentally only in the method of supporting the lath and plaster membrane and

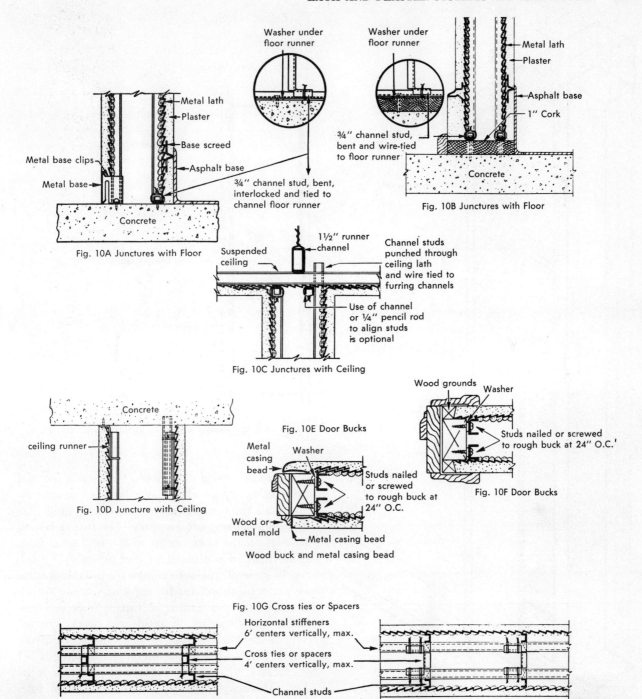

Washer under floor runner

Metal lath
Plaster
Base screed
Asphalt base
Metal base clips
Metal base
Concrete

¾" channel stud, bent, interlocked and tied to channel floor runner

Fig. 10A Junctures with Floor

Washer under floor runner

Metal lath
Plaster
Asphalt base
1" Cork

¾" channel stud, bent and wire-tied to floor runner

Concrete

Fig. 10B Junctures with Floor

Suspended ceiling

1½" runner channel

Channel studs punched through ceiling lath and wire tied to furring channels

Use of channel or ¼" pencil rod to align studs is optional

Fig. 10C Junctures with Ceiling

Concrete

ceiling runner

Fig. 10D Juncture with Ceiling

Fig. 10E Door Bucks

Metal casing bead
Washer
Studs nailed or screwed to rough buck at 24" O.C.
Wood or metal mold
Metal casing bead

Wood buck and metal casing bead

Wood grounds
Washer
Studs nailed or screwed to rough buck at 24" O.C.'

Fig. 10F Door Bucks

Fig. 10G Cross ties or Spacers

Horizontal stiffeners 6' centers vertically, max.
Cross ties or spacers 4' centers vertically, max.
Channel studs

Fig. 10 — Channel Stud Hollow Partition — Details

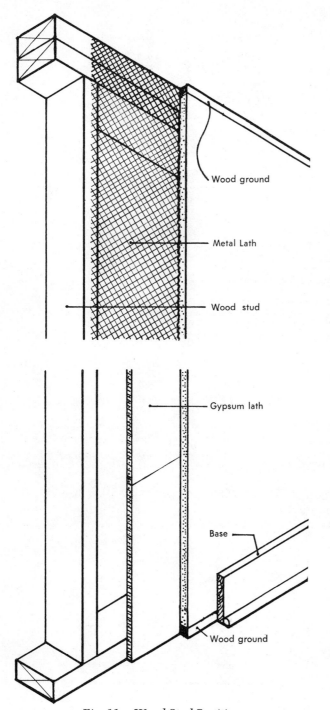

Wood ground

Metal Lath

Wood stud

Gypsum lath

Base

Wood ground

Fig. 11 — Wood Stud Partition

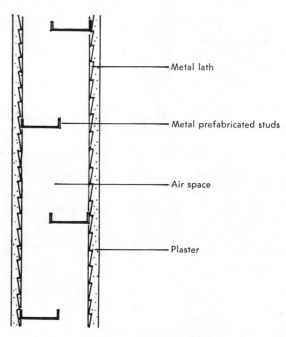

Metal lath

Metal prefabricated studs

Air space

Plaster

Fig. 12 — Staggered Stud Sound Insulating Partition

in the space provided between the membrane and the main structure above. A suspended ceiling includes all the components of a furred ceiling plus an additional support assembly. The furred ceiling includes all the components of the contact ceiling, again, with an additional support assembly.

In general, contact ceilings are suitable for use with structural systems having joist spacing within the maximum permissible lath span. Since this condition usually exists in residential work, contact ceilings are widely used in this type of construction. Where such a limitation on joist spacing is not practicable, a furred or suspended ceiling may be used. The suspended type allows maximum freedom in positioning the elements of the main structural system.

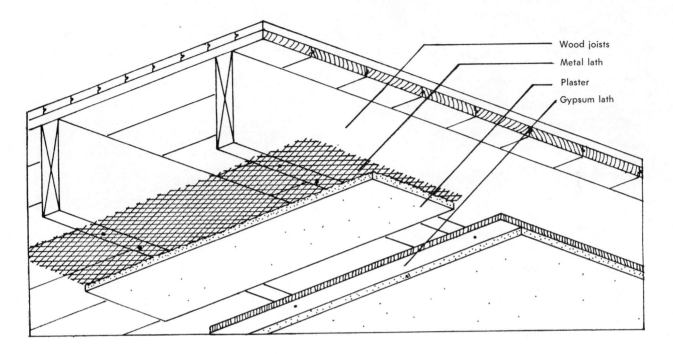

Wood joists
Metal lath
Plaster
Gypsum lath

Fig. 13 — Contact Ceiling — Wood Joists

The space provided between the ceiling and the deck above, in the case of contact ceilings, is governed by the depth of the joists, thus limiting the size of mechanical equipment that may be enclosed above the ceiling. The size of mechanical or electrical lines which run perpendicular to the direction of solid joists is severely restricted. This also is true, though to a lesser extent, with furred ceilings since the clearance provided between the ceiling membrane and the bottom of the joist usually is large enough to accommodate only small electrical lines. The cross-furring members, however, do give support to insulation, electrical and mechanical outlets, and conduit, that is not provided in a contact system. The suspended ceiling permits virtually any type of mechanical or electrical equipment to be installed above it, since hanger length may be varied to accommodate even

extremely large components. There is also no limitation in such instances on the direction in which lines and ducts may be run.

Contact and furred ceilings must follow closely the contour and height of the structure above them. Suspended ceilings, however, may assume virtually any form and may be suspended at any desired level.

The installation cost of contact, furred, and suspended systems rank lowest to highest, in that order.

Construction of contact ceilings. Due to the relative ease of fastening lath to structural members, wood and open web steel joists are more suitable supports for a lath and plaster contact ceiling than are concrete or large solid steel members. Methods of attaching lath to various structural elements are described in Chapter 3. Figs. 13, 14 and 15 show several contact ceiling systems that may

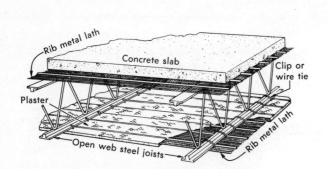

Fig. 14 – Contact Ceiling – Steel Joists

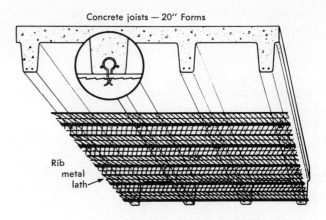

Fig.15 – Contact Ceiling – Concrete Joists

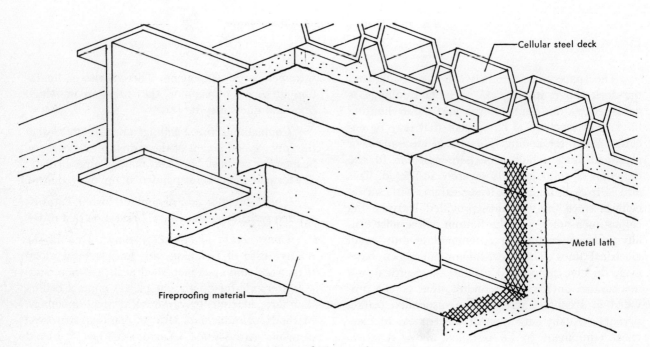

Fig. 16 – Sprayed Fireproofing Material

be used with wood, steel and concrete joists. Lath may be attached to cellular steel decks by means of punched flaps which are bent down and wired to lath.

Although not a contact ceiling according to the standard definition of the term, plaster applied directly to the underside of a roof or floor deck has similar characteristics. Chapter 4 describes the methods for applying bond plaster or a bonding agent, and a finish coat to concrete. A similar system involves spray application of a special fire-proofing or acoustical material direct to the underside of a deck and to its supporting structure. In addition to the acoustical properties afforded by this system, these materials provide effective fire protection for the structure. Fire rating periods of up to four hours may be obtained with a system similar to that shown in Fig. 16. (See Chapter 9.)

Construction of furred ceilings. The components of a furred ceiling are the same as for a contact ceiling, with the addition of furring channels, round rods, clips or other devices to provide a space between the supporting structure and the lath.

Furred ceilings containing gypsum or metal lath are adaptable to steel, concrete and wood structural systems. Figs. 17, 18 and 19 illustrate furred systems adaptable to steel, wood and concrete structural systems.

Construction of suspended ceilings. The standard components of suspended ceilings are lath and plaster, cross furring members, main runners, hangers, and attachment devices. In geographical areas where tornadoes, cyclones, hurricanes or earthquakes might be encountered that could exert upward pressures on a suspended ceiling, ¾ inch channels or struts (of heavier size where members exceed 4 feet on center) should be used as compression members. These struts should be so spaced as not to exceed 8 feet on center, and are in addition to the regular hangers. They serve to keep the ceiling from flut-

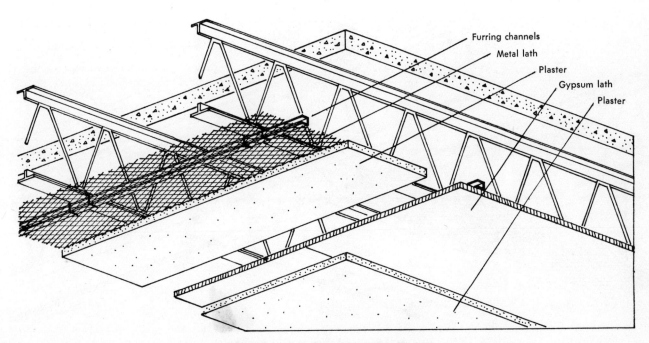

Fig. 17 — Furred Ceiling — Steel Joists

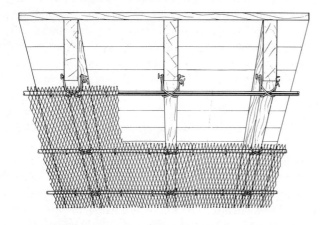

Fig. 18 — Furred Ceiling — Wood Joists

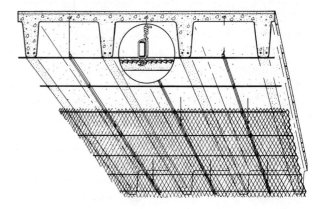

Fig. 19 — Furred Ceiling — Concrete Joists

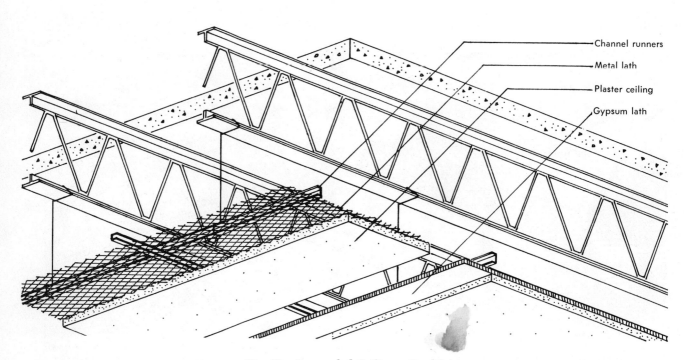

Fig. 20 — Suspended Ceiling — Steel Joists

tering or vibrating, and should not nullify the advantage gained by separation of the ceiling and the structure, inherent in the suspended system.

Suspended ceilings are adaptable to all types of structural systems. Figs. 20, 21 and 22 illustrate ceilings suspended from steel, wood and concrete construction.

In the standard method of constructing a suspended ceiling, furring channels are run at right angles to main runner channels. It has been found, however, that where furring channels support radiant heating coils, if the furring channels are run diagonally, heating coils may be run either parallel or perpendicular to main runners. This provides greater flexibility for the heating system with no loss in structural efficiency. Where ¾ inch furring channels are run diagonally to the main runner channels to allow greater flexibility for the installation of heating coils, the spacing between runners must be reduced to limit the span of the ¾ inch furring channels to a maximum of 4 feet. If a wider span between main runners becomes necessary the size and weight of the furring members must be increased accordingly. (See channel design tables, pp.149-153.) Where the ceiling is used to provide fire

protection for the structure above, the extent to which a suspended ceiling may be penetrated by heating and air conditioning outlets is limited by most building codes.

Flush mounted light fixtures may be installed in a fire retardant ceiling at no sacrifice in fire resistance if the fixtures are enclosed by lath and plaster troffers (Fig. 23).

Where ceiling penetrations required for heating or cooling must exceed the code limitations, a double ceiling may be a practical solution.

A double ceiling is two ceilings with a space between them. The upper ceiling, which may be in contact with the structure or suspended from it, provides fire protection for the structure. The lower suspended ceiling provides the finish ceiling surface. This type of construction is often used for luminous ceilings (Fig. 24).

The suspended ceiling is the only type where form is not dictated by the structure above it. In this type of system the ceiling membrane may assume virtually any geometrical or free form dictated by lighting, acoustics, esthetic considerations, or other requirements. Components used in this type of suspended ceiling are the same as those for

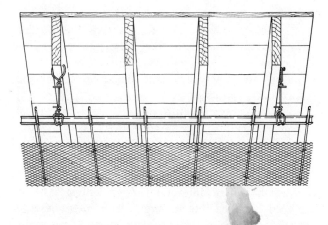

Fig. 21 — Suspended Ceiling — Wood Joists

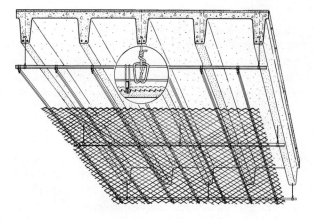

Fig. 22 — Suspended Ceiling — Concrete Joists

Fig. 23 – Lath and Plaster Membrane Enclosing Lighting Troffers

standard flat systems. Where compound curvatures are involved, diamond mesh metal lath is the most practical plaster base. Forms having limited curvature or angles may be produced with most standard lathing materials. Hangers can be used in two ways: they are always employed vertically to support the weight of the ceiling, and they may be installed at angles to resist the horizontal thrusts of domes or comparable forms. Suspension of the ceiling from a concrete slab is relatively simple, since hangers may be inserted in the formwork at any point desired. Special care should be taken in a lightweight joist structure not to exert too much lateral thrust on the structural members.

Ceiling details. The details that follow illustrate methods in general use for the solution of the juncture of ceiling with vertical elements, penetrations for mechanical and electrical equipment, and control joints.

Wall-ceiling juncture or junctures between columns and ceiling may be treated either as a continuous angle or as a discontinuity between horizontal and vertical membranes. Discontinuity or an unrestrained condition is particularly applicable to situations where differential movement may be expected between intersecting plaster membranes. A further discussion of the relative merits of restrained versus unrestrained junctures is in Chapters 4 and 6.

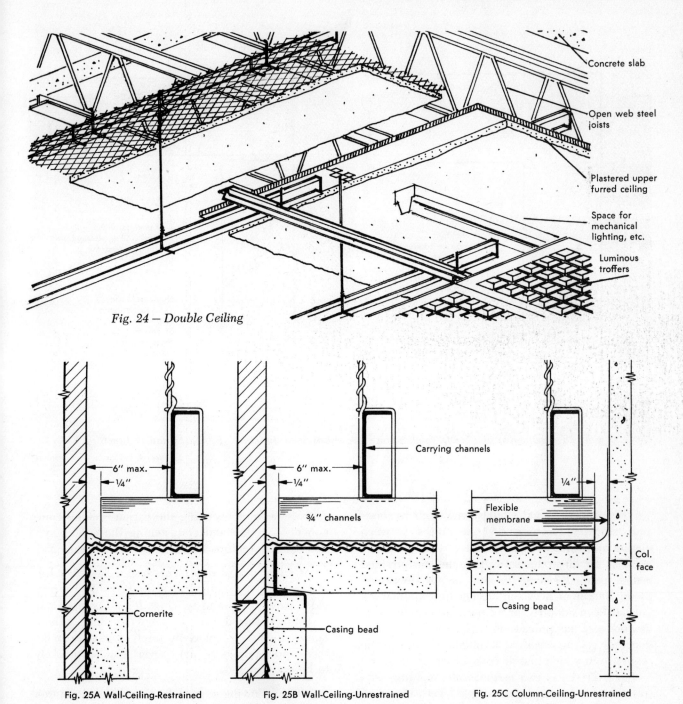

Fig. 24 – Double Ceiling

Concrete slab

Open web steel joists

Plastered upper furred ceiling

Space for mechanical lighting, etc.

Luminous troffers

Carrying channels

6" max.

1/4"

3/4" channels

Flexible membrane

1/4"

Col. face

Casing bead

Cornerite

Casing bead

Fig. 25A Wall-Ceiling-Restrained   Fig. 25B Wall-Ceiling-Unrestrained   Fig. 25C Column-Ceiling-Unrestrained

Fig. 25 – Restrained and Unrestrained Junctures.

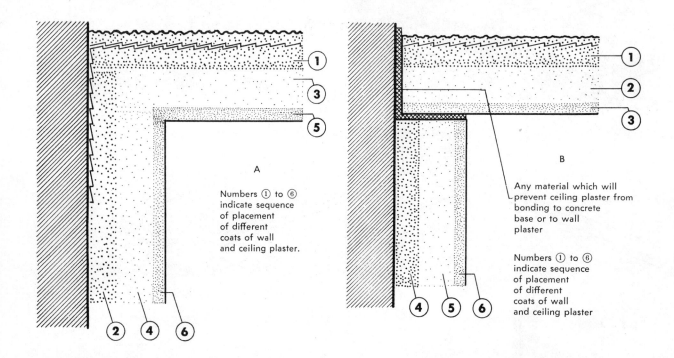

Fig. 26 — Sequence of Plaster Application — (A) Restrained Juncture (B) Unrestrained Juncture

Courtesy American Concrete Institute

Fig. 25 *A*, *B*, and *C* illustrates both methods and indicates recommended clearances between furring and runner channels and vertical elements.

Fig. 26 illustrates restrained and unrestrained wall-suspended ceiling juncture details developed by the Bureau of Reclamation. The unrestrained detail has been adopted for all portland cement plasterwork and has proved effective in reducing incidence of ceiling cracks. The numbers indicate the sequence in which plaster coats are applied.

Fig. 27 shows two methods of providing control joints in large plaster ceilings. The subject of control joints is discussed in detail in Chapter 6.

Methods of fastening the various ceiling components together and of fastening the ceiling system to the structure are described in Chapter 3.

Ceiling design data. The design data that follow are divided into two sections. Table IX provides sizes, spans and spacings for all components of contact, furred, and suspended ceilings. These figures include a sufficient safety factor to make them applicable to the most severe conditions likely to be encountered.

The following pages list more detailed data on ceiling components permitting more exact design.

Table IX.
Size and Spacing for Hangers, Main Runners, Cross Furring and Lath

A	MAXIMUM CENTER TO CENTER SPACING OF HANGERS ALONG MAIN RUNNERS									A	C	MAX. C. TO C. SPACING OF JOISTS OR CROSS FURRING			C
B	8'-0"	7'-0"	6'-0"	5'-0"	4'-6"	4'-0"	3'-6"	3'-0"	2'-6"	2'-0"	12"	16"	19"	24"	**B**
MAXIMUM C. TO C. SPACING OF MAIN RUNNERS — 2'-0"		#8 or 3/16" rod	#9 or 3/16" rod	#9	#9	#9	#9	#9	#9	#9	3/8" PR.	3/8" P.R. 3/4" CH.	3/8" P.R. 3/4" CH.	3/4" CH.	2'-0" — MAXIMUM C. TO C. SPACING OF MAIN RUNNERS
2'-6"			#8 or 3/16" rod	#9 or 3/16" rod	#9	#9	#9	#9	#9	#9	3/8" PR.	3/4" CH.	3/4" CH.	3/4" CH.	2'-6"
3'-0"				#8 or 3/16" rod	#8 or 3/16" rod	#9	#9	#9	#9	#9	✻	3/4" CH.	3/4" CH.	3/4" CH.	3'-0"
3'-6"	✻			#7 or 3/16" rod	#8 or 3/16" rod	✻	#9	#9	#9	✻	✻	3/4" CH.	3/4" CH.	✻	3'-6"
B 4'-0"	✻	✻		✻	#6 or 3/16" rod	#8 or 3/16" rod	✻	#9	#9	✻	✻	3/4" CH.	✻	✻	4'-0" **B**
RECOMMENDED RUNNERS	SPECIAL LIGHT STEEL STRUCTURAL MEMBER			2" COLD ROLLED CHANNEL			1½" COLD ROLLED CHANNEL			3/4" C.R. CH.					

Notes: Channels called for in table based on cold rolled data.

✻   Indicates spacing not recommended

🖛   Indicates type of lath that may be used

(1) 13½" recommended maximum span for metal supports

(2) 16" recommended maximum span for concrete or wood supports

LATH

		12"	16"	19"	24"
GYPSUM	3/8" Gyp. Lath	🖛	🖛	✻	✻
	½" Gyp. Lath	🖛	🖛	🖛	🖛
WIRE	Wire Lath	🖛	✻	✻	✻
	Wire Fabric	🖛	🖛	✻	✻
METAL LATH	2.75# Flat Rib	🖛	(2)	✻	✻
	3.4# Diam. Mesh	🖛	(1) (2)	✻	✻
	3.4# Flat Rib	🖛	🖛	🖛	✻
	3.4# + 4.0# 3/8" Rib	🖛	🖛	🖛	🖛
	4.5# Sheet Lath	🖛	🖛	🖛	🖛

Based on MLMA Table

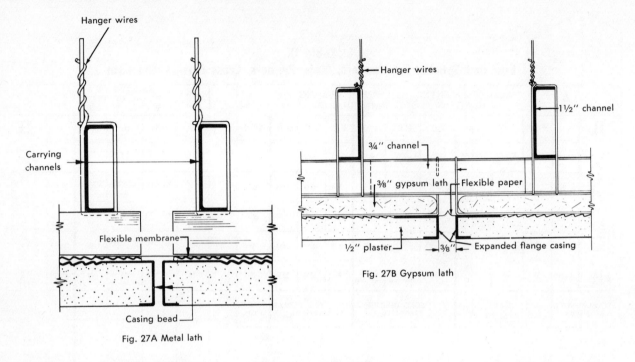

Fig. 27A Metal lath

Fig. 27B Gypsum lath

Fig. 27 — Control Joints

Miscellaneous lath and plaster systems. The systems included in this category are used for these purposes: wall (vertical) furring; fireproofing; backing for other surface materials; special uses.

Many systems within this category are unique constructions, devised to fit a specific and often non-recurring condition, but others, due to their general efficiency and applicability to recurrent conditions, have become more or less standard practice. The latter class are described in this section.

Wall (vertical) furring generally consists of a vertical membrane with plaster applied to the exposed side only. It is used in conjunction with exterior or interior walls to provide a finished surface which is separated from the wall by an air space. This type of system may be used to provide an inside finished surface for exterior masonry walls that will prevent condensation or to permit a treatment of the interior finish surface independent of the form of the exterior walls.

Wall or vertical furring may be of either the *braced* or *free-standing* type. Braced furring includes horizontal members which tie it in to the wall and provide lateral support. This type is more widely used than free-standing furring since smaller supporting and stiffening members may be used and greater heights obtained.

Fig. 28 illustrates two systems of braced vertical furring that use diamond mesh metal lath and long-length gypsum lath.

Table 15 lists the recommendations of the Metal Lath Manufacturers Association for heights and supporting member sizes of braced and unbraced furring that use metal lath and channel or prefabricated studs.

It is recommended that wall furring utilizing long-length gypsum lath not exceed 12 feet in height and that lateral bracing be placed at intervals not exceeding 36 inches vertically. Where regular-sized sheets of insulating gypsum lath are

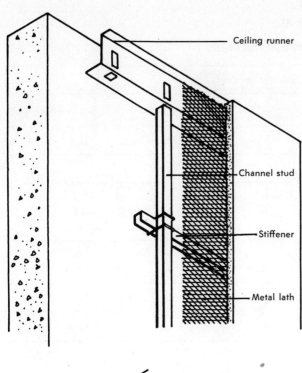

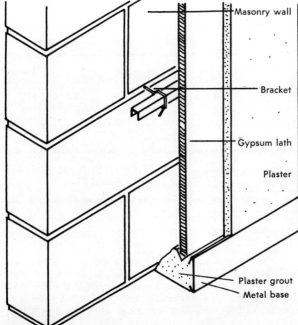

Fig. 28 — Furring on Inside of Exterior Masonry Walls

Table X.
Properties of Channels

Elements of Cold-Rolled Channels[1]

Depth	Flange Width	U.S. Gage	Weight per 1000 Lin. Ft.	S Inch³	I Inch⁴
¾″	⁷⁄₁₆″	16	300 lbs.	.0200	.0075
1½″	⁷⁄₁₆″	16	475 lbs.	.0538	.0404
2″	¹⁹⁄₃₂″	16	590 lbs.	.1005	.1005

Elements of Hot-Rolled Channels[1]

Depth	Flange Width	Web Thickness	Weight per 1000 Lin. Ft.	S Inch³	I Inch⁴
¾″	⁵⁄₁₆″	.072″	300 lbs.	.0191	.0072
¾″	⁹⁄₃₂″	³⁄₃₂″	400	.0190	.0071
¾″	³⁄₈″	.072″	400[2]	.0240	.0090
1″	³⁄₈″	⁵⁄₆₄″	410	.0356	.0178
1″	³⁄₈″	⅛″	680[2]	.048	.024
1″	³⁄₈″	⅛″	690[2]	.048	.024
1½″	³⁄₈″	¹⁄₁₆″	650	.073	.055
1½″	⁷⁄₁₆″	³⁄₃₂″	800	.090	.067
1½″	½″	⅛″	1120[2]	.108	.081
1½″	½″	⅛″	1120[2]	.133	.100
2″	½″	⅛″	1260[2]	.190	.190
2″	½″	⅛″	1330[2]	.198	.198
2″	½″	⅛″	1470[2]	.223	.223
2½″	¹⁵⁄₃₂″	⅛″	1500[2]	.267	.334
2½″	⅝″	³⁄₁₆″	2270[2]	.400	.500

Elements of Angles

Size	Weight per 1000 Lin. Ft.	Gross Area S	Gross Area I	Net Area S	Net Area I[3]
1½″x1½″x⅛″	1230 lbs.	.07	.08	.06	.07
1½″x1½″x³⁄₁₆″	1800 lbs.	.10	.11	.08	.09

[1] Properties S and I are computed about the strongest (X-X) axis of the channel.

[2] Listed in R222-46, "Hot-Rolled Carbon Steel Bars & Bar-Size Shapes."

[3] Allowance made for ⁷⁄₁₆″ bolt hole.

Table XI.
Table of Maximum Uniform Loads

Size	Member	Wt. in Lbs. per 1000 Lin. Ft. Wt.	24″ Hgr.	24″ W	30″ Hgr.	30″ W	36″ Hgr.	36″ W	42″ Hgr.	42″ W	48″ Hgr.	48″ W
	Channels											
¾″	HR	300	9	79	9	63	9	53	9	45	9	38
¾″	CR	300	9	81	9	65	9	54	9	47	9	40
¾″	HR	400	9	89	9	71	9	59	9	51	9	44
1″	HR	410			9	117	9	97	9	84	9	73
1″	HR	680			7	168	8	140	9	120	9	105
1½″	CR	475			6	224	6	186	8	160	8	140
1½″	HR	1120									6	248
1½″	HR	1120									¼″φ	309
2″	CR	590									7⁄32″φ	268
2″	HR	1260									BF	434
2″	HR	1330									BF	444
2½″	HR	2270										
	Angles											
1½″x1½″x⅛″		1230			¼″φ	280	6	233	6	199	7	175
1½″x1½″x3⁄16″		1800			BF	374	¼″φ	311	7⁄32″φ	267	6	233

Size	Wt.	12″ W	18″ W	24″ W	30″ W
Pencil Rods					
⅜″ round	376	72	37	20	13

BF = Bolted Flats
WF = Welded Flats

NOTE: Each member will support a safe load of "W" lbs. for the span indicated. This figure represents the maximum permissible design load determined by bending and torque or deflection. The maximum permissible load "W" for channels was calculated using a formula for channel design recommended by Professor George Winter of Cornell University. This formula determines the rotation stresses represented by the horizontal bending of the top half-beam and the total direct static stresses. The maximum permissible load "W" for angles was calculated using the design stress of steel @ 15,000 lbs. per sq. in. with the formula: $M = WL/9.33$ (Max. moment of 4 continuous spans). The maximum permissible load for deflection is reached when the ceiling load will produce a deflection equal to 1/360 of the length of the span. This was calculated from $\triangle$ or $L/360 = 2.5\, wL^4/384\, EI$.

Table XI. (continued)
Table of Maximum Uniform Loads

Member		Wt. in Lbs. per 1000 Lin. Ft.	54"		60" (5')		72" (6')		84" (7')		96" (8')	
Size		Wt.	Hgr.	W	Hgr.	W	Hgr.	W	Hgr.	W	Hgr.	W
	Channels											
¾"	HR	300										
¾"	CR	300										
¾"	HR	400										
1"	HR	410	9	65	9	58						
1"	HR	680	9	93	9	82						
1½"	CR	475	9	124	9	112	9	93				
1½"	HR	1120	6	210	6	198	7	165				
1½"	HR	1120	7/32"ø	274	6	247	6	206				
2"	CR	590	6	238	6	214	6	179	9	153	8	134
2"	HR	1260	BF	386	¼"ø	345	¼"ø	289	6	248	6	217
2"	HR	1330	BF	395	BF	357	¼"ø	296	7/32"ø	254	6	222
2½"	HR	2270			WF	695	BF	580	BF	497	BF	
	Angles											
1½"x1½"x⅛"		1230	8	155	8	140	9	117	9	100		
1½"x1½"x³⁄₁₆"		1800	6	208	6	187	8	156	8	133		

HOW TO USE TABLE XI

Example 1 Select a main runner to safely carry the load.

(A) Assume that the area of ceiling carried by each span of main runner will be 12 sq. ft. If gypsum-sanded plaster is used, the main runner will be carrying a dead load of 12 sq. ft. x 10 psf=120 lbs. (approx.). The 12 sq. ft. area is derived by multiplying the span times the center to center (transverse) spacing of the main runner. The dead load or weight of a lath and gypsum-sanded plaster ceiling is approximately 10 lbs. per sq. ft.

(B) From the Table select the main runner. If the hangers are to be 4' on centers, then under the 48" spacing of supports, find the lightest weight main runner that will carry the 120 lb. load. The 1½" cold-rolled channel at 475 lbs. per M ft. is selected since 120 lbs. is less than W.

Example 2 Design a suspended ceiling of gypsum-sanded plaster under steel roof joists spaced 30" on center.

(A) The area carried by each hanger or each span of main runner, using cross furring at 24"=2' x 2½'=5 sq. ft., making this dead load 5 sq. ft. x 10 psf=50 lbs.

(B) From the Table, a ¾" CR @ 300 lbs. per M ft. is selected as the main runner. (Alternate: Try selecting a channel using a 60" span.)

(C) If cross furring is spaced 12" o.c., the wt. on each cross furring member spanning 24"=1' x 2' x 10 psf=20 lbs. From the Table, ⅜" pencil rods are suitable for furring.

DATA USED IN CALCULATING "TABLE OF MAXIMUM UNIFORM LOADS" FOR SUSPENDED CEILING CONSTRUCTION

Channels and angles serving as main runners in a suspended ceiling are supported by hangers at regular intervals and are usually continuous over at least 4 or more supports. The dead load (or weight) of the ceiling is considered to be a uniformly distributed load.

I. In channel design the rotating (or warping) and bending stresses have been calculated by a method formula which is based on stress concentration at the first interior support $168/1568$ wL^2 and at the midpoint of the end span $121/1568$ wL^2 as shown in the diagram.

The total rotating and bending tension stresses, for each member, are used to determine "W" or the safe load that each main runner will support. In the formula a maximum design stress of 22,500 psi,

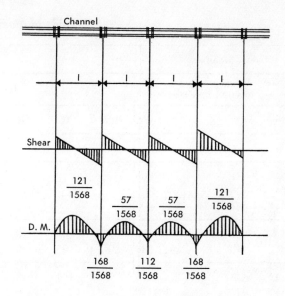

Table XII.

Maximum Uniform Loads for Main Runners Used in Suspended Ceilings Supported by Long Span Type Construction

(See Table XI for carrying capacities of lighter members)

Description of Runners	Span in Inches and Allowable Load in Pounds[1]															
	48″		54″		60″ (5′)		72″ (6′)		84″ (7′)		96″ (8′)		108″ (9′)		120″ (10′)	
	Hgr.	W	Hgr.	W	Hgr.	W	Hgr.	W	Hgr.	W	Hgr.	W	Hgr.	W	Hgr.	W
Angles																
2″ x 2″ x ⅛″ @ 1.65 lbs./ft.	BF	380	¼″∅	338	¼″∅	304	⁷⁄₃₂″∅	253	6	217	6	190				
2″ x 2″ ³⁄₁₆″ @ 2.44 lbs./ft.	BF	556	BF	493	BF	444	BF	370	¼″∅	317	¼″∅	278				
2″ x 2″ x ¼″ @ 3.19 lbs./ft.	WF	730	BF	648	BF	584	BF	487	BF	417	BF	365				
Channel																
3″ x 1½″ @ 4.1 lbs./ft.							WF	2140	WF	1835	WF	1600	WF	1425	WF	1285

W = Maximum permissible load or W = 0.33 f_sS/L.
BF = Bolted flats.
WF = Welded flats (See p. 153)

[1] The allowable stress used to determine the maximum loads was reduced to 15,000 lbs. from 18,000 lbs. This was done to compensate for the added stresses in the runners which are caused by rotation.

Table XIII.

Hanger Data for Mild Steel Rods, Flats and Wire

Type of Hanger	Gage or Dimension	Cross Sectional Area in Sq. In.		Safe Load in Lbs.[a]			Estimated Ultimate Strength[b]	Max. Area Supported per Hanger[c] Sq. Ft.
		Gross	Net[d]	Tied	Bolted[e]	Welded[f]		
Round Rod	3⁄16″	.0276		552			1656	25
Round Rod	7⁄32″	.0376		752			2256	25
Round Rod	1⁄4″	.0491		982			2946	25
Flat	1″x3⁄16″	.1875	.1055		680	3750	11250	25
Flat	1½″x1⁄8″	.1563	.1016		680	3126	9378	25
Flat	1¼″x3⁄16″	.2344	.1523		680	4688	14064	25
Flat	1½″x1⁄8″	.1875	.1328		680	3750	11250	25
Flat	1½″x3⁄16″	.2813	.1992		680	5626	16878	25
Wire	12 U.S.S.	.0087		156			552	8
Wire	10 U.S.S.	.0143		258			858	12
Wire	9 U.S.S.	.0173		312			1040	12.5
Wire	8 U.S.S.	.0206		372			1236	16
Wire	7 U.S.S.	.0246		443			1476	17.5
Wire	6 U.S.S.	.0290		552			1740	25
Wire	5 U.S.	.0337		607			2020	25

a Rod and flat hangers are based on a design or working stress of 20,000 psi. Wire hangers are based on a design or working stress of 18,000 psi.

b Based on ultimate strength of 60,000 psi of gross area.

c These areas do not utilize the full safe load of the hanger, but are based on spacings generally recognized and used in suspended ceiling construction.

d Arrived at by deducting area of 7⁄16″ diameter hole for 3⁄8″ diameter bolt.

e Safe load on net area of flat is greater than shown, but safe load on 3⁄8″ bolt in single shear is .068 sq. in. (root area) time 10 kips per sq. in. = 680 lbs.

f Based on strength of hanger only. Welds have not been calculated as job requirements vary depending upon load to be supported.

or a 25 percent overstress of the usual 18,000 psi allowable stress, was used where localized stresses only occurred.

Calculations for angles in the "Table of Maximum Uniform Loads" were at the point in the ceiling which has the greatest stress concentration: namely, at the first interior support.

The Bending Moment coefficients of wL^2 for angles are as shown in the diagram, and BM mx. (at first interior support) is $168/1568\ wL^2$, where w=load per foot and L=span. In making calculations, $BM=f_sS$, and wL (or "W")=9.33 f_sS/L (f_s=15,000 psi, S=Section Modulus of the channel, L in inches). The 15,000 psi working stress was used for these angles to compensate for additional stresses due to rotation. A reduced working stress was not necessary for channels because actual stresses resulting from rotation were calculated.

Table XIV.
Tie Wire Data

Safe Loads for Single Strands of Tie Wire Normally Used[a]

U.S. Steel Wire Gage	Diameter in Inches	Cross Section Area — Sq. In.	Safe Load in Lbs.[b]	Estimated Ultimate Strength[c]
18	.0475	.0018	32	108
16	.0625	.0031	56	186
14	.0800	.0050	90	300

a It must be remembered that this table lists a single strand of tie wire. When a single loop of tie wire is made, 2 strands support the load or when a double loop or saddle tie is made, four strands support the load. The safe load figure then will be multiplied by the total number of strands.

b Based on a design or working stress of 18,000 psi.

c Based on ultimate strength of 60,000 psi.

II. In addition to the flexure or bending moment design, deflection must be considered for all supporting members in order to prevent cracking of the plaster. A deflection equivalent to 1/360 of the length of the span has long been considered as the maximum; and the greatest deflection will occur in the end span (See Chapter 7). (The weight to produce this deflection is designated by Delta [△].)

Since this end span is neither a simple nor a fully restrained beam, we have estimated that the deflection will be approximately ½ that of a simple beam (the channel is continuous at the first interior support, and is partially restrained at the end). The formula evolved was $\frac{1}{2} \times 5wL^4/384EI$ (max. defl. simple beam) $= 2.5wL^4/384EI$ or W (wt./span) $= 384EI/2.5 (360)L^2$. ($E = 29,000,000$).

Table XV.

Maximum Recommended Heights of Wall Furring — Channel and Prefabricated Stud

a. BRACED FURRING

Recommended Maximum Distances "B" between Horizontal Bracing (Based on 16″ Spacings)

Stud	Heights (A)
¾″ Channel	6′-0″
1½″ Channel	8′-0″
2″ Channel	9′-0″
2½″ Prefab.	10′-0″
3¼″ Prefab.	14′-0″

b. FREE-STANDING FURRING

Recommended Maximum Unsupported Height, "A" (Based on 16″ Spacings)

Stud	Heights (B)
¾″ Channel	8′-0″
1½″ Channel	10′-0″
2″ Channel	11′-0″
2½″ Prefab.	12′-0″
3¼″ Prefab.	17′-0″

Horizontal Stiffeners, spaced same as Bracing in Table are recommended for all Free-Standing Furring. For furring more than 16″ o.c., use one-half these spacings, with minimum of 3′-6″.

It is recommended that wall furring utilizing long-length gypsum lath not exceed 12 feet in height and that lateral bracing be placed at intervals not exceeding 36 inches vertically. Where regular-sized sheets of insulating gypsum lath are used in conjunction with vertical stud supports, lateral bracing should be placed at intervals not greater than 54 inches.

Floor and ceiling attachment details for exterior wall furring are similar to those used in solid plaster partitions that use comparable materials except that trim is applied only to the exposed side.

Fig. 29 illustrates a proprietary device used to provide anchorage.

Fig. 30 illustrates a method of treating an opening in a furred exterior wall.

Fig. 31 illustrates two methods of constructing free-standing enclosures. While this is not "furring" in the usual sense, the construction is similar to wall furring, and is therefore included in this category. These systems are plastered and finished from the exposed side.

Fire resistance ratings for the systems illustrated in Fig. 31 are considered to be equivalent to those for metal lath and channel stud solid partitions of equal over-all thickness. (See Fire Resistance Rating Tables in Chapter 9.)

Instances often arise where it is desirable to construct furring over metal lockers, display cases, closets and other installations to create the appearance of a flush surface. In such instances it is often necessary to suspend the furring from the structure above. See Fig. 32 for several suspension details.

Column fireproofing. Surrounding a steel column with a membrane of lath and plaster is an efficient and effective means of increasing the length of time that the column can sustain its full design load during a fire. Fire tests performed on an unprotected steel column, and columns protected by lath and plaster, indicate respective fire resistance ratings of 10 minutes (see Chapter 9) and from one to more than four hours, depending on plaster type, thickness, and other factors.

Although there are countless specific methods for column fireproofing, most may be reduced to one of three basic systems: lath and plaster applied direct; lath and plaster furred; and plaster applied to gypsum block, clay tile, or similar materials, which have been built up around the column.

Fig. 33 illustrates direct application of self-furring metal lath and gypsum lath and plaster.

Fig. 34 illustrates a column fireproofed with diamond mesh metal lath furred by means of furring channels or metal lath spacers.

Where long fire resistance periods are necessary, plaster may be applied to grounds of 2 inches or more. These relatively thick applications, where gypsum lath is used, may require inclusion of supplementary hexagonal reinforcing mesh embedded

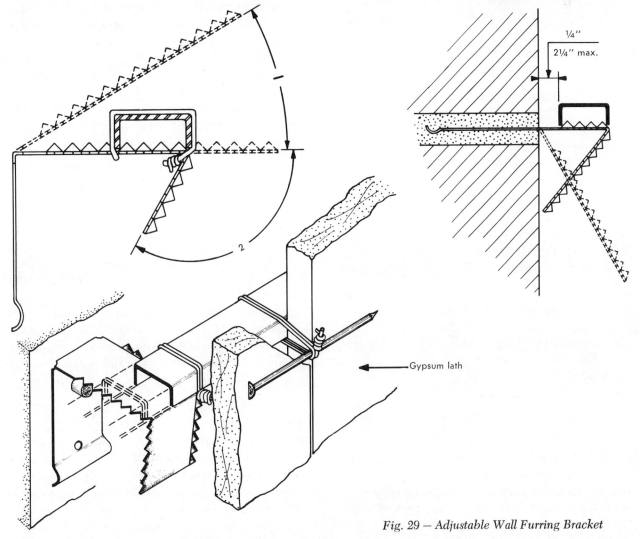

Fig. 29 — Adjustable Wall Furring Bracket

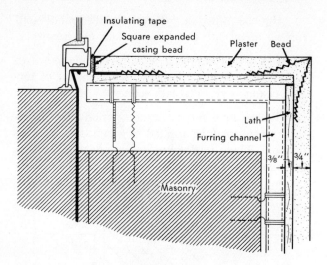

Fig. 30 — Horizontal Section of Window in Furred Exterior Wall

in the scratch or brown coat. This lends added support and reinforcement. (See Chapter 9.)

Column fireproofing consisting of plaster applied to block and tile is illustrated in the fire resistance rating in the tables in Chapter 9. These tables should be consulted for fire resistance ratings of all types of membrane column fireproofing, and for the specific construction details necessary to obtain them.

Beam and girder fireproofing. Lath and plaster membrane fireproofing of beams and girders may be provided either by a ceiling run continuously beneath them or by enclosing individual members separately.

Individual lath and plaster protection may be applied directly to the structural member, furred out from it, or suspended from the deck above, so as to provide complete enclosure.

Fig. 35 illustrates direct attachment of self-furring metal lath and plaster fireproofing. Furring channels wedged between flanges provide support at the beam sides.

The systems illustrated in Figs. 35 and 36 are two of the more generally used fireproofing methods. Many other methods are feasible. Fig. 37 illustrates two methods of protecting beams which support concrete slabs. Others are described in Chapter 9.

Backing for other surface materials and special uses. While the use of lath and plaster as a base for ceramic tile and other materials is often overlooked due to its concealed position, it constitutes a significant portion of the total volume of lath and plaster. In small residential work, usually the tile contractor installs the lath and applies the plaster setting bed. In large jobs, however, this is a function of the lather and the plasterer. Depending on locality, the lathing and plastering trades perform the work if more than four (in some cases two) bathrooms are to receive a plaster backing for tile.

Specifications covering materials and application of lath and plaster back-up are usually included in the lathing and plastering section of the general specifications.

Lath and plaster backing may be used either with the mortar setting bed method of tile application or with adhesive application. The following recommendations for lathing and plastering in both tile setting methods are derived principally from Standard (ASA 108) Specification for Installation of Ceramic Tile. Only those provisions applicable to the installation of the lath and plaster backing are considered here.

Installation of mortar setting bed. Lathing and plastering materials used in this method are identical to those for portland cement plastering, except that lime should be type S. Mortar is applied in up to three coats: scratch, levelling coat, and setting bed. Proportions for these coats are shown in Table XVI, and are used for application to masonry, concrete, or metal reinforcement.

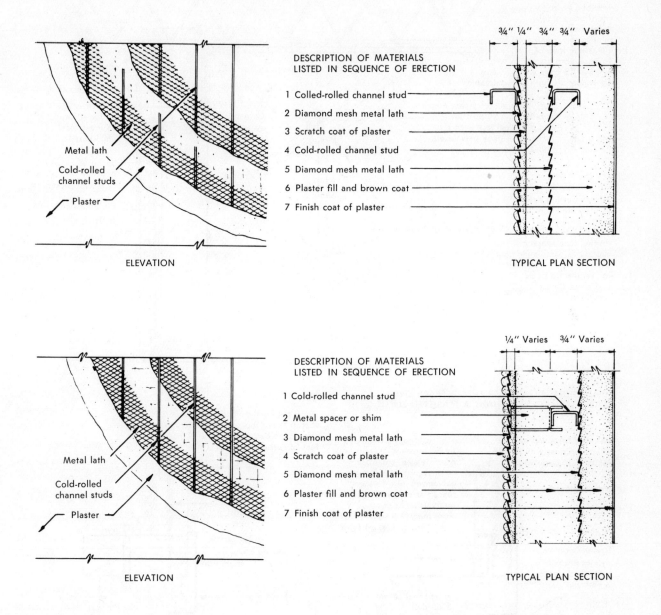

DESCRIPTION OF MATERIALS
LISTED IN SEQUENCE OF ERECTION

1 Colled-rolled channel stud
2 Diamond mesh metal lath
3 Scratch coat of plaster
4 Cold-rolled channel stud
5 Diamond mesh metal lath
6 Plaster fill and brown coat
7 Finish coat of plaster

Metal lath
Cold-rolled channel studs
Plaster

ELEVATION

TYPICAL PLAN SECTION

DESCRIPTION OF MATERIALS
LISTED IN SEQUENCE OF ERECTION

1 Cold-rolled channel stud
2 Metal spacer or shim
3 Diamond mesh metal lath
4 Scratch coat of plaster
5 Diamond mesh metal lath
6 Plaster fill and brown coat
7 Finish coat of plaster

Metal lath
Cold-rolled channel studs
Plaster

ELEVATION

TYPICAL PLAN SECTION

Fig. 31 — Two Systems of Free Standing Furring

CONSTRUCTION OF FURRED RECESS TO RECEIVE WARDROBE LOCKER

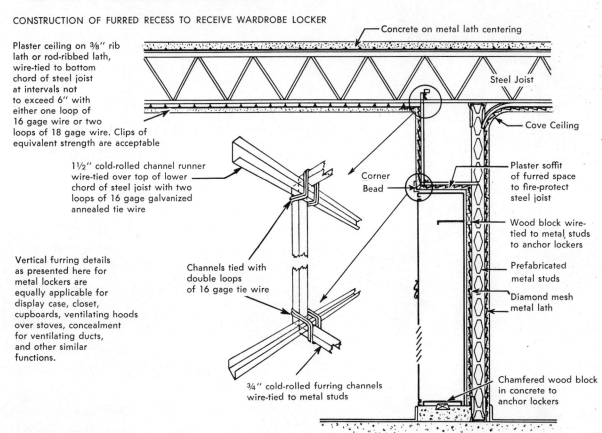

Concrete on metal lath centering

Plaster ceiling on ⅜" rib lath or rod-ribbed lath, wire-tied to bottom chord of steel joist at intervals not to exceed 6" with either one loop of 16 gage wire or two loops of 18 gage wire. Clips of equivalent strength are acceptable

Steel Joist

Cove Ceiling

1½" cold-rolled channel runner wire-tied over top of lower chord of steel joist with two loops of 16 gage galvanized annealed tie wire

Corner Bead

Plaster soffit of furred space to fire-protect steel joist

Vertical furring details as presented here for metal lockers are equally applicable for display case, closet, cupboards, ventilating hoods over stoves, concealment for ventilating ducts, and other similar functions.

Channels tied with double loops of 16 gage tie wire

Wood block wire-tied to metal studs to anchor lockers

Prefabricated metal studs

Diamond mesh metal lath

¾" cold-rolled furring channels wire-tied to metal studs

Chamfered wood block in concrete to anchor lockers

ALTERNATE DETAILS FOR FURRED SPACE OVER WARDROBE LOCKER WITHOUT A PLASTERED SOFFIT

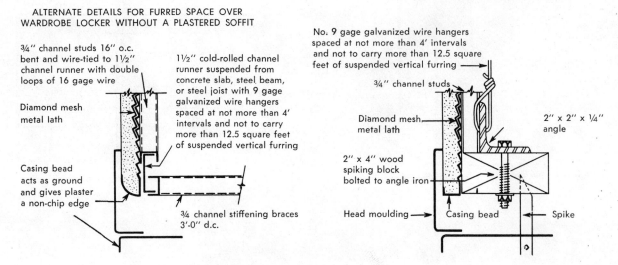

¾" channel studs 16" o.c. bent and wire-tied to 1½" channel runner with double loops of 16 gage wire

Diamond mesh metal lath

Casing bead acts as ground and gives plaster a non-chip edge

1½" cold-rolled channel runner suspended from concrete slab, steel beam, or steel joist with 9 gage galvanized wire hangers spaced at not more than 4' intervals and not to carry more than 12.5 square feet of suspended vertical furring

¾ channel stiffening braces 3'-0" d.c.

No. 9 gage galvanized wire hangers spaced at not more than 4' intervals and not to carry more than 12.5 square feet of suspended vertical furring

¾" channel studs

Diamond mesh metal lath

2" x 4" wood spiking block bolted to angle iron

Head moulding

Casing bead

2" x 2" x ¼" angle

Spike

Fig. 32 — Suspended Vertical Furring

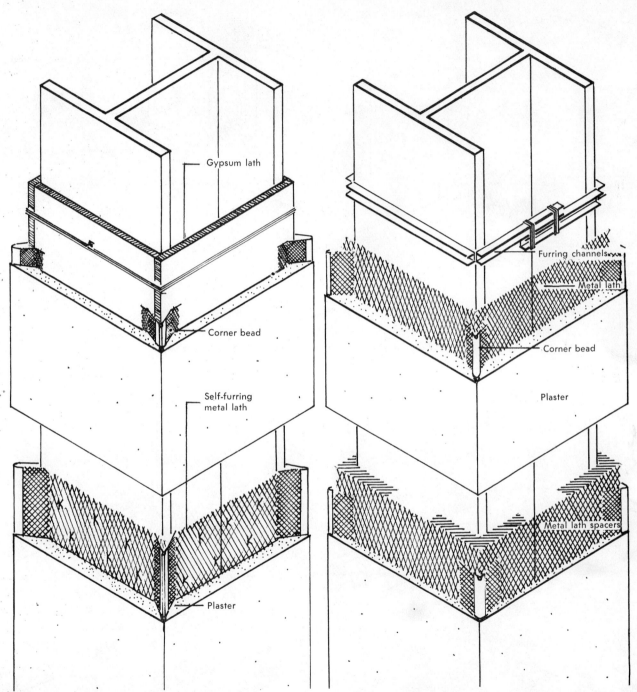

Fig. 33 — Column Fireproofing — Direct Application of Lath and Plaster

Fig. 34 — Column Fireproofing — Furred Application of Lath and Plaster

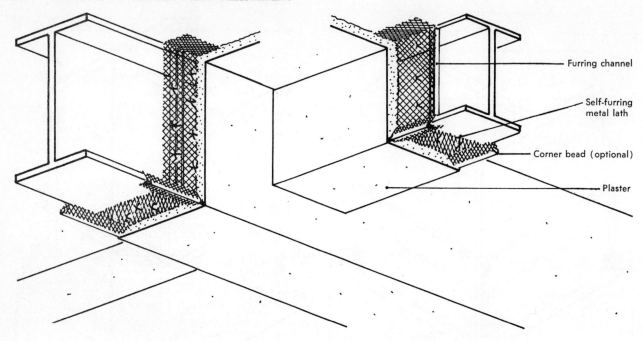

Furring channel

Self-furring
metal lath

Corner bead (optional)

Plaster

Fig. 35 — Beam and Girder Fireproofing — Direct Application

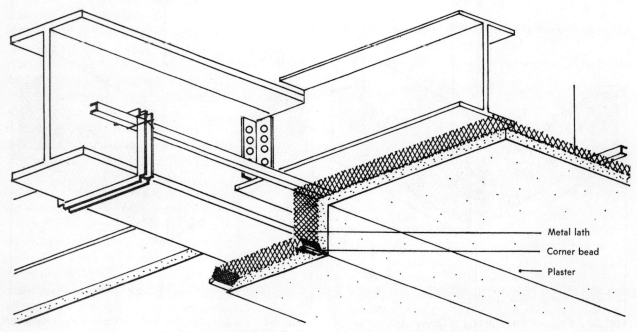

Metal lath

Corner bead

Plaster

Fig. 36 — Beam and Girder Fireproofing — Furred Application

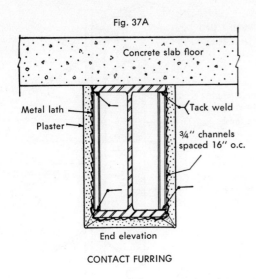

Fig. 37A

Concrete slab floor

Metal lath

Plaster

Tack weld

¾" channels spaced 16" o.c.

End elevation

CONTACT FURRING

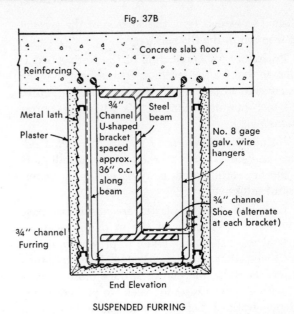

Fig. 37B

Concrete slab floor

Reinforcing

Metal lath

Plaster

¾" Channel U-shaped bracket spaced approx. 36" o.c. along beam

Steel beam

No. 8 gage galv. wire hangers

¾" channel Shoe (alternate at each bracket)

¾" channel Furring

End Elevation

SUSPENDED FURRING

Fig. 37 — Protection of Beams Supporting Concrete Slabs

Table XVI.

Mortar Proportions for Scratch Coat, Levelling Coat and Setting Beds

	Portland Cement	Lime	Sand
Scratch Coat			
Walls	1	.20	4-5
Ceilings	1	.50	2½-3
Levelling Coat and Setting Bed	1	.50	4-5

Proportions are by volume

Before metal lath can be applied to wood studs or to a gypsum plaster surface, a waterproof membrane must first be installed. Application of lath to steel studs may be direct, but provision for complete curing of the portland cement should be made. In shower stalls, metal reinforcement should be extended to within 2 inches of the floor and lapped over the metal sub pan.

Where recessed tile accessories occur, the metal lath is cut to allow positioning. A piece of metal lath two or three times larger than the hole is then cut and inserted, loosely rolled, through the hole. It is then unrolled vertically and jammed tightly into place, top and bottom to form a basket which is filled with mortar to receive the accessory.

Plaster application may be in two or three coats. The first, or scratch, coat may be omitted over welded wire reinforcement, self-furring tile-reinforcing mesh, and metal lath applied over a rigid backing.

Where the scratch coat is required, it is applied according to the standard practice for portland cement plastering described in Chapter 4.

The second and third plaster coats are termed the *levelling coat* and *setting bed*. The levelling coat is applied to a scratch coat that has been allowed to cure at least 12 to 24 hours. The maximum recommended grounds for this coat are ¾ inches. Expansion joints spaced a maximum of 16 feet on center horizontally and vertically, are established to extend from the surface of the scratch coat through to the tile surface.

Procedure for application of the setting bed is similar to that for the levelling coat, except that the area covered in one application must be limited to one which permits setting of tile while the mortar remains plastic.

Installation of plaster backing to receive adhesive and tile. In this method of tile installation, the mortar setting bed is replaced by a water-resistant adhesive.

Lath and gypsum plaster are a suitable base for adhesive application of tile in damp locations if special precautions are taken to prevent moisture from penetrating the tile surfacing. Over bathtubs and shower stalls, the plaster surface must be covered with a water-resistant sealer (to prevent moisture penetration) before the adhesive is applied for tile embedment. A ¼ inch space must be provided between the lath and plaster and such fixtures as bathtubs, at the rims and shower pans. The use of a plaster stop at this location is recommended. The use of foil-backed gypsum lath is not recommended for tile application.

Tile may be applied either to the brown coat that has been troweled to a smooth, dense surface, or to a hard white coat finish.

Plaster surfaces designed to receive mastic and tile must be plumb and level, and should not deviate by more than $\frac{1}{16}$ inch in 3 feet from the required plane. Trowel marks, ridges and grains should be less than $\frac{1}{32}$ inch above adjacent areas. **Special uses.** A recent use of plaster which appears to have economical advantages is in the fabrication of chalkboards. This use permits construction of chalkboards in schoolrooms and other locations by the same trade that does the plastering and at the same time.

Fig. 38 illustrates a chalkboard constructed first by surrounding a portion of wall area with curved point base screed and then applying a dense gypsum plaster basecoat. A high-strength gypsum-gauged lime finish coat is then applied and with a

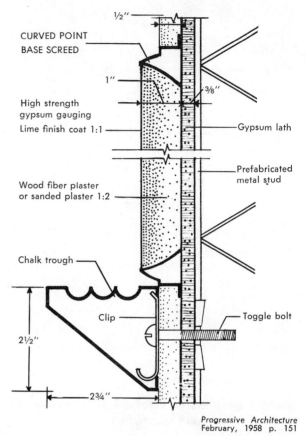

CURVED POINT BASE SCREED

High strength gypsum gauging
Lime finish coat 1:1

Wood fiber plaster or sanded plaster 1:2

Chalk trough

½″

1″

⅜″

Gypsum lath

Prefabricated metal stud

Clip

2½″

2¾″

Toggle bolt

Progressive Architecture
February, 1958 p. 151

Fig. 38 — Plaster Chalkboard

mechanical trowel brought to an extremely dense, smooth surface. After the plaster has dried, a coat of primer sealer and two coats of chalkboard paint are applied.

In addition to the uses described in this chapter, which are basically functional, there are many others which are purely decorative. Chapter 1 describes such uses as sand sculpture, graffito, and the construction of stage and motion picture sets.

EXTERIOR USES

The traditional systems in which plaster is used as an exterior wall finish include sheathed or unsheathed frame structures which are covered with metal reinforcement; and masonry which may be either plastered directly or first covered with furred reinforcement, depending upon the type and condition of the masonry surface. In addition, exterior plaster (stucco) is often an effective and economical means of resurfacing or overcoating other types of exterior finishes. Besides these systems, other newer ones are coming into use or being developed in which plaster performs functions other than simply providing a weather resistant and visually pleasing surface.

One of the most promising of these newer uses is the curtain wall, in which plaster may serve as the interior and exterior finish as well as the core. Another is the load bearing plaster wall.

Wall surfacing. There are two general methods of constructing a conventional stuccoed frame wall: one, known as the *open-frame* method, consists of stucco applied to metal reinforcement which is attached directly to the structural frame; a second method differs from the first only in that sheathing and a waterproofing layer are interposed between structural members and metal reinforcement. Open-frame construction may involve only a conventional plaster application to the outside face of the reinforcement, or it may include back-plastering, which is added to the stud side of the reinforcement.

If the frame is sufficiently rigid, open-frame construction is generally considered to have greater crack resistance than wood sheathed construction, since it eliminates movement caused by shrinkage or warping of sheathing. This is particularly true of open-frame construction where back-plastering is used. Investigations of stucco conducted by the Bureau of Standards indicated that back-plastered construction is second only to stucco on monolithic concrete with regard to freedom from cracking.*

Stucco applied over open or sheathed frame construction ideally should be treated as a thin,

reinforced slab which, though supported by the frame, is not in sufficiently rigid contact with it to permit direct stress transfer. Methods of providing this type of attachment are discussed in Chapter 6. Metal reinforcement should in all cases be furred out sufficiently from the studs or sheathing to provide for complete embedment in the stucco.

To insure maximum crack resistance in the stucco membrane, the supporting frame must be sufficiently braced to produce maximum rigidity. Also, particular care must be given to detailing of flashing and drips to prevent penetration of water behind the stucco where it could cause deformation or corrosion of structural members.

The frame systems now to be described are those included in ASA A42.2-1946, Specifications for Portland Cement Stucco. It is believed these systems are equally applicable to lime-portland cement stucco.

Wood frame. In wood construction, the back-plastered, open-frame system is superior to a system in which wood sheathing is incorporated. However, since sheathing always serves to provide rigidity, its absence must be compensated for by increased bracing. Studs should be bridged with 2″ by 4″ or larger at least once in each story height; corners should be braced diagonally with bracing let into studs; and trussings should be provided over all openings more than 4 feet wide (Fig. 39).

In back-plastered construction, stud spacing may be a maximum of 16 inches on center, and the moisture barrier omitted. If back plastering is not included, one of two alternate systems may be used. In the first, horizontal wires, 18 gage or heavier, are stretched taut across the face of the studs at 6 inch intervals to provide some rigidity for waterproof building paper which is subsequently applied and secured to the studs. Metal reinforcement is then applied utilizing furring devices. In the second, a paper-backed metal reinforcement eliminates the need for the horizontal wires and building paper. Paper-backed reinforcement must provide for complete embedment of the metal by the stucco (See Fig. 40).

* U. S. Department of Commerce, National Bureau of Standards; Stucco Investigations at the Bureau of Standards with recommendations for Portland cement stucco construction. Washington, D.C. (G.P.O. 1926).

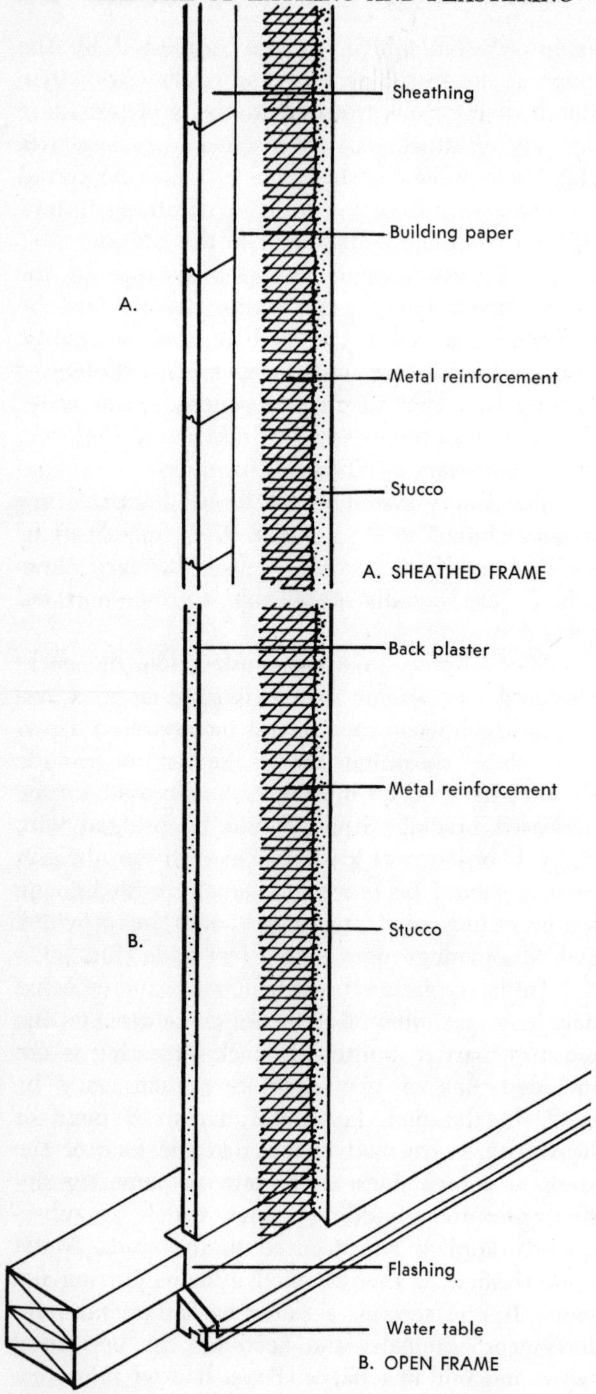

Sheathing

Building paper

A.

Metal reinforcement

Stucco

A. SHEATHED FRAME

Back plaster

Metal reinforcement

B.

Stucco

Flashing

Water table

B. OPEN FRAME

Fig. 39 — Exterior Plaster on Sheathed and Open Wood Frame

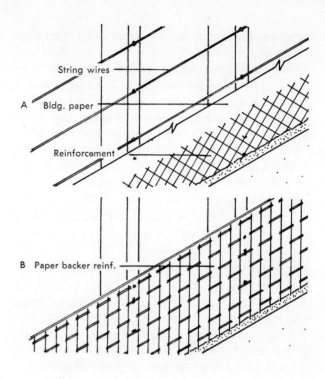

String wires

A   Bldg. paper

Reinforcement

B   Paper backer reinf.

A. STRING WIRES & BUILDING PAPER
B. SELF-FURRING, PAPER BACKED REINFORCEMENT

Fig. 40 — Exterior Plaster on Open Wood Frame

ASA A42.2 recommends that stud spacing in both of these alternate systems not exceed 12 inches o.c. There are many areas, however, where stucco is applied to open-frame construction with studs spaced 16 inches o.c.

If sheathing is incorporated, it should be of such a type and attached in such a way that minimum movement will result from shrinkage, expansion or warping. Building paper is applied to the sheathing prior to application of furred metal reinforcement. Stud spacing in this case should not exceed 16 inches o.c., except where water-repellent gypsum sheathing is used.

Light steel frame. The systems that have been described for wood frame construction are also applicable to light steel frame construction. The ASA recommends that stud spacing in light steel construction not exceed these limits:

Open Frame	
Back-plastered	32 inches*
Not back-plastered	16 inches**
Sheathed Frame	24 inches

Steel or reinforced concrete skeleton frame. Supports of the stucco membrane in this case should be channel studs or prefabricated metal studs. Stud supports should be tied into the main structure at both ends. Only back-plastered construction is recommended.

Masonry and monolithic concrete. Monolithic concrete and masonry possessing surface characteristics necessary for adequate bond (see Chapters 3 and 4) provide the best surfaces for application of stucco because of their inherent rigidity and the combined adhesive and cohesive bond obtainable.

Unlike frame construction, where the stucco is treated as much as possible like an independent membrane, stucco applied direct to concrete or masonry becomes an integral part of the backing. This renders the entire wall thickness effective in resisting internal and external forces.

Sometimes a concrete or masonry surface is not suitable for direct stucco application, because of insufficient key or suction or to friability or other weakness. In such instances it should be covered with building paper and furred metal reinforcement prior to application of stucco.

Stucco as an overcoating for an existing finish. For exterior remodelling work, stucco is an economical and effective means of resurfacing an existing finish. Stucco overcoating may be applied over virtually any surface having structural rigidity.

In most instances the application is done by first preparing the existing surface by replacing loose material and removing large areas of friable or rotten material. The existing surface is then covered with waterproof building paper and furred metal reinforcement prior to stucco application.

Where existing concrete or masonry surfaces provide suitable key and suction, direct application of the overcoating is possible. It should be noted that original projecting trim must be extended to provide necessary stucco grounds plus the desired projection past the stucco surface (Fig. 41).

Load bearing walls. During recent years increasing interest has been shown in systems comprised of plaster and standard plastering components which serve as exterior, load bearing walls.

Among the advantages of such a system are: construction of an entire wall assembly including structure; finish and insulation is accomplished by a single trade; and the advantages of a thin, monolithic, structural panel are obtained without the cost of form work.

"Thinwall" system. This system is made up of 3¼ inch or 4 inch prefabricated metal studs, placed on 16 inch centers. Studs are welded to a metal track at the top and bottom of the wall. Strip-back, paper-covered 2 inch by 2 inch 16 gage welded wire mesh is tied to the outside faces of the studs, with the paper to the outside. Two or three inches of 3,000 psi sand-portland cement plaster is applied mechanically to the mesh, 1¼ inches or 2¼ inches applied to the inside, and the remaining ¾ inch applied to the outside after the paper has been stripped off. Insulating portland cement-perlite plaster is then applied to the inside face of the sand-cement plaster to a thickness determined by the U factor required for the wall. The interior face of the wall consists of metal or gypsum lath fastened to the inside face of the studs and gypsum-sand plaster (See Fig. 42).

Application of the cement-sand concrete is done by machine in ¾ inch layers. The concrete is kept monolithic by allowing no longer than 24-hour intervals between application of succeeding layers. A series of loading tests on this system were conducted by the Plastering Development Center, Inc., of Chicago. Results of these tests showed that

---

* If stud spacing exceeds 16 inches o.c., ¾ inch channel or ⅜ inch round rod cross furring should be securely attached horizontally across studs at not more than 16 inches intervals.
** Stucco construction is often installed over load-bearing steel studs spaced 24 inches o.c.

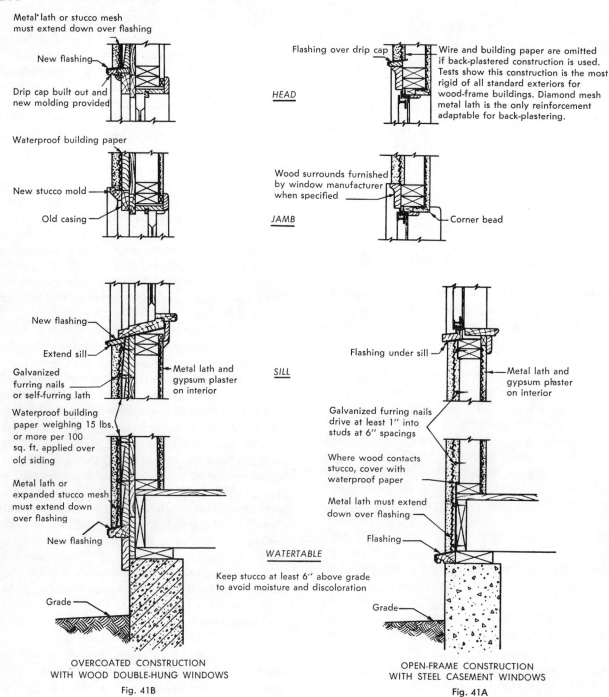

Metal lath or stucco mesh must extend down over flashing

New flashing

Drip cap built out and new molding provided

Waterproof building paper

New stucco mold

Old casing

Flashing over drip cap

HEAD

Wire and building paper are omitted if back-plastered construction is used. Tests show this construction is the most rigid of all standard exteriors for wood-frame buildings. Diamond mesh metal lath is the only reinforcement adaptable for back-plastering.

Wood surrounds furnished by window manufacturer when specified

JAMB

Corner bead

New flashing

Extend sill

Galvanized furring nails or self-furring lath

Metal lath and gypsum plaster on interior

SILL

Flashing under sill

Metal lath and gypsum plaster on interior

Waterproof building paper weighing 15 lbs. or more per 100 sq. ft. applied over old siding

Metal lath or expanded stucco mesh must extend down over flashing

New flashing

Galvanized furring nails drive at least 1" into studs at 6" spacings

Where wood contacts stucco, cover with waterproof paper

Metal lath must extend down over flashing

Flashing

WATERTABLE

Keep stucco at least 6" above grade to avoid moisture and discoloration

Grade

Grade

OVERCOATED CONSTRUCTION
WITH WOOD DOUBLE-HUNG WINDOWS

Fig. 41B

OPEN-FRAME CONSTRUCTION
WITH STEEL CASEMENT WINDOWS

Fig. 41A

Fig. 41 — Stucco   Construction Details

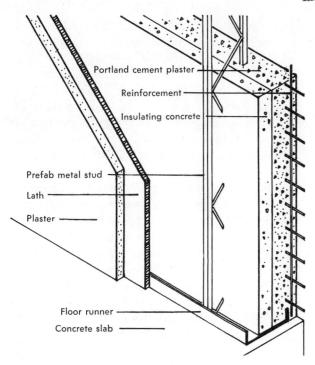

Portland cement plaster

Reinforcement

Insulating concrete

Prefab metal stud

Lath

Plaster

Floor runner

Concrete slab

Fig. 42 — Exterior Plaster Bearing Wall ("Thinwall" System)

panels having an unsupported height of 10 feet consisting of either 3¼ inch or 4 inch studs and 2 inches or 3 inches of portland cement-sand plaster, could support a combined vertical load of 8,000 pounds per lineal foot and a horizontal (wind) load of 75 pounds per square foot. Panels remained under these loading conditions for a 24-hour period, after which loads were removed. Horizontal deflection readings taken just before and after the load was removed showed a maximum deflection under load of .850 inches (average was .49 inches) and a minimum recovery after removal of load of 76 per cent (average was 86 per cent). Horizontal loads were applied to the exterior panel face in some tests and to the interior face in others. Resulting deflections were comparable in both cases.

Other similar systems have been investigated which utilize metal lath, standard cold-rolled channels and portland cement plaster. These systems

have shown considerable promise. Now, with the advent of the spray nozzle designed for plaster application to metal lath, these systems may be practical for certain load-bearing enclosure elements.

CURTAIN WALLS

The wide acceptance of that system of building enclosure commonly known as "curtain wall" has had a profound effect on the construction procedures employed in large buildings, and on the urban landscape as well. It is a rare current issue of any architectural periodical or Sunday real estate supplement that does not feature at least one curtain walled building. The sudden popularity of the curtain wall has caused some anxiety among architectural critics concerning the universal monotony that the standardization inherent in the method might produce in our cities.

The opportunity for repetitive manufacture of similar units of enclosure is one of the most easily recognized economic advantages of this approach to building. But while the advantage is, to be sure, an important one it is not necessarily fundamental to the general design concept that produced the curtain wall. Because designers of curtain walls so far have been preoccupied with the use of metal and other non-plastic materials, the problems of fabrication necessarily have taken on primary importance. For the most part, these problems have been solved by increasing the amount of prefabrication and off-site manufacturing of the building enclosure, a condition which is, of course, conducive to standardization of parts. When this uniformity is extended to the visual aspects of the enclosure, as in the case of the now familiar grid type metal curtain wall, visual sameness throughout the building, and from one building to another, naturally results.

For these and other reasons, increasing attention in design is being directed towards lath and plaster and other plastic materials that can be used more flexibly in the construction of lightweight, non-bearing exterior walls. Within the limits of this manual it is impossible to discuss all the curtain wall designs that have been developed recently. However, the basic criteria for the design of this type of enclosure will be set forth in this section insofar as they have been established. The part that plastering materials and methods can play in the fulfillment of these requirements will be particularly emphasized.

The concept of curtain wall. In building, the word *wall* is accepted as meaning a self-supporting, vertical surface that encloses, subdivides, or otherwise defines space; that provides protection of various sorts; and that permits the controlled passage of certain objects or forces such as light, heat, air, and sound. The definition of *curtain wall*, however, is neither so clear cut nor so universally accepted. The greater conflict in definition exists between that used by most designers and that used by certain of the more influential building codes. The code definition recognizes the curtain wall as only one of several special types, all of which are considered curtain walls as encompassed by the designer's conception. Thus, the codes regard a *curtain wall* as a non-load bearing wall, between columns and piers, that is not supported at each story; a *panel wall* is a non-load bearing wall, between columns or piers, that is supported at each story; and a *spandrel wall* is that portion of an exterior wall between the top of one opening and the bottom of another opening in the story directly above. For our purposes, however, this general definition is more useful, and is employed throughout: *a curtain wall is any non-load bearing exterior wall attached to and supported by the structural framework of a building* usually erected after the frame is in place. It is a system of construction that allows the skin of a building to be rapidly placed over the skeleton of the structure, and permits selection of the various components of the skin that can best fulfill the visual and physical requirements of a wall. The idea of a wall as a barrier, perforated and glazed to admit light and ventilation, has been expanded to the degree that, as Fitch observed, the wall no longer functions simply as a barrier. Rather, it acts as a filter that will control the passage, either to the interior or to the exterior, of elements influencing the environment within the building.[1]

A curtain wall is generally composed of three main elements: exterior surface, core, and interior surface. The materials used for each of these elements are selected for their ability to satisfactorily perform the environmental and other functions required by the particular conditions of use. These functions can be separated into four categories: visual, physical, environmental, and economic. It will be found that in most cases any given function will determine, or be determined by, the importance of other factors in the design of the wall.

The use of plaster in curtain walls. The use of materials and skills of the plastering industry has been widespread in the enclosure of buildings by curtain walls. Plaster in one form or another has been used as exterior facing material, insulating and fire resistant cores, and as the finished interior surface. As an exterior building material it has been known for hundreds of years, so it is no surprise to find increasing interest in its use for this purpose in curtain wall construction. As noted in Chapter 4, methods of mechanical placement and trowelling have been developed to produce surfaces that in many ways are superior to, and less expensive than, the fine stucco work of the past.

The development and use of perlite and vermiculite aggregates as core materials in curtain walls has made possible considerable savings in space and weight. These economies could not have been obtained had it been necessary to use dense masonry materials to provide the required fire-resistance, thermal and acoustical properties.

The preponderance of curtain wall installations during recent years have utilized metal, or other non-plastic materials, for their exterior and often their interior surfaces. The degree of prefabrication of these walls has ranged from those meeting all physical requirements (interior and exterior faces, insulation, and the like) in a complete package, to metal facing units that serve as a protection for job-applied core materials and interior finishes. The development of plaster curtain walls has been spurred by demands, both visual and technical, for construction methods that allow greater flexibility.

Here are some advantages and limitations of plaster in meeting these needs:

Form: Can be applied in any shape or form desired.

Continuous application: Work can proceed from any place on the structure. Application does not depend on progressive interlocking of units. Thus several crews can work simultaneously.

Materials and skills: Plaster curtain walls are constructed of materials that are readily available in all parts of the United States by crews drawn from a large corps of skilled mechanics. The nationwide distribution of workmen skilled in the techniques of plastering does not limit, economically, the use of plaster walls to metropolitan areas. Additional advantages are derived through the use of the same trades to enclose the building and to subdivide the interior spaces.

Fire resistance: The use of plaster and lightweight concretes to provide fire protection for curtain walls, as well as for building interiors, is well established. These materials afford economical means by which code requirements can be met. At the same time, due to their relatively light weight, they effect additional savings by reducing the dead load on structural members. Where lightweight concrete was used in the now famous Alcoa Building, it was estimated that approximately 1,500 tons of structural steel were eliminated that would have been required had heavier masonry or concrete been used for fire resistance.[2]

Prefabrication: Any degree of prefabrication from field installation of individual components to factory produced stud and lath grids is possible with plaster curtain walls. The flexibility of this type of construction does not limit its use to areas near shipping centers, and can eliminate costly pre-ordering and delays in delivery.

Structural properties: Lightweight concretes, in addition to their excellent thermal, acoustic, and fire resistant properties, are capable of withstanding substantial wind loads and other forces.

Surface finish: Plaster offers great flexibility in the selection of surface form, texture, and color. It can have integral color by the introduction of pigment or colored aggregates, or it can be painted to suit any taste. It is not necessary to impose a rigid grid pattern of joints on the inside or outside of the building, although any pattern can easily be obtained.

Erection: The advantages of continuous application have already been noted. Methods now are being developed for enclosing and heating the working area by means of translucent plastic films and unit heaters, thus allowing work to proceed regardless of weather conditions.

As noted in Chapter 4, recommendations have been made to reduce the time between the coats of exterior plaster to less than 24 hours, at the same time producing improved results.

Maintenance: Once in place, an integrally colored exterior plaster wall requires little if any maintenance. Any damage that might occur to the surface, either during or after erection, is easily repaired, and the patched section becomes an integral part of the wall.

Cost: The initial cost of complete plaster curtain walls compares favorably with that of other systems now available. It has been estimated that a wall composed of exterior plaster facing, steel stud and lath grid, 4 inch insulating lightweight concrete, and interior lath and plaster, costs less than $3 per square foot. To obtain the same fire resistance, thermal and acoustic values, and structural capabilities by other methods, it is usually necessary to spend greater amounts, often as much as $10 to $12.

Examples of use of plaster in curtain wall construction: The following buildings represent a cross-section of curtain wall construction in which plaster was used for either interior and exterior facing, core material, or a combination of the three uses.

a) 3325 Wilshire Blvd.
Los Angeles

Exterior plaster — lightweight concrete core
Interior plaster

b) First Security Bldg.
Salt Lake City, Utah

Porcelain enamel — lightweight concrete
core

c) Jefferson State Office Bldg.
Jefferson City, Mo.

Aluminum sheets — precast lightweight
concrete panels

d) Medical Towers
Houston, Texas

Porcelain enamel — lightweight concrete
core — plaster

e) Bank of the Southwest
Houston

Aluminum panels — lightweight concrete
core — plaster

f) Hillside Shopping Center
Chicago

Porcelain enamel panels — lightweight
concrete core and interior finish

g) Tecfab Plant — B
Beltsville, Md.

Exposed aggregate (stone) — lightweight
concrete core and finish

h) Doctors' Medical Center
Bellingham, Washington

Exterior plaster — insulation board —
interior plaster steel stud panel frames
and members

i) Moore's Store
San Francisco, California

Ceramic veneer — steel studs — interior lath
and plaster

j) Alcoa Building
Pittsburgh, Pa.

Aluminum panels — lightweight concrete
back-up — plaster

Structural considerations. By definition, a curtain wall is non-load bearing. However, there are forces, such as wind, that must be considered during its design. In an effort to combine the excellent fire resistant and insulating properties of lightweight concretes with structural properties, an investigation was conducted for the Vermiculite Institute by the firm of Severud-Elstad-Krueger, Consulting Engineers.[3] The methods and results of those tests are here summarized (See Table XVII).

Description of walls analyzed: The wall assembly consisted of vermiculite concrete, either 2 inches or 4 inches thick, 1½ inch by 1½ inch by ³/₁₆ inch steel channels, spaced on 2 feet centers. The channels were located 1½ inches from the outside face of the vermiculite wall. The structural value of any exterior facing material was not considered in these investigations. (See Fig. 43.)

The walls were analyzed for both wind pressure and suction at loads of 30 psf and 20 psf.

Design Data:
Vermiculite:

Ultimate compressive strength
$f'_c = 750$ psi

Allowable compressive stress
*$f_c = 0.45$, $f'_c = 337.5$ psi
$f_c = 337.5 + 112.5 = 450$ psi

Bond strength
$u = 0.045 \ f'_c + ⅓ * = 45$ psi

Allowable sheer stress
$V = 0.03 \ f'_c + ⅓ * = 30$ psi

Allowable tensile stress
$f_c = 0.03 \ f'_c + ⅓ * = 30$ psi

*This figure is increased ⅓ in consideration of wind forces:

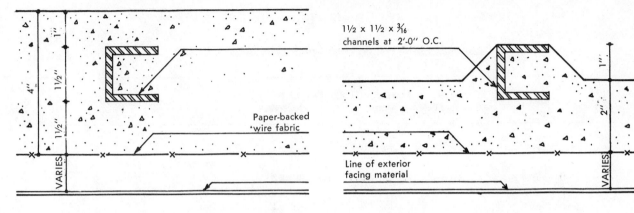

Fig. 43 — Horizontal Sections Through Vermiculite Concrete Wall Panels

Modulus of elasticity
> E = 300,000   n = 100

Steel channel:
> Maximum allowable stress
> $f_s = 20,000 + \frac{1}{3}* = 26,670$ psi
> Moment of inertia:
> $I_x = 0.27$ in.[4]
> In the 4″ wall the 1″ side in compression is critical. The moment of inertia for the composite section $I_{comp} = 58.55$ in.[4]

Thermal stresses. Stresses set up by changing temperatures have been a matter of concern in curtain wall construction. Rapid temperature changes, often in the magnitude of 100 degrees F., are not uncommon on the exterior surfaces of buildings; the resulting elongation, shrinkage, or deformation of the wall and structure can mar the appearance of, and even damage, exterior surfaces. Often the reappearing "oil-can" effect noted on many flat metal panel walls is the visual result of dimensional changes due to thermal activity.

While this problem is by no means limited to metal curtain walls, extensive effort has been directed towards finding means for controlling the expansion and contraction of metal sheets. One method that has been tried with some success is the lamination of the metal sheet to a more stable core material, such as lightweight concrete or plaster, by means of adhesive. Although the development of adhesives has been remarkable during recent years, there is still much to be learned about the performance of these materials over long periods. Until more is known of fatigue characteristics of adhesives under actual construction conditions, it is considered more reasonable to recommend mechanical bond, between the metal panel and the core.

Acceptable deformation of facing materials. At the present time, there are no standards to define the visually acceptable amount of deformation in the flat surface of a wall. The Princeton University study,[5] already outlined in Chapter 4, developed a set of values that can be used with stainless steel face-sheets. This study determined that the visually acceptable deformation allowable from a plane is related to the slope of the individual waves and to the reflectivity of the surface (see Fig. 44). The allowable deviation increases as the surface becomes duller. Until similar standards are established for all facing materials, it will be necessary to use rules of thumb for plastered surfaces, such as the ⅛ inch in 10 feet established by common practice.

As can be seen from Fig. 44, a deviation of ⅛ inch in 6 inches would cause the slope to be quite steep, and the wave readily visible. On the other hand, if the surface were to deviate ⅛ inch (h) in

Table XVII.

Allowable Wall Heights for Vermiculite Curtain Walls[4]

Wall Thickness	Wind Load or Suction (psf)	Method of Attachment	Maximum Height Determined By Moment	Deflection	Attachment Systems
4″	30	A	12′-10″	7′-7″	*A* Two simple supports
4″	30	B	12′-10″	10′-1″	$M = \dfrac{wL^2}{8}$
4″	30	C	15′-8″	12′-11″	
4″	30	D*	4′-0″	(A)	$\triangle = \dfrac{5wL^4}{384EI}$
4″	20	A	15′-8″	8′-8″	*B* One fixed One simple support
4″	20	B	15′-8″	11′-7″	$M = \dfrac{8}{wL^2}$
4″	20	C	19′-2″	14′-10″	
4″	20	D*	5′-1″	(A)	$\triangle = \dfrac{wL^4}{185EI}$
2″	30	A	10′-3″	5′-11″	*C* Two fixed supports
2″	30	B	10′-3″	7′-9″	$M = \dfrac{wL^2}{12}$
2″	30	C	12′-8″	10′-0″	
2″	30	D*	2′-9″	(A)	$\triangle = \dfrac{wL^4}{384EI}$
2″	20	A	12′-8″	6′-7″	*D* Cantilever
2″	20	B	12′-11″	8′-11″	$M = \dfrac{wL^2 + PL}{2}$
2″	20	C	15′-6″	11′-6″	
2″	20	D*	3′-8″	(A)	

* Based on a wall with a window 7′-0″ in height. Moment only, considered for height limit.

(A) "Deflection limits, when considered, are not easily fixed for a cantilevered wall. A greater deflection than the ratio of L/360 as set for a wall supported at both ends would appear permissible even if plaster finish is the controlling factor."

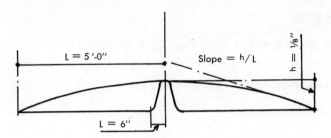

Fig. 44 — Visually Acceptable Surface Deformation

5 feet (L) the slope would be very slight and the surface would appear to be much flatter.

An additional consideration of temperature in the design of curtain walls concerns the fact that entrapped air in hermetically sealed panels can create substantial pressures within the wall as the temperature changes. The exterior surface of a wall can easily reach 150 degrees F. due to solar heat, even when the outside air is cool. The effect of temperature variation on sealed panels was illustrated by Tyler Rogers at a conference held by the Building Research Institute.[6] It was noted that if the pressure or the vacuum created is not dissipated through the panel surface, stresses are induced that can destroy vapor seals. Perhaps, as in the case of plaster, this pressure can produce discontinuity in the inner or outer layer of the wall.

Panel restraint. If a panel is not sealed, but the edges of the wall are so constructed that the inner and outer faces are bound together so that all movement caused by thermal expansion and contraction is restrained, deformation will occur in either the interior or exterior surface. This depends upon the temperature differential of the two sides of the wall. (See Fig. 45.) The principles described in Chapter 6 outlining the relationship of cracking in plaster panels to the degree by which the panel is restrained, apply also to the design of curtain walls in which plaster is used. Steps should be taken to allow movement without the induction of high stresses in the plaster slab.

While Fig. 45 shows a homogeneous wall unit with bound and unbound edges, more exaggerated conditions can be visualized where the wall unit is composed of a number of materials with varying coefficients of expansion. In the selection of materials for the various components of the wall and thin attachments, proper consideration should be given to differences in the coefficients of expansion. Table XVIII illustrates the thermal coefficients of expansion for various curtain wall materials.

Panel joints. Joints between panels, between panels and structure, and the joints around wall openings are matters of some concern in the design and fabrication of curtain wall units. The method by which joining problems are solved is a critical one because of the multiplicity of functions the joints must perform. In addition to providing a means by which the expansion and contraction of the panel surface can be controlled and accommodated, the joint must be weather-tight; it must allow simple and easy panel erection; it must be so connected to the structure that through conductivity of heat is minimized; and the joint must be composed of materials that will not deteriorate. An excellent discussion on joints in metal curtain wall construction is in Study No. 2 of the Curtain Wall Research Project conducted at Princeton University.[7]

Methods for providing efficient joints in exterior plaster walls have also been developed, some of which have been known for many years. Metal casings and expansion joints provide numerous control techniques that have been readily adapted for use in curtain wall construction.

Basic considerations common to all types of wall construction, such as provision for drips on horizontal overhangs, must be noted and incorporated also into the design of plaster curtain walls.

The ready availability of multi-formed plastering accessories provides the designer and builder with great flexibility in finding acceptable solutions to many such problems. Fig. 46 illustrates possible joints for exterior use in vertical locations. Additional information is included in this chapter

Table XVIII.

Thermal Coefficients of Expansion (in. per in. per degree F. x 10⁻⁶) From 32°F. to 212° F.

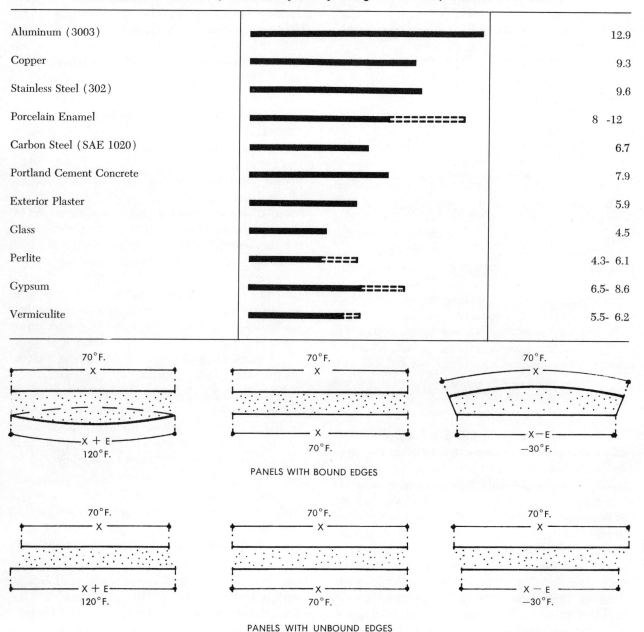

Aluminum (3003)		12.9
Copper		9.3
Stainless Steel (302)		9.6
Porcelain Enamel		8 -12
Carbon Steel (SAE 1020)		6.7
Portland Cement Concrete		7.9
Exterior Plaster		5.9
Glass		4.5
Perlite		4.3- 6.1
Gypsum		6.5- 8.6
Vermiculite		5.5- 6.2

PANELS WITH BOUND EDGES

PANELS WITH UNBOUND EDGES

Fig. 45 — Effect of Temperature on Wall Panels

under "Exterior Plaster," and in Chapter 4 under the same heading.

Although improved methods of applying and curing exterior plaster, as outlined in the preceding chapter, have greatly reduced the possibility of shrinkage, the use of casing bead accessories similar to those illustrated in Fig. 46 will adequately cover hair cracks occurring at the line of the joint.

Steel and concrete structural frames cannot be erected with the precision necessary to provide perfect alignment of curtain wall units. In multi-story buildings differences of 2 inches are not uncommon in the plumb line of the surface of the structure. With prefabricated panel units, it is therefore necessary to use a method of attachment for the wall panels that will provide adjustment in three directions to compensate for these discrepancies in alignments. Fig. 47 diagrammatically illustrates a connection employing this principle.

In addition to the requirements for adjustment, there are several other functions that attachment devices must perform:[8]

(1) *Required strength:* All wall units should be supported independently at each floor level. Care is to be taken that compressive forces are not transferred to the non-bearing wall panels from floors and walls above. The method of attachment, as noted in Table XVII, also affects the allowable clear span between floors of the curtain wall units.

(2) *Positive fastening:* Care should be taken to insure against attachment failure due to building movement, thermal expansion and contraction, etc., after the panels have been installed.

(3) *Fire resistance:* Attachment devices must be adequately protected to prevent their failure during a fire; the release of wall units caused by this failure will endanger the lives of persons fighting the fire. A highly successful method for meeting this requirement is to spray lightweight plaster around all connection devices (See Fig. 48).

(4) *Corrosion resistance:* The element used for the attachment of wall units must not deteriorate. The attachment devices should either have inherent corrosion resistant properties or be adequately pro-

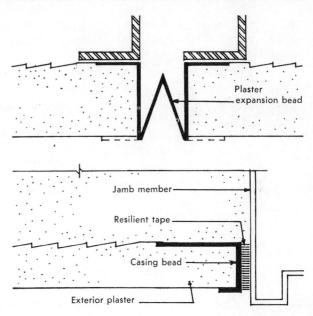

Fig. 46 — Joining Techniques for Exterior Plaster

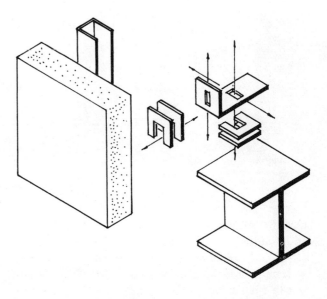

Fig. 47 — Three-Way Adjustment of Curtain Wall Attachment

Fig. 48 — Spraying Connections with Lightweight Concrete

tected from exposure to moisture, electrolysis, and other injurious conditions.

(5) *Installation of Panels:* Ideally, all curtain wall units are attached from the inside of the building in such a manner that the units are sealed in place on tall buildings without having to rely on scaffolds or other exterior platforms. However, re-cent developments in scaffolding equipment have improved exterior working conditions where interior installation is impracticable. In some cases scaffolding has been eliminated by the design of the building.

Fire resistance. Early developments in curtain wall construction were greatly hampered by archaic building codes that required all exterior non-bearing walls to be constructed of 8 inch to 12 inch masonry. During recent years, however, there has been an increasing trend on the part of building officials to accept performance standards for fire resistant construction that specify results, rather than methods or materials.

The most important national model codes, upon which the majority of municipal building codes are based, generally require from one to two hour fire resistance in curtain wall construction. One exception should be noted, as found in the National Building Code recommended by the National Board of Fire Underwriters. This document states that all curtain walls must have a three hour rating.

The method for establishing wall ratings is detailed in Chapter 9, in the description of "Standard Methods of Fire Tests of Building Construction, ASTM E-119."

Perlite and vermiculite concretes and plasters have been used extensively to provide the required fire resistance and thermal insulation in curtain walls.

The structural properties of lightweight concretes already discussed have provided an additional advantage from the point of view of fire protection. In the event of disintegration of the curtain wall facing material, the fire resistant core will remain sufficiently strong to prevent collapse of the wall units with the subsequent spread of fire from one area to another around the periphery of the building, or to adjacent buildings.

Although the re-examination of existing codes has effected a trend towards lowering the fire resistance requirements on exterior walls, a great deal of research is still needed. There is still controversy on the proportion of glass to fire-proofed wall, the vertical distance required between windows to prevent the spread of fire, the flame spread properties of various components of the wall, the control of toxic gases emitted during a fire, and on the very nature by which fire tests are conducted. So far, there have been no major fires in which the adequacy of requirements for curtain walls could be tested.

Insulation. The thermal and acoustical properties of a curtain wall system to a large extent are determined by the material chosen for the core of the panel. These points should be considered when selecting insulating material:

Thermal conductivity – required "k" value.

Coefficient of noise reduction and transmission loss.

Fire resistance.

Weight.

Moisture resistance – permeability.

Resistance to deterioration when exposed to moisture.

Structural properties.

Flame spread values.

Resistance to emission of toxic gases when heated.

Dimensional stability.

Cost.

The thermal properties of a curtain wall, as with any exterior wall, play an important part in the maintenance and operational costs of a building as well as in the comfort of the occupants. Heat transmission through a wall assembly represents a loss of heat during winter, and a heat gain in summer. The thermal characteristics of plaster are discussed in Chapter 8.

The thermal considerations of the non-glass areas of a wall become less important as the ratio of glass to solid wall increases. The heat transmission of glass, per unit area, is three to five times as great as an equivalent solid panel area.

A significant observation was made by Rogers[9] with respect to the thermal protection of structural framing members:

"Curtain walls hung over the exterior of metal or concrete frames have a distinct functional advantage over those supported by floors extending to the outside: they tend to keep all parts of the structural frame at nearly the same temperature. With modern heating and cooling adding to high operating costs, plus the tremendous fly-wheel effect of the building mass, there appears to be a major advantage in locating the insulating element entirely outside the structural frame."

Fig. 49 illustrates approximate temperatures that can be expected at the structural member. The temperature of the structural steel will more nearly approach that of the inside room temperature in both cases, if an equal mass of lightweight concrete in lieu of stone concrete is used for fire protection.

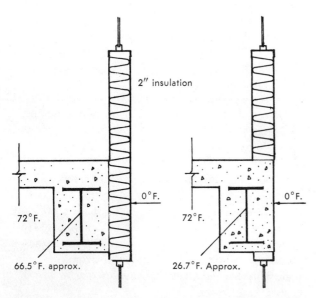

Fig. 49 — Influence of Temperature on Structural Members by Location of Curtain Wall Units

Condensation control and vapor transmission. Unless controlled, condensation that occurs either on the surface of a curtain wall or within the panel itself can be a source of trouble and expense. A detailed discussion of this subject is included in Chapter 8. Condensation will occur when the temperature of a surface drops below the dew point of the air adjacent to it. The vapor pressures on the interior of heated buildings are invariably higher than those outside the building. This difference in vapor pressure is caused by moisture generated within the building, and by the fact that outside air entering the building, although possibly near saturation, is capable of holding more moisture as the air temperature is increased. When a vapor differential exists the vapor will seek its way through openings or porous material to the lower pressure area on the outside of the building. If at any point within the wall the vapor is prevented from continuing its path because it encounters an impermeable barrier such as the exterior metal skin of the building, and the temperature of that barrier is below the dew point of the air-vapor mixture, condensation will occur on the surface of the barrier. On the other hand, if the exterior surface has a higher permeability, such as exterior plaster, the vapor will continue through the outer layer and will not condense inside the wall unit.

Fig. 50 illustrates the U values required to prevent condensation on the interior surface of a wall under varying interior and exterior dry bulb temperature conditions.

The problem of condensation in curtain wall construction has been handled in several ways. The basic methods are shown diagrammatically in Fig. 51.

Panel A consists of a wall assembly where a vapor barrier is placed on the inside surface of the wall. This method prevents any water vapor from entering the panel. In practice, it is seldom possible to obtain completely satisfactory results by this method since most impermeable materials require joints which are difficult to waterproof.

Where a porous material, such as plaster, is used for the interior surface, an effective vapor barrier can be obtained by sealing the surface with two coats of high gloss or aluminum paint plus a final finish coat.[10] But any scratches that occur in this surface will naturally tend to cut down its resistance to vapor penetration.

Panels B and C are similar insofar as water vapor is allowed to permeate the inner surface of the wall. While the condensation can be removed from the panels by gravity, Panel C has the advantage that any outside air entering the panel through the vent openings will not by-pass the in-

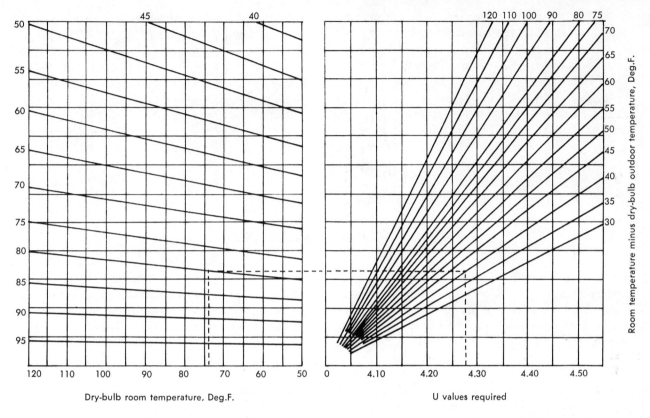

Fig. 50 — "U" Values for Prevention of Condensation

Hunt, W.D., "The Contemporary Curtain Wall," New York, 1958, F. W. Dodge Corp.

sulation to reduce its effectiveness. An air wash, as shown in Panel C, can assist in removing any water that does occur in the panel. The openings in the wall, through which outside air is introduced and expelled, must be large enough to preclude their becoming closed in freezing weather. Vent holes ¾ inch in diameter have proved adequate for the venting and prevention of closure due to ice.[11]

Panel D shows a wall that contains no vapor barrier. All materials in this unit are permeable enough to let water vapor travel unimpeded to the side of the building with the lower vapor pressure. Because porosity and permeability are related, there is the possibility of wind-driven rain accumulating within the panel and temporarily lowering its thermal insulating properties.

If properly installed, metal foils and sheets, plastic membranes and sprayed sealants can all be used with excellent results for the vapor barriers shown in Panels B and C. Table V in Section II of Chapter 8 shows the vapor permeability rates for various materials used in building construction.

Because lightweight concretes are so frequently sprayed into curtain wall units, sometimes directly against a metal exterior panel, methods have been devised to provide ventilation between the skin and the concrete in order to prevent frost accumulation and the subsequent destruction of bond between the two materials. A successful method is shown in Fig. 52, where cardboard tubes are fastened to the exterior skin prior to spraying on the lightweight insulating material. Moisture is drawn into these

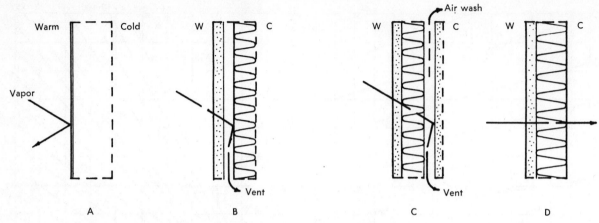

Fig. 51 — Control of Condensation in Curtain Walls

tubes and is dispelled by means of vents at the top and bottom of the panel. To be most effective, the tubes should be at least ¾ inch in diameter (inside).

A final consideration relating to spraying lightweight concretes into curtain wall panels deals with the type of backing sheet used during the spraying operations. The wall shown in Fig. 53 consists of exterior skin, air space, wire mesh or metal lath with a paper backing, insulating lightweight concrete, air space, foil vapor barrier, and interior lath and plaster.

A means must be provided for allowing the water contained in the insulating concrete to be dissipated before the wall becomes sealed. In a series of tests conducted at Pennsylvania State University this observation was made concerning a panel constructed similarly to that shown in Fig. 53. The backing for the "sprayed on" material should be permeable enough to the flow of water

vapor to allow the sprayed material to dry rapidly. It was found in the laboratory that: "the relatively warm temperatures during the accelerated drying period drove the moisture inboard to condense on the aluminum foil vapor barrier and spoiled its heat reflective properties."[12] It should also be noted that a more permeable backing would prevent the accumulation of water on the cold surface of the wall.

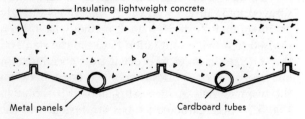

Fig. 52 — Removal of Water from Curtain Wall by Means of Porous Tubes

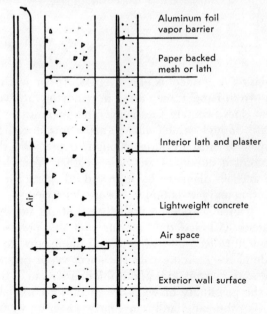

Fig. 53 — Curtain Wall Section Showing Air Spaces

CHAPTER 6

FUNCTIONS AND QUALITY OF LATH AND PLASTERWORK

"Quality plasterwork" is a term almost never defined, but widely used. It is generally associated with a plaster job that adequately meets traditional visual requirements such as flat, unblemished surfaces and square, clean-cut angles. To utilize the full potential of plaster, however, this association of over-all quality with visual performance alone is inadequate, because it considers only one of several functions that the material can perform. Plaster is used in certain instances primarily for its fire resistant, acoustical, or thermal properties. Therefore, a useful definition of plaster quality must be related to all the functions the material may be selected to perform.

This chapter will aim, first, to suggest a definition of quality plasterwork, and second, to enumerate and discuss some of the more important factors which affect it.

I. QUALITY AND ITS DETERMINATION

A complete definition of quality necessarily must be in terms of performance of all functions for which a material has been selected. Therefore, for a given system, the degree of quality obtained is determined by how nearly actual performance of all the required functions approximates the maximum capability of the system with respect to these functions.

Before a system or the materials and assemblies comprising it can be selected, the functions to be performed must be established as well as the degree of performance required. If the degree of performance required lies beyond the maximum capabilities of the system selected, it is obvious that the system cannot perform satisfactorily. On the other hand, if the maximum performance capability of a system greatly exceeds the degree of performance required, the system is inefficient and wasteful. The designer always endeavors to select the system possessing capabilities that most nearly meet all performance requirements, and yet not exceed his budgetary limits. As a result, it is usually necessary that the maximum performance potential of a system be realized in practice. In other words, that the highest possible quality be obtained.

While the visual quality of plasterwork may be easily evaluated by inspection, determination of plaster quality with respect to other functions may be more difficult.

How quality is obtained. Responsibility for the degree of quality produced in plasterwork is shared by the designer, general contractor, plastering contractor, material producer, the mechanics, and laborers involved in all phases of the work.

Initially, the responsibility for quality rests with the designer. Opportunities for control available to him fall into the general categories or stages of the work: first, the selection of a lath and plaster system that performs all the required functions; second, the influence the designer brings to bear on execution through drawings and specifications, contract administration, and inspection.

The general nature of plaster. Probably the most outstanding characteristic of plaster is its extreme versatility and ability to adapt to widely diversified requirements encountered in performing its various functions. This versatility is provided by the plastic state of the material when it is applied. This enables virtually unlimited freedom in creating form and surface treatment. It is further augmented by the great variety of capabilities provided by the many available plastering materials and techniques.

In many respects the characteristics of plaster are closely related to those of concrete. Both materials are much stronger in compression than in tension (in plaster the ratio is usually around five to one, compressive to tensile) and relatively inelastic compared with wood or steel. Plaster is inorganic matter and is not subject to decomposition by organic agents; it is incombustible and effective in preventing the spread of fire or the transmission of high temperatures. The density of cured plaster varies widely, but generally it is one third to two thirds that of concrete. After application and subsequent setting or hardening and drying, plaster becomes relatively stable; however, some plasters, during the period when excess mixing water is leaving the newly applied plaster, shrink considerably. In gypsum plaster, this shrinkage is offset by ex-

pansion due to hydration, resulting in a negligible total volume change.

The acoustical and thermal properties of plaster vary widely. Specialized plasters are effective in absorbing sound and reducing heat transmission. Standard hard-wall plasters are effective in reducing sound transmission. Surface hardness also varies from the relatively soft and friable acoustical materials to the high-strength gypsum gauging plasters which may be considerably harder and stronger than concrete.

Depending upon the materials used in its formulation, plaster is suitable for use in virtually any location and under all conditions of exposure.

II. FUNCTIONS OF LATH AND PLASTER AND FACTORS AFFECTING PERFORMANCE

As we saw in Chapter 4, in building construction plaster generally serves as one lamination of a composite enclosure membrane. Its presence results because it possesses characteristics which no other component of the assembly can provide. In virtually all instances, plaster aids in performing the general function of space enclosure or space subdivision, and it can perform or aid in performing these specific functions: visual, acoustical, thermal, fire protection, nonvisual surface, and structural. Each of these functions will be discussed in terms of performance and quality of plasterwork.

Visual function. The most commonly recognized — and one of the oldest — functions of plasterwork is essentially a visual one. Chapter 1 described the visual capabilities of plaster as it is used to create new form or to conceal, refine or enrich forms inherent in its supporting structure.

Performance of the visual function is measured by how its various forms, textures, and colors appear to the observer; whether or not its visual characteristics represent the intent of the designer; and whether or not the initial appearance can be maintained permanently.

The visual characteristics of plasterwork which have been selected by the designer and which provide a basis for subsequent performance and quality evaluation are, in the final analysis, chosen subjectively (by personal preference, taste, and the like), and can therefore vary widely from one job to another. While this makes it impossible to measure visual performance in all cases on the basis of a single series of arbitrarily established characteristics, certain attributes of plasterwork by tradition and universal acceptance have come to be generally used as performance criteria. Foremost among these are:

(1) Uniformity and consistency of the plaster-surface treatment with regard to color and texture.

(2) Precision with which the forms have been executed as manifest in plumb, level, flatness of surfaces; sharp, true angles, and the like results.

The first criterion depends upon materials, application and finishing procedures, trowel skill of the plasterer, and freedom from defects or blemishes. The second is related to the skill of the lather, the degree of geometric control established in the construction of the base as well as in the application of the plaster. If visual performance were confined to these factors alone, evaluation of quality could be absolute. However, since the objective configuration of the plaster forms themselves is never evaluated, but rather the appearance of the form to a particular observer, the evaluation of quality becomes relative.

The pages that follow will discuss the major factors affecting both the actual configuration of plaster forms and the appearance of these forms as they are affected by illumination, relative position of the observer, visual references, and other factors.

Factors establishing the visual quality required. In virtually all buildings, visual performance requirements vary considerably according to the function of individual spaces. In residential work this variation might not warrant individual treatment of each space according to its function. However, in larger buildings having wider variation in functions, differentiation of visual characteristics according to individual requirements often will prove advan-

tageous with regard to costs, if not absolutely necessary from a performance standpoint. For example, in a manufacturing plant, visual requirements in the office and reception area in all likelihood would be much different from those in production areas, which, in turn, might vary considerably from requirements of storage or utility areas. Here it is likely that visual requirements could be relaxed, while other surface characteristics become more important.

Situations often arise in the use of plasterwork where selection of visual characteristics is restricted by controls imposed by adjacent materials. Where plaster must finish flush with window and door frames, wainscoting, tile, etc., the deviation from plumb and level permissible in the plaster will be established by the nature of these adjacent materials. Similarly, use of wood or metal trim around the perimeter of a plaster panel often will limit the allowable degree to which the plastered surface may deviate from a true plane. It may also affect the roughness of surface texture that may be used.

The relation in which plasterwork appears with respect to scale, size of space, position, distance from observer, and other associated factors often determines the degree of perfection of finish required. For example, a wooden floor is not required to be so highly finished as a table top.

Factors affecting visual quality. One of the great advantages of plaster over other interior and exterior surface materials is the virtually unlimited variety possible in surface treatment. It has often been said that textural possibilities are limited only by the imagination and skill of the plasterer, and that color selections are limited only by the variety of pigments available either in the form of paint or pigments integrally mixed with the plaster. While in a general sense, these statements are true, the choice of colors and textures involve a number of other factors that affect visual performance under specific conditions of use.

Texture. Several examples of interior and exterior textures have been illustrated in Chapter 4, along with the general procedures used to obtain them. As these examples indicate, the suitability of a particular texture is determined by the manner in which the plaster is applied (hand or machine), environmental conditions (airborne dirt, rainfall, and the like), properties of the finish coat plaster (plasticity, time of set, and other factors), nature and properties of the basecoat, and other considerations.

As a general rule, to obtain a high degree of visual quality, very smoothly troweled finishes should be confined to interior uses over basecoats with relatively high resistance to defects. The most obvious reason for this recommendation is that minor defects or deviations from the intended degree of precision often will be concealed by a rougher texture, whereas they are apt to be more readily apparent if the surface is very smooth. Furthermore, the aggregate, usually added to finish coat material when a rougher texture is to be produced, serves to reduce the coefficient of thermal expansion of the finish coat plaster. This brings it closer to that of the basecoat and reduces the risk of cracking or separation of the finish due to differential expansion.

In exterior plaster, selection of a suitable texture is generally more critical than in interior applications. This is because of the more severe exposure conditions found in the former case.

Table I was originally published by the British Department of Scientific and Industrial Research in a booklet entitled *External Rendered Finishes for Walls*. It indicates the suitability of various finishes for various environmental, exposure, and backing conditions.

It is almost universally recommended that integrally colored interior or exterior plaster be finished with other than a smoothly troweled surface. The uniformity of an integrally colored surface is extremely sensitive to many factors involved in proportioning, mixing and application. For example, slight variations in use of pigment proportions, amount of mixing water, mixing time, base suction, trowel or float pressure, and water used for finishing can produce within a surface noticeable chroma

and value variation. Joinings between two plaster applications are also virtually impossible to conceal if the surface is smooth. These factors are particularly important in hand mixing and application since the degree of procedural uniformity obtained is usually less than the machine operations. In either case, however, it is advisable to use a texture no smoother than a sand float finish. For exterior work a texture comparable to the "rough-cast" is usually advisable because the modulation of light on the rough surface helps conceal joinings, uneven deposits of dirt, and pigment concentrations.

To insure that the texture intended is the one obtained, it is often advisable to make final texture decisions on the basis of sample panels made up on the job by the journeymen who will do the actual work. Although generally not necessary where a smoothly troweled finish is specified, this practice may save considerable time and cost when it involves a more complicated texture where a verbal description could be misconstrued.

A final consideration is whether or not the texture desired can be readily executed in the finish material selected, and whether it is readily produced by the application method used. Either very smooth trowel finishes or finishes utilizing textural characteristics involving precise detail should usually be attempted only with materials having relatively high plasticity. For example, it would be extremely difficult, if not impossible, to produce the fan texture illustrated in Chapter 4 with a finish material such as a one part lime to four parts Keene's cement which is "rubbery" and difficult to manipulate with a trowel or float. (An exception to this might be production of a smooth finish with this material, using a mechanical trowel.)

Time of set may also affect selection of texture. In general practice the plasterer regulates the set of the finish coat material by adding retarder to permit sufficient time for the finishing or texturing operation. However, in instances involving a complex finishing operation, set time may influence the size of panels that may be finished in one operation

Table I.

The Suitability of Various Exterior Surface Textures to Various Backing Materials, Environmental and Exposure Conditions.[1]

Treatment	Suitability of Various Backing Materials	Suitability for Various Environments	Suitability for Various Exposure Conditions	Requirements
Pebble-dash or dry-dash	Not suitable on weak types of brick or lightweight concrete	All areas, but particularly suitable for rural or coastal areas	Particularly suitable for severe conditions	Less susceptible to defects and deterioration than all other types
Roughcast or harling	All except very weak backing materials	do	do	Durable—Low Maintenance
Scraped finishes	All backing materials	All areas, but coarser finishes less suitable in the dirtier urban atmosphere	All conditions	Greater freedom from crazing and patchiness of appearance than smooth finishes
Textured or floated finishes	All backing materials	All areas; in the dirtier urban atmospheres tend to accumulate dirt, but are not so prone to streakiness as the smoother finishes	All conditions	Similar to scraped finishes
Smooth finishes	All backing materials	All areas, but see note in last column	All conditions	The type most likely to develop defects, including crazing, cracking and patchiness of appearance
Machine applied finishes	All backing materials	Often less suitable for urban conditions, as they show dirt rather badly	All conditions	Do not craze but become patchy or streaky under some conditions
White or light colors in any of above finishes	All backing materials	Less suitable for urban areas	All conditions	Will probably require some maintenance to keep good appearance in urban areas

without joinings or the size of the finishing crew required, or both.

The method of manipulating the finish coat will also affect the suitability of texture selection. An obvious example would be an attempt to produce a texture which is a direct expression of trowel manipulation, such as the fan texture in a mechanically troweled finish coat material.

Painting and color. A large proportion of the plasterwork produced today is colored either by painting some time after completion of the finishing operation, or by including color pigments or colored aggregate integrally with the plaster material. Each of these methods of obtaining a colored plaster surface has particular characteristics, advantages, and limitations which makes it more or less applicable to solution of certain visual requirements.

The method of providing color by integral pigment is not as widely used as painting. It has perhaps its widest application in exterior plastering. Finely divided inorganic color pigments, such as metallic oxides, are incorporated either during manufacture in the case of proprietary ready-mixed color finishes, or during mixing of the plaster mortar at the job site. Since gross variation in color uniformity can result from minute variations in quantities of mixing water, proportioning and mixing of materials, and many other factors, the greatly increased accuracy in formulation and standardization possible with factory-mixed products recommends their use universally.

Two advantages of integral color are the savings in time that otherwise would have been required for curing and drying before painting could commence, and the savings in cost of painting materials and labor. These savings are generally significant only when periodic maintenance or redecoration is less frequent. Therefore integral color is often well adapted to exterior applications where dirt accumulation is not a problem. A further advantage of integral color over a painted surface lies in the color homogeneity throughout the full finish coat thickness. Whereas removal of a nail or picture hanger from a painted surface may leave a white chip mark, a similar chip in an integrally colored surface will not be as apparent.

Recent developments in mechanical application and finishing of integrally pigmented finish materials indicate possibilities of a much wider future use as the problem of color uniformity is overcome. Use of machines also make possible a wider range of colors than can now be obtained with hand application which tends towards the lighter shades.

The painting of plaster presents an entirely different set of problems. A film of paint may be considered as an independent lamina of an enclosure assembly having a series of intrinsic characteristics. While some of these characteristics exist independently and are in no way affected by the base over which the paint is applied, others are directly related to the back-up material.

Although consideration of the general subject of painting is beyond the scope of this manual, some attention to the special relationships of paint to plaster is warranted. In addition to providing color, paint may be used to conceal or modify various characteristics of a plaster finish. Some paints, particularly the cement and latex emulsion types, can effectively conceal minor surface blemishes in plaster such as fine hairline cracks and dull or slick spots. Nearly all types modify surface properties by changing porosity, light reflectivity and, in some instances, sound absorption.

When using paint in conjunction with plasterwork the greatest problems arise when newly applied plaster is to be painted for the first time. The success of the initial union between the two materials depends primarily upon the adhesion between them and their compatability (that is, absence of harmful reaction).

The adhesion developed between paint and plaster is a function of mechanical bond, and develops as paint penetrates plaster pores; or *specific adhesion,* the attraction of paint to a smooth but unglazed surface of low porosity.[2] Specific adhesion, while generally producing the greatest bond strength, is greatly reduced if plaster is damp at the time paint is applied. Specific adhesion will also be temporarily reduced if plaster, which though dry when painted, is subsequently wet. When that happens, nonporous paints may blister while the moisture is present and return to their original state, with the possibility of significant reduction of initial adhesion as the plaster dries.

Several manufacturers produce moisture meters, which are designed to indicate the moisture content of plaster and wood, according to the electrical resistance measured across two contact electrodes. It is usually difficult to calibrate these instruments to read the actual moisture content of plaster. The only completely safe practice is to assume that if the meter indicates the presence of any moisture, the plaster is too damp to paint. Even this method of moisture content determination may sometimes be misleading due to variable moisture conditions at various depths within the plaster and at various locations on its surface. But it is considerably more reliable than the "match test" which consists of striking a match against the surface and determining adequate dryness by whether or not the match will light.

The actual amount of moisture permissible in plasterwork before painting can safely proceed varies somewhat with the type of paint to be applied. Porous paints, such as cement and latex paints, are less sensitive to moisture than are sealers which are less permeable to water vapor such as varnishes or pigmented oleoresinous primer-sealers. Once an impermeable sealer is applied, it prevents further drying of that surface.

In addition to loss of adhesion and possible peeling and blistering, excessive moisture remaining in painted plaster, particularly in plaster applied direct to masonry, may carry soluble salts from the masonry through to the plaster surface. Here they may crystallize as efflorescence and push the paint film away from the plaster and produce bumps and bulges.

These conditions can be prevented by allowing sufficient time for initial drying to take place and by providing furring, vapor barriers or other methods of preventing recurrence of high moisture conditions within the plaster.

The time taken for initial drying varies with plaster thickness, type of aggregate, ventilation, humidity conditions, and many other factors. The fastest drying may be expected when plaster is exposed to air circulation on two sides. The slowest drying condition is where plaster is applied direct to masonry.

Occasionally a gauged-lime putty finish will be chalky; it will appear dull, and if brushed, a white powder will rub off. Oil paint should not be applied to plaster in this condition because peeling may result. BMS Report 121, "Investigations of Failures of White-Coat Plaster," explains the condition as resulting from a tendency of lime to be floated to the surface during troweling, much in the manner of "fines" in portland cement plaster. The condition appeared more severe in instances where a lime-gauging plaster finish had been applied to a "green" basecoat.

Some types of paint are liable to deteriorate if the binder or pigment is exposed to an alkali such as is sometimes present in plasters containing lime or portland cement. Linseed oil, oleoresinous, and alkyd binders may saponify or turn to brown soaplike substances in the presence of an alkali while Prussian blue, chrome yellow, and chrome yellow-green pigments may discolor or fade. Usually these reactions occur only when paint has been applied before sufficient moisture has been removed from the plaster. To prevent this type of defect, it is always advisable to use an alkali-resistant paint over plaster that contains lime or portland cement. (These products are so labeled by the manufacturer.) For interior uses, self-priming paints based on phenolic resin, chlorinated rubber or latex emulsions are generally recommended since they are resistant to attack by alkali. Where other types of paint must be used, the plaster should be allowed to dry completely and should then be primed with an alkali-resistant sealer. For exterior applications, cement paints or latex emulsions usually are recommended.

Prior to the development of alkali resistant paints, often a zinc sulphate solution was used prior to painting, to neutralize alkalinity on plaster surfaces. It was discovered that zinc sulphate applied to a lime putty finish coat reacted with the recarbonated material on the surface, breaking it down and causing the surfaces to become soft and porous. For this reason the zinc sulphate treatment should never be used.[3]

So far, application of paint to new plaster has been discussed only as it affects the paint. However, premature painting can also cause trouble in a plaster finish containing lime. To a large extent, the hardening of a lime finish coat depends on progressive recarbonation of lime putty from the surface inward, which in turn depends upon absorption of carbon dioxide from the air and subsequent release of moisture. Once the plaster surface has been sealed with a nonporous paint, absorption of carbon dioxide can no longer take place, and the lime finish is unable to further harden. If a lime finish must be painted before 60 to 90 days after completion of plastering, a porous paint should be used that will permit passage of carbon dioxide and water vapor, so that hardening by recarbonation can be completed.

Appearance of plaster forms is influenced by such factors as the texture and reflectivity of their surfaces, direction and intensity of illumination, relative position of the observer and his opportunity to relate to adjacent reference lines and points.

While performance depends upon the relationships between actual configuration and these factors affecting perception, degree of quality depends upon whether or not this relationship is complementary.

Although in many cases it is impossible to predict the conditions of illumination under which plasterwork will be observed or the relative position of any observer, there are recurrent cases present in several building types where these conditions are predictable. An example would be the long interior corridor common to hotels, schools and hospitals. In instances such as this it is often possible to estimate the degree of precision in execution of the plaster forms necessary to produce a given appearance requirement.

The actual degree of precision with which plaster forms are executed depends to a large extent upon the number of opportunities for control that are available in the furring, lathing, and plastering methods used. For example, if a lathing specification requires direct application of lath to structural members that are badly out of plumb, the resulting plasterwork must also be out of plumb. However, if furring had been called for, an independent opportunity would have been provided for controlling the plumb of the plaster surface. Similarly, a surface more nearly approaching a true plane can be more readily obtained with a three-coat plaster application than with a double-up or two-coat application.

The two-coat method offers less control since the full basecoat thickness is built up in what is essentially a single operation, thus reducing the opportunity for intermediate leveling adjustments. If necessary, even greater precision may be obtained by using screeds or dots and screeds to control thickness and surface plane (see Chapter 4).

To determine whether or not a surface appears plumb or level, an observer usually refers to the line of intersection of the observed surface with an adjacent surface. If this line appears parallel or perpendicular, as the case may be, to the other reference lines provided by trim, doors, windows, and other features, then the surface is adjudged plumb or level.

Conditions where deviations from plumb or level would be most readily apparent are those where several adjacent parallel surfaces meet a surface perpendicular to them, as in the case of a series of parallel beams or columns.

Where conditions such as these occur, and where a high degree of visual quality is necessary, it will probably require special control of layout and application procedures. In the case of plumb and level, the greatest opportunity for control occurs in the furring or suspension operations where it is possible to correct for gross deviations. The brown coat should not be forced to correct for more than very minor deviations, since uniformity of thickness is important. The finish coat should never be used as a means of final straightening, because its performance is even more sensitive to thickness variation.

Flatness of surface is one of the more readily recognized characteristics of plasterwork. Several standard specifications require that plaster be applied with sufficient precision so that the surface does not deviate from a true plane by more than 1/8 inch from the line of a 10 foot straightedge placed at any location on its surface. While this is an arbitrary standard and does not limit slope of surface bumps and depressions (see Chapter 4) its general acceptance indicates that it is usually a satisfactory criterion of whether or not a surface will appear flat.

There are other conditions, such as the previously mentioned long interior corridor, where apparent surface flatness is often extremely difficult to obtain. Light striking a surface at an angle approaching the surface plane brings into high relief even the slightest waviness. Similarly, an observer standing close to a surface and sighting along it immediately detects waviness that would not have been apparent had the angle of vision been 90 degrees.

Waves and depressions become even more apparent if the surface is very smooth and has high reflectivity. For this reason, where apparent flatness is desired in plasterwork and the observer's angle of illumination or probable angle of vision, or both, is such that slight deviations are likely to be noticeable, use of a rougher texture or decoration with a flat paint will aid considerably in restoring apparent flatness.

Squareness and alignment of angles are another important visual characteristic. Many accessories such as corner beads and casing beads, etc., are available that make it very easy to obtain projecting angles of excellent appearance, When properly installed, these devices provide control of plaster thickness and insure positive alignment.

Re-entrant angles require somewhat greater skill during the plastering operation to make them appear sharply defined and straight since there is generally in this case no pre-installed guide. Where the highest visual quality is desired, re-entrant angles are troweled and the line of intersection incised with a featheredge. (See Chapter 4.) In less demanding situations (for example, in residential work), the angle is formed more rapidly but less accurately with a paddle. These operations are applicable to "restrained angles." If "unrestrained" angles are specified, casing beads, modified expansion joints, or other devices may be used to form the re-entrant angle, thus providing both grounds and alignment control.

ACOUSTICAL FUNCTIONS

Plasterwork invariably performs some acoustical function. This is true regardless of whether plaster has been selected primarily on the basis of its acoustical capabilities whether these were a secondary consideration, or whether they were totally ignored. Since this capability always exists to some degree, its full exploitation in all instances would result in a generally higher level of over-all plaster performance, and therefore higher over-all plaster quality.

Chapter 8 includes a comprehensive section on the subject of acoustics, with particular emphasis on the relation of plaster and plastering systems to the general subject. Discussion in this chapter will therefore be limited to a general consideration of what acoustical functions plaster can perform, and how over-all plaster quality may be affected by improving the efficiency of its acoustical performance.

The acoustical functions of plasterwork are divided into three categories: sound absorption, reduction of sound transmission, and reflection of sound. Sound absorption depends upon what percentage of the total sound energy striking the enclosure surface can be held just within the plaster membrane, and immediately dissipated there in the form of heat. A sound absorptive plaster must therefore contain surface openings through which the sound waves may enter, and a porous, cellular interior where they will become trapped.

The only plastering materials having these characteristics are those which have been designed specifically for the purpose and without exception are proprietary, mill-mixed products requiring only addition of water at the job. Whether actual performance results in maximum capability depends on the strict adherence to the manufacturer's instructions with regard to mixing, application and finishing, and decoration and maintenance.

The acoustical material should be at least ½ inch thick and the open cellular structure must be preserved if it is to remain effective. For this reason excessive troweling and compaction should be avoided, and where painting is required a thin, non-bridging material should be used. Acoustical plaster should be confined to locations not subject to abrasive wear or requiring frequent cleaning.

In the reduction of sound transmission the efficiency of a plaster wall or ceiling depends upon the interaction of a series of factors, many of which are not directly connected with the plasterwork itself. As with a fire resistance rating, the sound transmission loss for a particular assembly or system is determined by a standard test which measures only over-all performance. It is therefore impossible to isolate and evaluate in quantitative terms the effect of any single variable. This, however, does not preclude estimation of relative contribution of similar components to over-all performance (based on observation and general theory).

While in theory sound transmission loss is directly related to the mass of the sound barrier, in practice, this pure relationship is often destroyed by openings such as doors or mechanical fixtures.

It is considered that for each doubling of the mass, average transmission loss is increased by 6 decibels. Since the mass per unit area of a homogeneous membrane varies with plaster density and membrane thickness, in most cases these factors will relate directly to transmission loss performance, except as they are influenced by the presence of openings. The mass law is most applicable at higher frequencies; in the lower range, membrane stiffness affects transmission by reducing it as sound frequency decreases.

The reflection of sound is a function more limited in application than absorption or transmission loss. It is of use in theaters, concerts halls and auditoriums and other locations where sound distribution is important. Plaster is an extremely efficient means of distributing sound, since a smooth troweled plaster surface generally reflects up to 97 per cent of the sound striking it. Also, the freedom of form possible enables accurate control of the direction in which the sound waves rebound.

In this case quality depends upon the precision with which the forms are executed and the degree of control of surface characteristics maintained.

THERMAL FUNCTIONS

Among the functions that plaster can perform is that of thermal insulation. In conventional applications plaster may, to a very limited degree, supplement the insulation provided by another layer of material included specifically and only for this purpose. However, in other, newer applications such as curtain wall cores, plaster alone provides the heat insulation.

Although essentially fire resistance involves insulation against heat transfer, it has been discussed separately in another section of this chapter and in Chapter 9. It involves exposure conditions and characteristics of plaster not directly related to performance as insulation in the normal ambient range.

A second function involving the thermal properties of plasterwork is its use in radiant panel heating installations. In this instance, resistance to heat flow is not desirable, and plaster is used to distribute, by way of radiation, heat supplied by coils or wires embedded within it.

The discussion of thermal properties that follows is confined to only those factors which directly affect performance and quality. A more complete and detailed coverage is included in Chapter 8.

Insulation. The most important single factor in determining the relative heat insulating values of various plasters is the type and amount of aggregate that they contain. In comparable proportions, gypsum plaster containing perlite or vermiculite is generally somewhat more than four times as effective as a sanded gypsum plaster. It should be noted that in the case of sanded plasters, insulating efficiency decreases as the proportion of sand increases, while in lightweight aggregate mixes, the converse is true, with efficiency increasing with the aggregate proportion.

As with virtually all other functions, plaster thickness is an important factor in determining performance as thermal insulation. The over-all insulating performance of a wall or ceiling assembly which contains a layer of specialized insulating material usually is not appreciably affected by minor variation in plaster thickness. However, the performance of a curtain wall panel which relies entirely upon a plaster core of a given thickness for heat insulation could be quite sensitive to thickness variation.

To be fully effective, reflective insulation such as insulating gypsum lath must be installed so that the shiny foil surface is spaced at least ¾ inch from the next layer of the wall or ceiling assembly. In addition, the foil should not come in direct contact with steel members, since heat is readily transferred by conduction between the two materials.

Radiant panel heating. Performance of a plaster membrane designed as a radiant heating panel depends upon the efficiency with which heat is transferred to the membrane surface from supply elements embedded within it. The transfer should be accompanied by sufficient lateral distribution to produce a uniform temperature at the radiating surface.

Since high conductivity is desirable, acoustical plasters, or plaster containing lightweight aggregates, are not as efficient as sanded plasters and ordinarily should not be used in radiant panels. The type of cementitious material and lath used depends upon the design temperature at which the system will operate. If the operating temperature is less than 125 degrees F., any type of lath and cementitious material may be used; above 125 degrees F. metal lath and lime or portland cement plaster should be employed.

For some time there has been controversy over the question of whether to place tubing above or below metal lath. Recent experiments indicate that, if certain precautions are taken, placement above the lath offers several advantages over the other method. (See Chapter 8.)

Plaster thickness varies with the system used, but it is generally agreed that where coils are placed above metal lath, at least ¾ inch should be maintained between the membrane surface and the face of the coils.

In the case of gypsum lath or in instances where heating coils are placed below metal lath, ⅜ inch should be maintained between the face of the coils and the plaster surface.

A final precaution: the heating system must never be used to hasten drying of the plaster. It should be started up only after the plaster is completely dry, and then only according to the procedure outlined in Chapter 8.

FIRE PROTECTION FUNCTION

Possibly the most vital function of plaster is the protection of lives and property from fire. Its ability to confine flame, smoke and super-heated gases to the area in which a fire originated, while protecting the structure against exposure and collapse, places plaster in a class by itself among surface materials.

The performance of a plaster membrane with regard to fire resistance is measured in terms of the period in hours between the time of initial exposure to a controlled fire, and the time at which failure occurs as determined by standard criteria. A description of the standard fire test procedure is included in Chapter 9. Also in Chapter 9 are tables which give the fire-resistance ratings in hours for a large number of wall, ceiling, and column systems.

Since building codes, virtually without exception, recognize only those ratings that are based on actual tests, quality of plasterwork with regard to fire resistance depends upon how precisely the rated assembly is duplicated on a job.

NONVISUAL SURFACE FUNCTIONS

Sanitation. Plasterwork properly selected and finished provides one of the most sanitary surfaces obtainable. Its great advantage over other materials with comparable surface properties, lies in its freedom from joints which could harbor dirt and vermin.

One of the prime requisites of a material selected on the basis of sanitation is a smooth surface that will not collect dust and dirt and that can be cleaned easily. For this reason a very smooth trowel finish will generally be required. Although this type of surface can be produced with most conventional finish coat materials, a Keene's cement-lime putty finish is particularly hard, and like other lime putty finishes it can take a highly glass-like polish. Final finishing with a mechanical trowel will produce the maximum degree of smoothness and surface densification.

The type of basecoat used also is of great importance. Crack resistance of the entire plaster membrane is highly important since cracks, if they occur, tend to reduce efficiency.

Resistance to impact and abrasion. All conventional hard plasters possess sufficient abrasion and impact resistance to withstand the blows and scratches encountered under normal wear and tear. In instances where unusually severe impact or abrasion is anticipated, such as walls or partitions in warehouses, or corridors in schools, to insure adequate performance it may be necessary to select plaster materials particularly suitable to these conditions.

The resistance of a plaster membrane to damage caused by impact is primarily a function of the plaster's resiliency, its thickness, and the mass and rigidity of the entire assembly (that is, a 2 inch solid plaster partition has greater impact resistance than a ¾ inch lath and plaster membrane.) While not classified as impact resistant materials, the relatively low moduli of elasticity of lightweight aggregated plaster, compared with those of sanded plasters, allow the former to deform to a relatively greater extent without cracking when exposed to impact.

The effect of plaster thickness on resistance to impact cracking was studied in the plaster investigation conducted by the Armour Foundation.[4] This test involved dropping a 60-pound sandbag through a known distance onto the center of a horizontal plaster panel supported on two steel rollers. Drops were made from increasing heights until the first crack was observed. The table that follows shows

the effect of increasing plaster thickness over metal lath from ¼ inch to 1 inch.

Table II.

Effect of Increasing Plaster Thickness on Impact Cracking

Plaster thickness	¼″	½″	¾″	1″
Height of drop when first crack occurred	6″	8″	24″	48″

(Comparable results were obtained with gypsum lath and plaster panels.)

Rigidity of the plaster base is also an important consideration. Tests performed by a manufacturers' association indicated a marked increase in resistance to impact cracking of plaster applied to certain masonry bases, over plaster applied to lath bases.[5] [See Figs. 1(A) and 1(B)].

Resistance of plasterwork to damage caused by abrasion depends almost entirely upon the hardness of the plaster surface.

As stated before, hardness in plaster generally varies directly with strength. Finish coats of extreme hardness can be produced with gypsum plaster, Keene's cement, or portland cement. Portland cement will usually give the hardest finish, with Keene's cement next, and special high-strength gypsum gauging plaster following.

Weather resistance means the ability of exterior plaster to resist the penetration of water, and to maintain its surface integrity when exposed to temperature and moisture cycling, and freezing and thawing. Since portland cement and lime are the materials recommended for exposed exteriors, this discussion will be confined to their capabilities.

The degree of weather resistance required in stucco depends upon the severity of climate (that is, temperature extremes, amount of rainfall, and rapidity of freezing and thawing cycling) and the degree of exposure of the plaster (orientation, location, and the protection afforded by overhangs). The most critical factor in weather resistance is plaster's

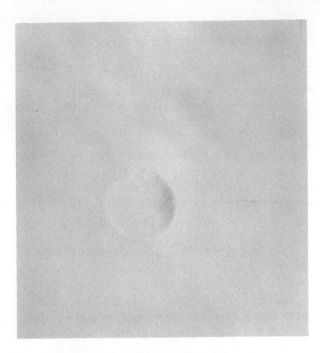

Fig. 1 (A) — Plaster on Rigid Masonry

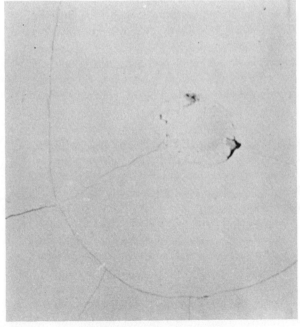

Fig. 1 (B) — Plaster on Lath

ability to resist penetration of water from its exposed face through to the backing where it may produce warping, corrosion, efflorescence, breakdown of bond, and other problems. In frame construction, the moisture barrier generally applied prior to plastering protects the underlying structure. However, complete embedment of metal reinforcement in the plaster is also necessary to insure against corrosion.

Direct application of exterior plaster to masonry involves somewhat different considerations. Since there is no moisture barrier between plaster and backing, water penetrating the plaster can enter the masonry either by capillary action or through cracks at joints. Also, substances contained in some types of masonry, when in solution, can cause bond failure from sulphate reaction, or may result in efflorescence appearing on the plaster surface.

As a general rule, plaster mixes rich in cementitious material should be avoided (that is, proportions should always be three or more parts of aggregate to one part of binder). While a rich mix produces strong, dense, impermeable plaster, it is subject to relatively high shrinkage upon loss of mixing water, and thus is more susceptible to cracking. Rain water tends to run down the surface of this type of material. Upon penetrating a crack the water becomes trapped, since the material is not porous enough to permit migration back to the surface and subsequent evaporation. A leaner, more porous mix, while absorbing more rain water, absorbs it evenly over its entire surface and allows it to return to the surface to be evaporated without penetrating through to the backing.

The surface treatment used on exterior plaster also affects its weather resistance. (Table I relates surface texture with adaptability to various environments and exposure conditions.)

STRUCTURAL FUNCTION

At the present time plasterwork performs no function that could be classified as purely structural. The solid plaster partition, as a self-supporting, free-standing element, while most nearly approaching a truly structural use, is always considered non-bearing. Estimates of the ultimate capabilities of plaster and lath to become reality (discussed in Chapter 1), will entail a degree of quality control similar to that now used in concrete work. Work towards establishment of the necessary controls is now in progress. However, much more remains to be done before it will be possible to set up design standards and construction procedures.

III. CAUSES OF CONDITIONS WHICH IMPAIR QUALITY

As a surface material, plaster must present a pleasing appearance while serving as a visual barrier between the observer and the other structural and service components within a wall or ceiling assembly.

Because it is exposed and the other components concealed, plaster is often blamed for surface blemishes which are in fact direct manifestations of defective conditions originating behind it. For example, warpage of a "green" wood stud may produce stresses in a plaster membrane of such magnitude that a crack results. In other instances, a staining material originating in a masonry plaster base may be dissolved by water leaking in from the exterior. This solution may eventually migrate through to the plaster surface where the evaporating water deposits a stain. In instances like these, the tendency is often to overlook the cause to blame the plasterwork for the result.

This section will describe methods of insuring the required plaster performance by eliminating the causes of conditions which tend to impair it.

Cracking. A plaster crack is a break or fissure originating on the surface of or within a plaster membrane. Cracks vary in severity or intensity according to the width, length, and depth of the fissure. They are differentiated by severity and by the characteristic patterns or forms in which they generally occur. Cracking is due to only one primary cause: a concentration of stresses which, in magnitude,

exceeds the maximum strain capacity of the material. Once this critical point is passed, stress relief will occur in the form of a break. Stresses are always present, even though plaster is seldom considered as carrying any load or materially supplementing the load-carrying capacity of the structural system. They may be transferred to the plaster from the structure, set up in the plaster itself by dimensional changes due to varying temperature and moisture conditions, or they may result from some other type of external force such as impact or vibration acting directly on the plaster.

Stress build-up in the plaster membrane may be controlled in three ways:

(1) Reduction of stress transfer from the structure;

(2) Increasing the inherent load capacity of the plaster membrane (by providing thicker grounds, increasing strength, or other means).

(3) Provision of integral stress-relief mechanisms in the plaster membrane.

The performance capability of a plaster system with regard to crack resistance depends upon the extent to which these operations are implemented. Quality will vary with the effectiveness of the implementation.

Structural cracking has been clearly described: ". . . a large, prominent crack extending across the surface and through the plaster, is probably a structural crack. It may start at the corner of a door or window and extend diagonally to the edge of a wall, or it may run along the corner between two walls or a wall and ceiling. The name indicates that it is due to some movement of the structural members of the building, and not to any fault in the plaster"[6] (See Fig. 2).

Structural cracking is caused by direct transfer of stress from the structure to the plaster membrane. These stresses usually result from movement of structural members caused by warping, shrinkage, expansion, unequal settlement, or deflection. Cracking tends to be directional, to follow planes of greatest stress in the plaster membrane. Fig. 3 illustrates typical locations of structural cracks.

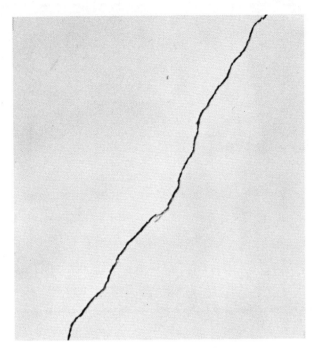

Fig. 2 – Structural Cracking

The measures required for control of structural cracking will vary in each individual situation according to magnitude of a structural movement expected. Often when an initial settlement of a building followed by relative stabilization is anticipated, it may be more practical to allow initial cracking to occur and then to patch and fill the cracks. Circular No. 151 of the National Bureau of Standards states:

"It might be possible to construct a building sufficiently massive and rigid so that this type of crack would not occur. A more practical expedient, however, is to let the cracks form, and then, after the building has "found itself," point them up. Unless the structure is poorly framed, the chances are that they will not reopen, and the plaster will be better than new."[7]

In practice the probability of a structure ever arriving at a completely stabilized state is slight. Therefore, assurance of obtaining a given performance usually entails some precautionary considerations when selecting plastering materials and systems as well as other building components.

Reduction of stress transfer from the structure. Stress transfer may be reduced in two ways. Movement and resulting stress build-up in the structure can be minimized by insuring adequate sizing of joists, bracing, and footings. Or by isolating the plaster membrane from the structure with respect to stress transfer through use of flexible or resilient mountings for attachment of the membrane. Or stress transfer may be reduced by employing both methods. (See Fig. 4.)

When resilient or flexible mounting devices are used, it is important that all parts of the lath and plaster unit be equally isolated from the structure. If edges are held by grounds or casing beads which are rigidly attached, while the center of the plaster area is independent of structural movement, little has been gained toward crack prevention.

The extent to which dissociation of structure and plaster membrane need be carried depends upon the performance required of the plaster. Use of loose or resilient mountings is not standard practice in average residential work, and usually entails higher initial cost than the standard direct attachment. But regardless of the method of mounting, no plaster bond should occur at junctures with other materials. (See Chapter 5.)

The deflection of structural frames under load is one of the more recurrent causes of plaster cracking. A plaster ceiling that is attached to the underside of a deflecting floor is in the position of the extreme fiber of the system taken as a structural unit, where the forces causing the deflection are resolved into tensile forces acting in the plane of the plaster membrane. When these forces exceed the maximum resistance of the material, cracking must occur.

For many years it has been more or less arbitrarily assumed that if deflection in ceiling joists due to live loads is kept below 1/360th of the span of the joists, plaster attached below the joists will not crack. This rule of thumb was investigated extensively by the Armour Research Foundation in

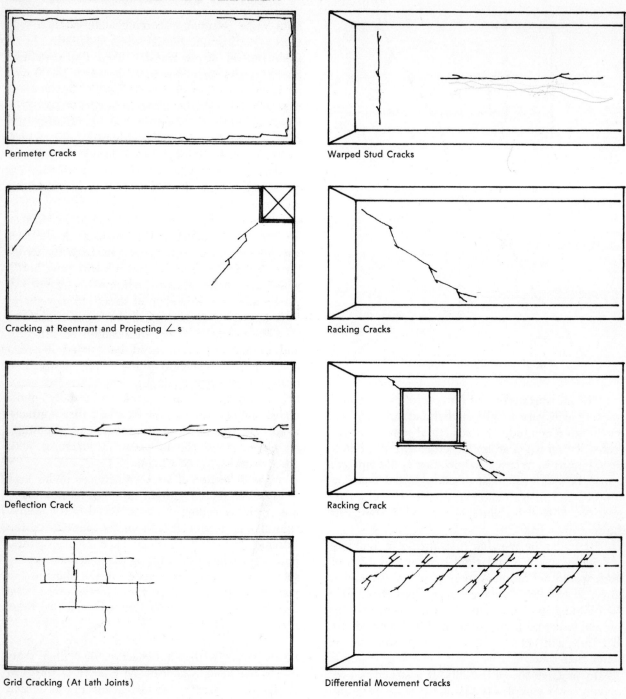

Perimeter Cracks

Warped Stud Cracks

Cracking at Reentrant and Projecting ∠s

Racking Cracks

Deflection Crack

Racking Crack

Grid Cracking (At Lath Joints)

Differential Movement Cracks

CEILINGS

WALLS

Fig. 3 — Typical Locations of Structural Cracks

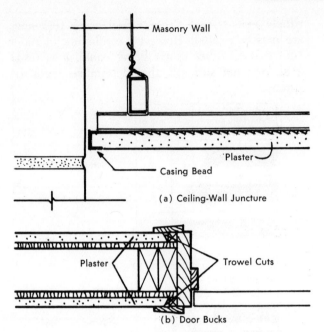

Fig. 4 — Preventing Plaster Bond with Structure

1948 under the auspices of the U. S. Department of Commerce. Its report, entitled "Standardized Lathing and Plastering Practices," states: "The allowable deflection under live load permitted by 1/360th of the span length is not a dependable basis for limiting deflections which will produce plaster failures."[8]

The conclusion was drawn from a series of tests made on full-size samples. The samples were of 2 inch by 8 inch and 2 inch by 12 inch wood joist construction spanning 15 feet and 18 feet. It was determined initially that relationships between cracking, span length and deflection would hold as well for steel structures as for wood.

Three types of lath and plaster ceilings were tested:

(1) Metal, gypsum, and fiber insulation laths nailed directly to the underside of wood joists;

(2) Metal and gypsum laths attached to the underside of wood joists by means of resilient clips;

(3) Metal and gypsum laths fastened to furring and runner channels suspended from the underside of wood joists.

In the case of direct attachment of lath to joists, it was found that the joist and plaster membrane tended to act together much as an inverted T-beam. In this case deflections well within the 1/360th limit caused cracking. However, in cases where the plaster membrane was attached with resilient mountings or suspended from the joists, the joists and membrane acted as separate beams. Deflections in these cases were measured well in excess of the 1/360th limit (up to eight times as great) before the first crack occurred.

The dimensions of the ceiling also affect its tendency to crack under deflection. A rectangular ceiling that is long and narrow, with joists spanning the long dimension, may crack well before the deflection reaches L/360 with L equal to the joist span. Fig. 5 shows the deformation in relation to both A-A and B-B. Although the latter is in the direction of the joists, the allowable deflection should be limited by span A-A and not B-B.

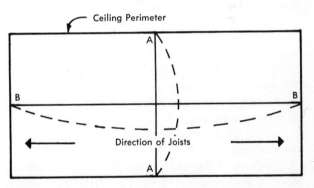

Fig. 5 — Effect of Ceiling Dimensions on Plaster Deformation Under Live Load

The following is also one of the conclusions of the Armour Foundation report: "In ceiling construction better structural performances could be attained either by strengthening the joint between adjacent lath or by employing greater unbroken lengths of lath in the direction parallel to the joists; starting with a lath (several feet long) centered at midspan, the region of weakness (the lath joints) then would be subjected to lesser stresses from joist deflection."[9]

The Armour Foundation's report recognized that in practice there are countless examples where plaster ceilings have performed perfectly when directly attached to joists. This has been attributed to the fact that floor systems seldom reach maximum design deflection since in design practice the loading usually assumed is higher by some factor of safety than that actually imposed in the use of the structure.

Increasing the inherent load capacity of the plaster membrane. Resistance to stress concentrations of critical magnitude may be provided either by taking steps to reduce unit stresses developed under load, or by increasing the stressing capacity of the plaster and lath membrane. In the first instance, under a given load the unit stress developed varies with membrane thickness. In the second, the stressing capacity varies with the strength and strain characteristics of the materials and assembly used.

Plaster thickness. The importance of strict adherence to minimum thickness recommendations was mentioned in Chapter 4. It should be reiterated that no other single factor affects plaster performance with regard to all its functions to the extent that its thickness does. Since in-place thickness can be measured, it is one of the most effective methods of general quality control.

That thickness determines crack resistance has been proved conclusively in several investigations. The effects of varying plaster thickness in the deflection tests conducted by The Armour Research Foundation are shown graphically in Fig. 6.

The feasibility of reducing minimum plaster thickness below the present minimum standard of ½ inch specified by ASA[10] and other nationally recognized standards for plastering over gypsum lath, has been extensively tested. The unanimous conclusion is that reducing thickness below ½ inch substantially increases the likelihood of cracking.

Strength. The subject of the relationship between plaster strength and its resistance to cracking involves considerable controversy. The opinion most widely held is that strength and crack resistance are closely related. However, conflicting opinions hold that all other things being equal, it is resilience, and not strength, that determines crack resistance.

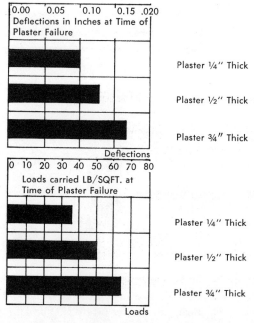

Standardized Lathing and Plastering Practices Armour Research Foundation

Fig. 6 — The Effect of Plaster Thickness on Load Carrying Capacity and Deflection at Time of Failure (Gypsum Lath Used)

The results of an analysis of all available information on the subject seem to justify a position somewhere between the two cited above. A crack occurs in a plaster membrane only if a stress develops that produces a deformation which exceeds the maximum strain capacity. Therefore, the relationship of stress to strain or the modulus of elasticity of a material must be considered in addition to either tensile and compressive strength or the ability to deform alone.

From the relationship:

$$e = \frac{S}{E}$$

e = unit strain (tensile or compressive)
S = unit stress (tensile or compressive)
E = modulus of elasticity

Strain capacity increases as stress capacity increases and modulus of elasticity decreases. Theoretically, plaster with a high strength and a low modulus of elasticity has both high-stress and high-strain capabilities, and will have relatively high resistance to cracking.

Due to technical testing problems, plaster strength figures are generally given in terms of p.s.i. compressive strength. However, in crack resistance it is usually the tensile strength of the material that is critical. Since in most plasters there is not a straight line relationship between tensile and compressive strength, the compressive figures are useful only as an approximate indication of relative tensile strengths.

Crack resistance is clearly related to strength. However, tensile or compressive strengths in themselves are not alone responsible.

The cementitious material, the aggregate, and their relative proportions, exert the greatest influence on plaster strength. (See Chapters 2 and 4.) The ratio of cementitious material to water is of next importance. In practice, within certain limits, the amount of water added to a dry mix is determined more by desired workability than by strength considerations. The amount of water required to produce a given mortar consistency may be reduced by insuring proper proportioning and gradation of aggregate, but specifically by avoiding excess "fines."

Table III

The Effect Of Mixing Water Proportions On The Strength Of A Set Neat Plaster Of Paris (Of Given Consistency)[11]

Water Lbs. per 100 lbs. plaster	Modulus of Rupture p.s.i.	Tensile Strength p.s.i.	Compressive Strength
50	1520	450	2540
60	1210	310	1970
75	870	230	1450
100	545	165	920

Addition of admixtures in general, and particularly retarder, purposely or accidentally in the form of impurities, results in reduced strength. The set time of most gypsum plasters is regulated by adding retarder during manufacture. Further addition, except where absolutely necessary, should always be discouraged. (See Fig. 7.)

Entrainment of air in plaster serves to weaken it by displacing solid material with air bubbles. This reduces the plaster cross section effective in resisting tensile forces. Entrained air in sanded gypsum plaster, regardless of the mix, runs from about 4 per cent to 6 per cent. In lightweight aggregated plasters, the entrained air runs from approximately 9 per cent in a 1:2 mix to 22 per cent in a 1:4 mix. The strength reduction due to increasing aggregate parts is proportional in sanded and lightweight mixes. However, the increased amount of air entrained in over-aggregated lightweight mixes further reduces strength.

Moisture content of hardened gypsum plaster exerts a pronounced effect on its strength. The effect of adding 1 per cent of water to a completely set and dry gypsum cast made with retarded plaster was to reduce the modulus of rupture by 44 per cent. Strength drop due to water content is greatest when gypsum plaster goes from a dry state to a small (1 per cent to 2 per cent) water content. Subsequent strength loss due to increase in water content is consistent but of smaller magnitude (from 2 per cent to saturation results in a further cumulative strength loss of 16 per cent).[13] Since, in practice, plaster often has a water content of greater than 2 per cent and seldom approaches complete saturation, variation of strength due to moisture content changes is not of particular importance as far as variation of in-place plaster strength. However, it is of great importance in determining in-place strength from laboratory specimens. ASTM includes this stipulation in the procedure for testing strength of gypsum plaster: "[After storing cubes until weight becomes constant within 0.1 per cent] . . . place the dry test specimens in a desic-

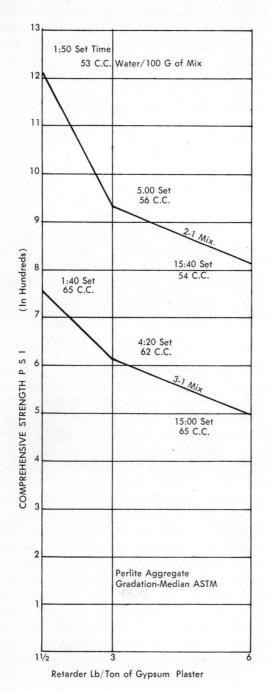

Fig. 7 — Effect of Retarder on Compressive Strength of Gypsum Perlite Plaster[12]

cator over anhydrous calcium chloride for 24 hours, remove, and test immediately."[14] It is clear that use of laboratory "dry strength" figures for design load purposes is not valid. Testing specimens in a standard condition would be far more realistic for determining in-place strength, since a margin of safety would be incorporated.[15]

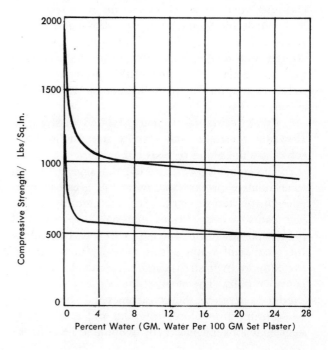

Fig. 8 — The Effect of Moisture Content on the Strength of Set Plaster of Paris[16]

The effective strength of a lath and plaster system depends on factors other than plaster strength alone. The type of lath, the methods of joining lath sheets to one another and to supporting members, weight and spacing of furring and main runner channels, all these are important considerations. The type of lath used affects over-all membrane strength in two ways. Gypsum lath as a "suction" base draws some excess mixing water from newly applied plaster mortar, and by thus lowering the water-plaster ratio increases plaster strength. Metal lath when completely embedded, while having no effect on intrinsic plaster strength, increases the over-all strength of the plaster assembly by providing reinforcement.

The sizes, weights, and spacing of members constituting the membrane supporting system are highly important in providing crack resistance. Chapter 5 includes several tables which permit rapid determination of the requirements for any given situation.

Since plaster containing a lightweight aggregate is less dense than sanded or neat plaster, it might seem to follow that a correspondingly lighter framework would suffice to support it. This is not true. Though it is lighter, lightweight plaster is not generally as strong as sanded plaster. Therefore it requires a relatively stronger and more rigid supporting framework. For this reason, the same recommendations for supporting members apply to both sanded and lightweight plasters.

Provision of integral stress-relief mechanisms in the plaster membrane. There are a few conditions involved in the use of plasterwork where stresses are likely to develop that cannot be accommodated by methods already outlined. In such instances it is usually advisable to provide some sort of stress-relief mechanisms that will at least control, if not prevent, cracking. Cracking of this type, though usually structural in origin, may also result from stresses caused by cumulative shrinkage or expansion within the membrane. Cracks may be classified by the location at which they usually occur in a plaster membrane.

If plaster is carried as a continuous membrane over a 90 degree angle such as usually occurs at junctures of walls and ceilings, the cross section at the apex of the angle normally is placed under considerably greater stress than an average cross section taken at random through either of the abutting membranes. The sharp angle results in the maximum stress concentration possible under a given set of conditions by reducing to a minimum the opportunity for distributing the differential movement stresses.

Because plaster will readily assume curvilinear form, and because its use as a membrane is analogous to thin shell reinforced concrete work, the principle of maximum distribution of stress throughout the entire system, universally followed in the latter, would seem applicable to plaster. On the basis of photoelastic studies, the Report of the Armour Foundation concluded that "... photoelastic studies indicate that sharp corners in walls are much more serious stress-raisers than are corners containing fillets."[17]

Fig. 9 illustrates two bakelite test specimens under the same racking load condition. The opening in (A) has 90 degree corners, while the corners in (B) contain fillets.

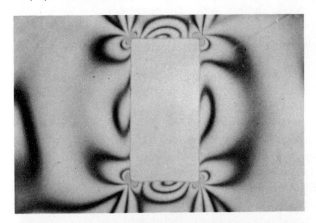

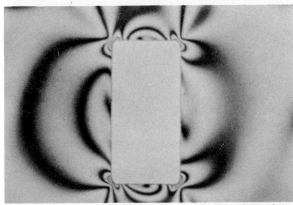

Standardized Lathing and Plastering Practices Armour Research Foundation

Fig. 9 — Stress Distribution in Photoelastic Models of Walls Containing Windows

For reasons of economy and adherence to traditional visual characteristics filleted corners have not become widely accepted.

If plaster is applied continuously over a surface comprised of two or more different backing materials, the probability of a crack occurring over the juncture(s) is relatively high. This is particularly true when the backing materials have widely varying coefficients of expansion.

A final example involves the condition where a plaster membrane is carried continuously over a large area. Stresses produced by cumulative dimensional changes tend to concentrate at planes of weakness such as lath joints, penetrations for mechanical equipment, locations where vertical elements project into the membrane, or at places where smaller projections of the membrane meet the large field. Unless stress relief is provided for, cracking at these locations is probable.

As already stated, prevention of perimeter cracks, dissimilar backing cracks, and cracks at weak areas in large membranes, often may prove extremely difficult. However, in these cases, use of special reinforcement such as cornerite or flat strips of metal lath often will be effective where limited stresses are encountered. An attempt to reinforce the juncture of two backing materials where considerable differential movement can be expected usually results in an extension of cracking throughout and around the reinforced area. Stresses which are well beyond the strain capability of the reinforced membrane section will tend to skirt around it into the unreinforced field.

Although prevention is uncertain, control of this type of cracking is relatively easy. It is done by providing "ready-made cracks" or control joints at critical locations in the membrane field and by eliminating restraint at the membrane perimeter. In this way, stresses are never permitted to reach critical magnitude.

A recent investigation into the causes of cracking in suspended ceilings of relatively small areas (such as hospital rooms) strongly indicated a relationship between perimeter restraint and field cracking. It was demonstrated that as perimeter restraint was lowered, field cracking was correspondingly reduced; and *vice versa.*

It is generally recognized that use of control joints is an effective means of preventing uncontrolled cracking at the juncture of different backing materials and at various critical locations in large plastered areas as has been described. There is, however, no generally accepted recommendation for the maximum plaster area that may safely occur between control joints. The figure of 3,600 square feet or maximum distance of 60 feet each way has been used with apparent success.

Fig. 10 shows several methods of eliminating restraint and providing control joints.

Before ending this discussion of structural cracking, a final factor which seems to affect its occurrence should be mentioned. In the investigation already mentioned, of cracking in relatively small suspended ceilings, the type of finish coat used appeared to have a remarkable effect on crack resistance. With minor exceptions, two finishes were used throughout the tests. The first was a standard lime-gypsum gauging trowel finish, the second a lime-Keene's cement sand-float finish. Statistical analysis revealed that the ceilings finished with the lime-Keene's sand-float finish were virtually devoid of field cracks. This was true regardless of the strength of basecoat plaster, degree of restraint, and other factors which together are generally assumed to determine crack resistance. However, the lime and gauging trowel finish showed defects that normally could occur under the conditions encountered. On the basis of these tests, the conclusion was reached that the type of finish coat (lime-Keene's sand-float) primarily determined the degree of crack resistance. The only apparent explanation for this phenomenon is minute stress relief provided by the aggregate in the finish coat. Instead of fracturing along a single well-defined line under excessive stress, the aggregated finish forms many minute breaks around and between aggregate particles. These, while relieving the stress, are not

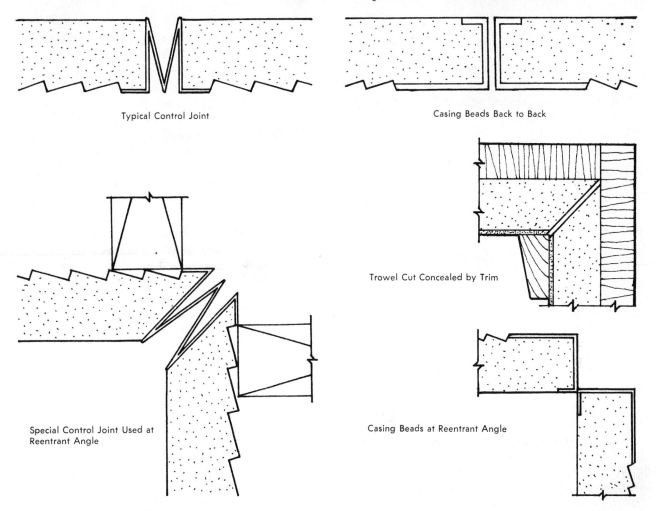

Typical Control Joint

Casing Beads Back to Back

Trowel Cut Concealed by Trim

Special Control Joint Used at
Reentrant Angle

Casing Beads at Reentrant Angle

Fig. 10 — Methods of Providing Controlled Discontinuity

visible because of their fineness and the texture of the floated surface.

Random or "map" cracking. Circular No. 151 of the Bureau of Standards thus describes random or "map" cracks: "This type is less prominent than a structural crack. It goes through the plaster, but it does not extend entirely across the surface. Instead, a system of cracks running at various angles, will form more or less geometric figures over the sur-face. These figures are usually large (more than 6″ across) and well-defined, and the figure is re-peated at different places on the surface."[18]

The basic cause of random or map cracking is the same as for structural cracking (a stress concen-tration causing deformation which exceeds the strain capability). However, the origin of the forces producing the stress concentration is not the same. Almost invariably, the forces that cause map crack-

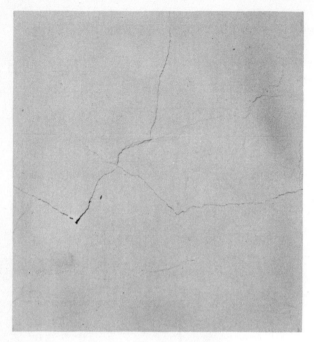

Fig. 11 – Random Cracking

ous backing materials. It has been generally proven that certain masonry backings offer greater adhesion values with gypsum and portland cement plasters than do the laths. The difference is essentially an academic one, however, since it has been demonstrated that the plaster base providing the lowest adhesion value on the basis of direct tension tests, still provided a safety factor of 38.[19] Although many bases are potentially suitable for plaster application some, namely masonry, may require preparation in the form of cleaning or equalization, or both, and reduction of suction before plastering. (See Chapter 3.) For uniformly adequate adhesive bond to be developed, a certain amount of suction must be present and, more important, this suction must be uniform.

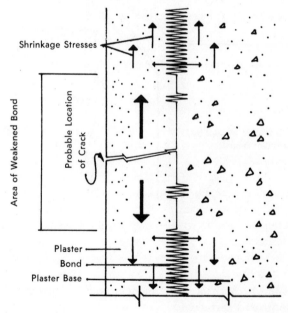

Fig. 12 – Stress Concentration in Plaster Due to Bond Failure

ing result from differential shrinkage or expansion between the plaster membrane and backing, or between individual plaster coats within the membrane.

If bond between laminae is uniformly strong, the stresses produced will be evenly distributed throughout the membrane. However, if bond is weak or nonexistent at any place on the interface, a stress concentration will occur in the lamina undergoing dimensional movement. (See Fig. 12.)

Elimination of random or map cracking to a large extent depends upon uniformly strong bond and minimization of differential movement between membrane and backing, and between individual laminae within the membrane.

The nature of plaster bond was discussed in detail in Chapter 4. Consideration of the subject in this chapter will, therefore, be confined to a treatment of the factors affecting bond as it, in turn, affects plaster performance.

Much has been written and many tests have been performed on the adhesion of plaster to vari-

Suction in the brown coat as it relates to application of the finish coat entails considerations that will be discussed in the section on craze cracking.

Differential movement between individual plaster coats and between the plaster membrane and backing may be effectively controlled by so selecting materials and mixes that stresses produced will be well within bonding capabilities. Before gypsum bond plaster was developed, it was considered bad practice to apply gypsum plaster directly to monolithic concrete, since many instances of bond failure had been recorded. It was found that in most cases, failure had been due to differential movement between the two materials. Subsequently it was discovered that additions of small amounts of hydrated lime to gypsum plaster resulted in a material having expansion-contraction characteristics closely approximating those of concrete. Through its use, bond failures between gypsum and concrete have been greatly reduced.

Most standard recommendations call for an increase in the proportion of aggregate added to gypsum plaster when applied to masonry surfaces. Since various types of masonry bases have widely varying expansion-contraction characteristics, no single plaster material could coincide with all of them. Use of a lean mix is the most practical solution, because it provides greater flexibility to accommodate dimensional changes without visible failure, than could be obtained with a stronger material.

In rare instances, plaster bond may be impaired or destroyed by a chemical reaction between substances occurring in the adjacent laminae. It is generally recommended that gypsum and portland cement plasters not be applied directly to each other. If moisture is present, there is a possibility of a "sulphate reaction" that can eventually destroy adhesion between the two materials.

Thermal shock. Random cracking is often attributed to sudden large changes in ambient temperature, or "thermal shock." A review of some of the basic concepts and factors involved in thermal shock should provide a better understanding of the condition as it applies to lath and plaster. Changes in temperature introduce stresses and distortions into any construction material or system. The success of the material or system in withstanding those stresses, or adjusting to them without fracturing, depends upon the amount of the stress, the speed of the change, and the inherent nature of the material or system.

It would appear that in most instances, the time element in temperature change is more important than the over-all temperature change. Lath and plaster construction often are able to compensate for stresses introduced slowly into the system, but the same stresses, if introduced suddenly, might crack the plaster.

Both plaster strength and elasticity are factors in resisting sudden stress build-up. It would appear that with equal moduli of elasticity, the stronger of two plasters can withstand a greater thermal shock. With equal strength, the plaster with the lower modulus of elasticity will withstand greater shock.

A system involving plaster on a solid backing will demonstrate greater shock resistance than an open frame system, because of its rigidity and its slower heat transfer.

Typical thermal shock cracks are likely to appear as partially concentric circles around the center of the slab, with more or less straight radial cracks extending from the center. The most effective means of preventing this occurrence is the control of temperature and ventilation and the elimination of strong drafts, particularly during wintertime. **Craze cracking** is variously termed "checking," "chip cracking," and "shrinkage cracking." It is confined to the finish coat of interior and exterior plasterwork and appears as a series of fine hairline cracks in patterns similar to random or map cracks, but with only an inch or less between cracks. In severe occurrences the small areas defined by cracks may become concave, with the perimeters cupping out from the basecoat. A similar pattern often may be observed on the surface of silt remaining in a pond which has been dried up by the sun.

Craze cracking is caused by shrinkage of the finish coat plaster as it loses water after application. In a properly prepared and applied finish, crack-

Fig. 13 — Craze Cracking

ing is prevented by troweling or floating the material while it is drawing up and before the gauging sets.

To counteract excessive shrinkage, the proper quantity of gauging material must be added, basecoat suction controlled, and troweling started at the right time. Chapter 4 defines these conditions.

In a portland cement plaster or stucco finish, over-troweling or over-floating should be avoided because a thin film of cement paste tends to work to the surface. Upon drying, this film will shrink considerably, and may cause crazing. Final finishing should be postponed until the material has hardened enough to resist migration of fine particles to the surface.

SURFACE IMPERFECTIONS

Latent expansion of various impurities inadvertently incorporated in a plaster mix or in the plaster materials themselves, usually is responsible for this type of blemish. Its occurrence, always relatively rare, may be virtually eliminated by observing a few simple precautions. The type of expansion that causes these conditions is not to be confused with normal cyclical expansion and contraction due to temperature and humidity changes. **Popping and pitting** produce one or a series of small bulges or craters in the plaster surface. Usually less than ⅜ inch in diameter, their depth depends upon the location in the plaster membrane of the unstable particles that produced them.

Fig. 14 — Popping and Pitting

Pops and pits are caused by accidental incorporation into the plaster of small particles of impurities such as seeds, lignite coal, pyrites, bits of iron, or overburned quickline. These particles either fall into the plaster mortar during preparation and handling, or enter with one of the plaster ingredients. Sand occasionally is contaminated with lig-nite coal, pyrites and iron. Artificial sands such as crushed slag are more apt to contain these impuri-ties than are natural sands. In rare instances, par-ticles of overburned quicklime core inadvertently will be incorporated in hydrated lime during manu-facture, due to a defective sieve. If these particles are large enough not to pass a No. 50 sieve, even-tually they may hydrate and expand with sufficient force to produce a pop in hard plaster.

All the impurities mentioned will expand only in the presence of moisture. The length of time required for expansion of sufficient magnitude to cause popping and pitting varies from weeks to years, depending upon the type of impurity and the moisture content of the plaster.

This condition can be overcome by observing ordinary precautionary measures in specifying aggre-gate materials and lime, and exercising reasonable care during mixing and handling of plaster mortar. The mortar tender must be sure that no pipe filings, wood chips, or other foreign matter is allowed to fall into the plaster.

Blistering, known also as "turtle backs," usually is confined to finish coats. A blister may form at points where bond between the finish coat and basecoat is extremely weak or non-existant.

Blistering usually occurs during or immediately after application of a finish coat. It is generally caused by a "green" basecoat which does not have sufficient suction, or by adding too much mixing water to the finish coat mortar.

STAINING — EFFLORESCENCE — SHADOWING

Discoloration of a plaster surface may take several forms. Some examples are rust streaks on exterior plaster, streaks or blotches of various colors on interior finishes, appearance of a joist or wood-lath pattern on ceilings.

The type of plaster and the backing to which it is applied seem to make little difference in whether or not the discoloration will appear and to what extent it does occur. Moisture conditions are a prime determinant. It has been observed that plaster remaining damp for long periods or going through many damp-dry cycles is far more subject to discoloration than plaster that remains in a dry state. In most cases these conditions may be pre-vented by proper detailing to keep moisture out of plastered assemblies (provision of flashings, drips, adequate sealing of joints, and so on) and by insur-ing that no stain or efflorescence-producing mate-rials are inadvertently incorporated in the plaster or placed in contact with it.

Staining. These are some of the more common sources of staining materials:

Tar paper used behind plaster as a vapor barrier;
Creosote used to treat framing lumber;
Organic impurities in sand;
Unvented temporary heaters;
Open fireplaces;
Unseasoned pine lumber in mixing boxes;
Dirty tools;
Oxidation of metal trim.[20]

Stains on exterior plaster (stucco) are usually traceable to oxidation of metal brackets, flashings, trim, and other accessories, which make contact with or penetrate the stucco membrane. This con-dition may be prevented by using a non-staining metal such as zinc or lead. It is advisable, where fastening devices pierce the membrane, to enclose them in lead sleeves, as illustrated in Fig. 15.

Rain water should not be permitted to cascade down the face of a stucco membrane. It may pick up staining substances from the roof or gutters and deposit them as a streak on the stucco surface.

Efflorescence may appear on both interior or ex-terior plastering as a white or grayish film on the plaster surface. In advanced cases, crystal growth or "whiskers" may occur.

The surest way of preventing this condition is to prevent access of water behind the plaster by proper detailing and flashing, since without water to act as a vehicle no surface deposit can be formed. In addition, masonry should be examined for signs of efflorescence prior to applying plaster. If efflores-cence is present, plaster should not be applied directly to the masonry. Sometimes sand contains soluble mineral impurities which if incorporated in plaster may produce efflorescence. Use of sand that has been tested in accordance with ASTM C35 "Specifications for Aggregates for Use in Plaster" (see Chapter 2), will greatly reduce the occurrence of this defect.

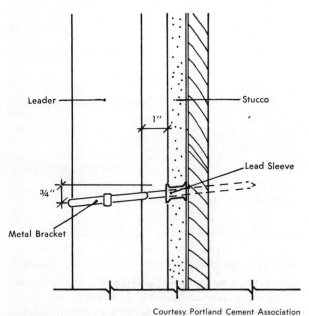

Courtesy Portland Cement Association

Fig. 15 — Attachment of Metal Bracket to Stucco Surface

Shadowing, also known as "pattern soiling," and "ghost marks," is caused by variation in the surface temperature of plasterwork. This phenomenon is produced by uneven insulation or changes in backing materials.

Dust accumulates on cold surfaces more readily than on warm ones. The rate of accumulation varies with the surface temperature so that plaster having wide differences in surface temperature will develop noticeable shadowing more quickly than surfaces whose temperatures are uniform.

The condition is common in buildings which are not properly insulated. It may occur in radiant heating panel installation where the tubing is placed too close to the radiating surface to permit a uniform surface temperature.

The minimum requirements of the Federal Housing Administration indicate that a differential of 6.5 degree F. temperature on a surface constitutes a serious problem. In *Design of Insulated Buildings for Various Climates,* T. S. Rogers has observed that even a differential of 3 degrees to 5 degrees F. will necessitate acceleration of redecoration cycles.[21]

To reduce this condition to a point where normal redecoration cycles are sufficient to provide a satisfactory appearance, the insulation value at all points on a surface should be balanced with the maximum possible degree of exactness.

"Sweatout" and "Dryout" are attributable to the rate at which mixing water is removed from newly applied plaster by suction of the backing and by evaporation. A sweatout occurs only in gypsum plaster and is identified by damp, soft spots in a gypsum wall or ceiling, that are darker in color than the surrounding plaster. When the condition has been allowed to remain uncorrected for an extended period a musty odor will be noticeable.

This condition occurs if water remains in plaster in sufficient quantity to inhibit proper drying, thus resulting in abnormal recrystallization and drastically reduced strength. As soon as a sweatout is observed, immediate steps should be taken to correct it by providing ventilation and dehumidification, and tempory heat if necessary. If a sweatout exists for a long period the plaster will lose its strength and eventually disintegrate, necessitating its complete removal and replacement.

A dryout may occur in gypsum and portland cement plasters. It occurs more frequently than a sweatout but is more easily corrected and rarely impairs the performance of the plaster. The condition is identified by light colored, friable spots of chalky appearance, often adjacent to doors and windows.

A dryout occurs if water is allowed to leave the plaster too rapidly prior to set (that is, by direct exposure to hot dry wind), so that enough does not

Fig. 16 — Shadowing

remain for complete hydration of the gypsum or portland cement. To remedy the situation, a water-alum solution is applied to gypsum plaster (water only to portland cement) in a fine spray until droplets begin to appear on the surface, thus indicating that the plaster is saturated. Wall openings should be screened to prevent too rapid evaporation. After being sprayed, the affected area of the plaster will continue to hydrate normally with no deleterious effects.

SPECIFICATIONS FOR LATHING AND PLASTERING

The first part of this chapter dealt with the effects on plaster performance of a selection of various materials, assemblies and procedures. As has been stated, that selection establishes only the maximum performance capability of plasterwork. Actual performance depends upon the degree of control subsequently exercised to insure that the selected system is executed as intended. Since the

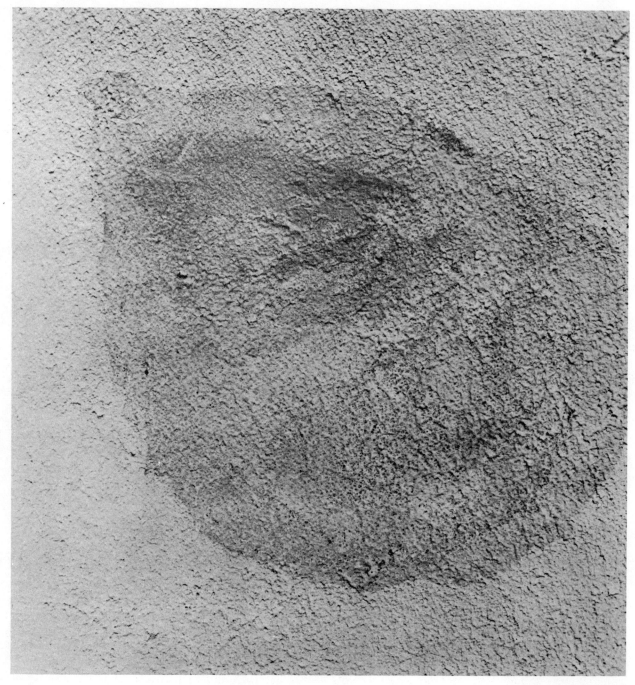

American Technical Society,
Chicago, Illinois

Fig. 17 "Sweatout"

American Technical Society,
Chicago, Illinois

Fig. 18 "Dryout"

specification provides probably the greatest opportunity for this control afforded the designer, the degree of completeness and accuracy with which it is written relates directly to the quality of the finish plasterwork.

Standard specifications. The American Society for Testing Materials, the United States Government, the American Standards Association and manufacturers publish recommended standards and specifications for many of the materials used in plastering and lathing. In general, the limits specified by ASTM are relatively broad.

Many organizations publish recommended general specifications for lathing and plastering which, unlike the material standards, apply to all phases of plasterwork and include proportioning, mixing, application, and other related considerations. Foremost among these issuing bodies are the American Standards Association, manufacturers' associations, building code authorities, and contractors' organizations. These specifications have done much to standardize practices throughout the nation. However, they are not, nor are they intended to be, blanket recommendations that may be incorporated into individual specifications verbatim or by reference.

All materials standards and recommended general specifications are offered as *minimum* recommendations, intended primarily to produce a degree of *visual* performance that is generally acceptable. Exceptions are the fire resistance requirements included in most building codes which, when applicable, must be followed precisely to comply with local regulations.

Most standard specifications consist of a series of provisions which permit several alternative procedures. For example, proportioning may be done by weight or volume, mixing by hand or machine, and application in two or three coats. Since the degree of control possible with each of these alternatives (and in many cases the cost) will vary considerably, it is usually not sufficient to specify, for example, that "basecoat application shall be done in accordance with ASA A42. 1." Similarly, in the case of material controls, to specify that "Gypsum plaster shall comply with ASTM C-28" is to permit use of any one of five different types of gypsum plaster.

The specification check list that follows enumerates in sequence the subjects which are covered by most standards, generally paralleling the chronological order in which the operations take place.

SPECIFICATIONS CHECK LIST

1. General and special provisions.
2. Scope of the work.
   Work included in this section.
   Work excluded from this section.
3. Scaffolding and protection.
4. Ordinances.
5. Preliminary inspection.
   Provision for correcting unsatisfactory conditions which could adversely affect plasterwork.
   Responsibility for undetected unsatisfactory conditions.
6. Cooperation with others.
   Coordination and scheduling.
7. Patching of plaster repairs.
   Defects in plasterwork.
   Damage by others.

8. Materials.
   Delivery and protection.
   Lathing and furring materials — accessories.

Material	Paper backing
Type	Grounds provided
Dimensions	Weight
Integral vapor barrier	Gauge
Rust protection	Mesh size

   Plastering materials.

Material	Gradation
Type	Noise reduction coefficient
Control standard	Purity

9. Systems (partitions, walls, ceilings and furring).
   Type
   Tie-in to adjacent structure.
   Members.

Sequence of erection	Spacing
Attachments	Location
Spans	

10. Lathing — Interior and exterior.
    Spacing of supports.
    Direction of lath.
    Attachment.
        To supports   At corners
        To adjacent lath   To other materials
    Temporary bracing.
    Openings.
      Bucks
      Reinforcement
    Provision for embeddment of lath.
    Workmanship — Tolerances
      Plumb   Alignment
      Level   Grounds
      Flatness

11. Plastering, interior and exterior.
    Preparations.
      Temperature and ventilation control
      Masonry surfaces
      Monolithic concrete surfaces
      Metal grounds
      Inspection of plaster base
    Basecoat
      Ready-mix
        Type
      Job-mix
        Materials
        Proportions

Mixing
  Hand
    Time
  Machine
    Time
  Sequence of material additions
Application
  Number of coats
    Sequence
  Thickness
  Compaction
  Provision for bond
  Curing
  Workmanship — Tolerances
    (see lathing and furring)

Finish coat
  Type
  Proportion
  Preparation and mixing
  Application
    Thickness
  Finishing
    Method
    Texture
  Curing

12. Clean-up.

CHAPTER 7

ECONOMICS OF LATH AND PLASTER

I. SUPPLY OF BASIC PLASTER MATERIALS

The basic materials of lath and plaster construction are lathing materials, cementitious or binding materials, aggregates, and water. The characteristics of these materials are discussed in detail in Chapter 2, and their combination and preparation in Chapter 3. In each of the categories there are a limited number of materials in common use. There are three basic cementitious materials; gypsum, which accounts for most of the interior basecoat plasters; portland cement, used for some interior plasters and extensively for exterior plastering; and lime, used mainly for finishing coats and as a plasticizing admixture with portland cement plasters. Lime can also be used effectively over certain plaster bases as the cementitious material for most basecoat plasters. Lathing materials tend to be more highly fabricated than the cements and aggregates. The lathing materials in common use are: lightweight, hot and cold rolled structural shapes, various fastening devices and wire materials used for furring, suspension

and other structures supporting the plaster base; metal lath of various patterns and weights; gypsum lath in several standard sizes and thickness; and wire mesh, also available in several types. The aggregates and the cementitious materials are mineral or mineral-like products. Since the location of the source of supply of these materials is determined by the geographic site of the mineral deposit, the relationship to point of use is accidental. Because aggregates and cements are heavy or bulky with respect to value, transportation costs often constitute a large portion of the final price.

Depending on the material and the mix, the cementitious material required for a cubic foot of plaster mortar ranges from 15 to 50 pounds. At the job this will cost from 0.7 cents to 1.5 cents per pound. From 50 to 100 pounds of sand per cubic foot of mortar will be required at a cost of 0.065 cents to 0.21 cents per pound. Lightweight aggregates, such as perlite and vermiculite, cost from 3.0

to 4.0 cents per pound, but only from 4 to 8 pounds are required per cubic foot of mortar. The importance of cost of transportation to the total cementitious and aggregate material cost can thus be seen. In many cases, this cost is greater than that of the material itself at the mine or quarry.

Although in the cementitious materials and the processed aggregates, a reduction in weight is usually effected by the refining process, sometimes it appears to be less expensive to ship raw materials to processing plants near large market centers. This seems to be general practice, particularly with the processed aggregates, and possibly is due to differential freight rates for raw and finished materials. Sand, however, is rarely shipped any great distance from the point of original production. No doubt, this is primarily because sand is abundant and widely distributed and acquires little added value by process or manufacture.

GYPSUM

Location of abundant gypsum deposits of a quality suitable for processing for construction purposes are widely distributed throughout the world. Calcium sulphate ranks fourth among the salts found in sea water. Frequently beds of gypsum are found associated with common salt deposits. In 1956 production in the United States was reported from 63 mines and quarries located in 20 states. Five widely distributed states (Michigan, California, Iowa, Texas and New York) produce 64 per cent of the total produced in the United States.

At present there is said to be no shortage indicated in the supply of raw gypsum in North America. While some of the older mines in the United States are approaching depletion, some new deposits have been discovered, the volume of imports has been increasing, and new mines were opened in Indiana and Nova Scotia during 1954 and 1955. In 1956, the production of crude gypsum throughout the world was estimated at 34,200,000 tons. Of these, the United States produced 10,316,000 tons and imported an additional 4,336,000 tons. It consumed more than 42 per cent of the estimated world production. A minor portion of this consumption may have been re-exported in the form of processed or fabricated products.

There is no customs duty on crude gypsum imported into the United States. Of that imported in 1956, 87 per cent was produced in Canada. Imports from all other countries producing gypsum for export, including Mexico, Jamaica, the Dominican Republic and the United Kingdom, amounted to 3.9 per cent of total United States consumption.

Of the total gypsum products sold in the United States in 1956, 24.9 per cent was uncalcined; 18 per cent of this went into the manufacture of portland cement, mostly as retarder, and the remainder into agricultural and other industrial uses. Of the total gypsum sold, 75.1 per cent was in calcined products ranging from 2.6 per cent for industrial uses to 72.5 per cent as building materials. Of the total calcined uses, 22.1 per cent was for plaster while 50.4 per cent went into prefabricated gypsum products, which includes gypsum lath, wallboard, sheathing, tile, roof planking and similar products.

Authoritative published figures for gypsum plaster production in 1956 indicate that 2.9 million tons were sold or used as cementitious material. This tonnage can be estimated to have yielded approximately 400 million square yards of finished plaster. In the same year, 297 million square yards of gypsum lath was used.

Between 1935 and 1956, the total volume of gypsum produced in the United States increased more than five times. An increase occurred in all categories of use. Gypsum produced for plaster increased over this period from 1 million to 2.9 million tons.

Prices of the various gypsum products held fairly close to the same index line throughout the eight years between 1950 and 1958, and have in general, followed slightly under the "Wholesale Price Index" for all building materials published by the U. S. Government. Over the same period, the wholesale price index for gypsum materials as well as for all building materials increased more steadily than did the index for all commodities. Calculated by the Federal index, the wholesale price of gypsum since 1950 has increased 27.4 per cent.

LIME

Limestone is produced widely and is available in most states in varying amounts and qualities. In 1954 Ohio, Missouri, Pennsylvania, and Texas, in that order, led in production. A large dolomitic deposit in northern Ohio yields a very fine finishing lime. It is said to supply most of the lime used for plastering in the United States east of Denver, Colorado. The total annual tonnage of lime produced in the United States has increased from 3.4 million tons in 1930 to 8.6 million tons in 1954, an increase of 155 per cent. Over the same period there has also been some consolidation in the lime-producing industry. A total of 375 plants produced the 3.4 million tons in 1930, whereas 154 plants produced the 8.6 million tons in 1954. A large portion of the added production was sold for agricultural and industrial uses. Lime used for building purposes, including masonry mortar, constituted 35.6 per cent of total production in 1930, and 13.1 per cent of the production of 1954, while construction tonnage remained approximately the same. The wholesale price of hydrated finishing lime, as determined by the wholesale price index, has increased 20.6 per cent on tonnage price, f.o.b. plant, from January 1955 to December 1957.

SAND

Sand is usually produced in the locality of the point of use. It varies considerably in quality and physical properties from one place to another. Production statistics on a national basis are not available. Average wholesale prices of construction sand per ton, f.o.b. plant or bank, have been reported as having increased from $1.15 per ton in 1955 to $1.30 per ton in December 1957. This rise of approximately 13 per cent, appears to be in line with the

wholesale price index for all building materials during the same period.

PERLITE

Perlite in its crude form is a volcanic rock found in western United States. Production elsewhere in the world is minor and data pertaining to such production are based largely on estimates. Some production, however, is known to occur in Australia, Canada, Ireland, Italy, Japan, Mexico and New Zealand. Transportation costs substantially prohibit the expansion of international trade in perlite. Some crude perlite, however, is exported from the United States to Canada, from Ireland to England, from Italy to England and France.

In 1955 the production of crude perlite was reported by 11 companies operating 14 mines in 6 Western states. Of the total, 51.7 per cent came from New Mexico; the other producing states, in order, were Colorado, Nevada, California, Arizona and Utah. An increase in production of 117 per cent occurred between 1951 and 1955: from 154,174 tons to 335,187 tons. In 1955, 77 per cent of the expanded perlite produced was used in plaster aggregates, 13 per cent for concrete aggregate, 5 per cent for oil-well drilling muds and cementing, 1 per cent for filtering, and 4 per cent for miscellaneous purposes.

Recent reports indicate, although complete data are not available, that since 1955 the non-aggregate uses of perlite have been increasing substantially. The Perlite Institute states that in 1954 perlite was used as the aggregate of 40 per cent of all basecoat plaster, and that this percentage increased to 44 per cent in 1955, and to 53 per cent in 1957. Expanded perlite sales increased 85 per cent from 1951 to 1955. Considerable variation occurs from one area to another in published average prices of perlite. Little correlation exists between these variations and mine and plant locations. Although no conclusions can be drawn, it is apparent that the market conditions under which perlite aggregate is sold permits active fluctuations from time to time. This makes it difficult to plot price and value trends, or to establish relative indexes.

VERMICULITE

In the United States vermiculite ore is produced in quantity only at Libby, Montana, and at several sites in the northwestern part of South Carolina near Travelers Rest. Since one company owns the mines at both places, the U. S. Government does not publish production data by states, in compliance with the disclosure rule. Vermiculite ore has been found in 12 states, and at various times commercial production was carried on in 7 of them. In 1954 Arizona and Colorado were producing states but by 1955 the output was confined to Montana and South Carolina, with a small amount coming from North Carolina. Production of vermiculite outside the United States is limited to the Union of South Africa, which exports crude ore to the United States and Canada. Vermiculite is admitted duty free into the United States.

Vermiculite ore reserves at Libby, Montana, are estimated at from 25 to 100 million tons. Reserves in Colorado, presently not being worked, are estimated at about 0.5 million tons. Exact information as to the reserves in southern United States is not available but they are believed to be substantial.

Production has increased more than 1,300 times between 1926 and 1955, 12 times between 1940 and 1955, and has more than doubled since 1946. The average value per ton of vermiculite concentrates during the same period has decreased approximately 50 per cent. In 1955 it was valued at approximately one-third of the highest value reached in 1928.

Imports of vermiculite from the Union of South Africa decreased from 1950, when 16,500 tons were imported, to about 7,000 tons in 1953. Since 1953 vermiculite ore imports have increased to 10,600 tons in 1955. This amounts to about 5 per cent of the total tonnage consumed in the United States.

II. FACTORS AFFECTING COST OF LATH AND PLASTERWORK

The actual amounts paid for particular jobs of completed plasterwork have been analyzed at various times from different points of view. It has been found that costs depend on variable factors so numerous that they preclude useful mathematical formulation for the purposes of re-projection. Where a sufficiently detailed history of the work is available a specific completed job can be analyzed, and cost factors isolated and evaluated; but being an after-the-fact method, it is of little direct use in any projection more precise than an estimated cost of a job that is about to begin. Statistical data compiled from cost analyses, however, provide the body of experience information upon which such estimating judgments are based.

Various sources of this kind of information are available to those of whom such judgment is required. However, like the data given in Section III of this chapter concerning relative unit costs, these are generalized and reveal nothing of the particular conditions to be encountered in specific work. In fact, such statistics are deliberately compiled on the widest possible sample base, for the very purpose of eliminating specific and peculiar variables. Usually cancelled out are influential factors such as geography, local market conditions affecting material and labor prices, productivity, and specific job conditions. Yet, the influence of factors peculiar to a given job very often are as important to cost as the total quantities of labor and material. For example, it is obvious that a specific number of yards of finished plaster surface in a single, unbroken plane, easily accessible for the delivery of mortar, presents a vastly different construction cost situation than does an equal area in a highly subdivided or remote space. For the man concerned, then, with the probable cost of projected work, the differences between the general case represented by statistics and the particular case of his project can be compensated only by his knowledge of the nature of the factors involved, how they vary, and over what range. This section will examine some of the more important aspects of this problem and endeavor to provide an elementary base from which the quality of such judgment can develop.

COST INFORMATION AND THE ARCHITECT

The problems of cost projection vary with different purposes. In design, a special case is developed. The importance of cost prediction to any rational decision is recognized as fundamental in the selection of materials and methods of building construction. The quality of a design can be evaluated, for utilitarian purposes, only in the economic terms of cost versus performance. Even in cases where the selection is based primarily on aesthetic considerations, economics can seldom be completely ignored. Selections of materials and methods are made with the solution of particular problems in mind, and the predicted performance is measured against the requirements of this problem, with cost as the yardstick. In some cases one of these two factors may be more dominant than the other. For example, in the case of fire protection where the degree of performance is critical; or conversely, in a simple ceiling demanding only visual performance, where cost is critical.

Unlike the contractor's estimator, who usually has a completely described job before him, no very analytic method of cost projection can be employed by the designer in the early stages of his work. Clearly it would be uneconomical for an architect to produce the several complete designs that would be necessary for measurement and comparison by "take-off" methods. The designer's decisions must be based, therefore, on some preconception of costs, the accuracy of which depend in large measure upon his general knowledge of the relationships in construction cost factors. But regardless of the extent of his knowledge and the soundness of his judgment, the designer has a risk, for in all cases he gambles his own time and effort. He must find an acceptable solution within a given fixed budget on, if possible, the first trial.

For this reason there is an understandable tendency on the part of all designers to narrow the field of selection to those materials and methods the ultimate cost of which are most easily projected, and to those having variable factors not subject to influences extraneous to the designer's control. It is reasonable to assume, therefore, that the greater the designer's familiarity with a particular material or method, the greater his control and the less apt is he to be disappointed in matters of either cost or performance. Such knowledge also widens the design vocabulary and permits more effective utilization of the methods and materials selected.

ESTIMATING METHODS

There are two attributes of all cost estimating methods that are of principal interest to those obliged to rely upon them. Perhaps the most universally important of these is numerical accuracy; the other, usually of equal concern to the designer at least, is the sensitivity of the method. Sensitivity, in this case, is thought of as the facility offered by a particular method to permit quick comparison of the cost effect of the one component, condition, material or method with another.

The quantity survey method. In varying degrees of detail, the "quantity survey" method of estimating is the most commonly used. By far, the most sensitive and accurate method of estimating known today is the detailed and comprehensive quantity survey made from a complete set of building plans and specifications that usually supports a contractor's bid. The procedure requires that analysis of the work be done in terms of quantities measured in market units, labor time estimates, and a detailed study of the working conditions under which the construction will proceed. The necessity for reducing quantities to market units demands a separation of labor and material by trades and type of product. For example, cubic yards of concrete must be priced separately from the form work, and pounds of gypsum must be separated from cubic feet of aggregate. As noted before, sensitive and accurate though this method be, it is relatively useless to the designer who at the time of his decision has nothing before him to measure.

A more useful modification of the quantity survey method has been devised which can be applied at various stages of preliminary and advanced design. This method employs functional units of measurement rather than market units. That is to say, quantities are measured in units related to performance rather than to those used in purchasing or production. Examples of such units are: a square foot of finished surface, a square foot of enclosure, a square foot of floor area, a foot-candle of lighting intensity, and a ton of air conditioning refrigeration. Approaching price thus in terms of units of effectiveness relates performance to cost directly, and greatly simplifies the evaluation of information upon which a sound design decision can be based.

A major disadvantage of this method, however, is its wide variation in accuracy and sensitivity. Costs do not always vary with the quantity of functional units. Also, since this is an analytic method that requires a form of quantity survey, some design work must have been done prior to its application. The more advanced the design at the time of analysis, the more realistic the results to be expected. The most elementary cost unit of this kind is the square foot of floor area. It is widely used throughout the construction industry for rule-of-thumb estimating and appraising. The idea that the cost of a building is very closely related to the quantity of floor area is quickly disproved, however, by the realization that building unit costs when measured in this way ranged in 1959 from less than $8.00 per square foot for simple unsubdivided structures such as warehouses, to more than $30.00 per square foot for institutional buildings. From this it appears that the unit cost of floor area is more significant in measuring the utility value and efficiency of buildings than it is in predicting costs of construction.

The measurement of cubic content is another common method of statistical estimating of this form, although it is more complex and perhaps both less sensitive and less accurate than the preceding method. Like the floor area unit method, this one also chooses its units in terms of space, and the provision of space is generally recognized as the primary function of buildings. But, since space measured by volume is less closely related to utility, and has little more relation to building cost than does space measured in terms of floor area, the method is now widely considered to be inferior.

The enclosure unit method. Although not currently so widely employed as the preceding examples of statistical estimating, the use of units of enclosure has been developing in recent years as a method which is far more satisfactory to the designer. This newer approach to early cost prediction is slightly more complex than the floor area unit method. It is considerably less complex than the measurement of cubic contents, but is both more sensitive and more accurate than either. It offers the additional advantage of being applicable at almost any stage of design.

The procedure is to collect data in terms of construction costs per unit of enclosure surface (square feet or yards) of exterior walls, partitions, floors, and roofs. These units vary determinately with respect to the functional units of building space on one hand, and to the quantities of construction materials on the other. For practical purposes, the bulk of materials employed in a building constitutes its enclosure.

The convenience of this method of predicting costs is easily demonstrated. Given a sufficient amount of statistical information and a knowledge of construction cost factors, a designer can correlate cost with performance information very quickly to solve a specific problem. A man working on the design of a floor plan with enclosure cost statistics in mind, virtually envisions constantly how much money he is spending as he draws the lines indicating walls and partitions. Like the floor area unit method, however, he must understand that his line representing three lineal feet of partition, nine feet high, involves not only the quantity of three yards of plaster and partition construction, but a unit price as well, and this varies independently of the quantity. The extent of this variation must be known or assumed. Herein lies the principal need for the designer's understanding of the various factors affecting the cost of construction. However, any discrepancy that must be corrected here usually is much smaller than in the method using the quantity of floor area to measure building costs.

Plaster, although by no means limited to that function, is customarily thought of as a surfacing material. Therefore, it is measured in surface area units, usually square yards. This measure coincides closely with the quantities involved in the enclosure unit area method of projecting the costs of construction.

RELATION OF COST FACTORS PECULIAR TO LATH AND PLASTER

The unit cost of lath and plaster is influenced by (and with considerable effort might be measured in terms of) more than twenty important variables. These range from the unit prices of materials and the productivity of labor, to the cost of calendar time per unit of production. Although not completely determinate for any given projection, the variables can at least be separated into three main categories: those which are controlled or influenced primarily by acts or decisions of the architect; those controlled or affected primarily by acts or decisions of the contractor; and extraneous influences over which neither the architect nor the plastering contractor has control.

The first category above includes items which are directly affected by the other two, and vice versa. Among those so classified are the total quantity of the finished product along with such influence as this may exert on the quantity of labor and materials, the complexity and general difficulty of the work, and the degree of quality desired in the work. Those matters classified as responsibilities of the contractor are related to the resources required by the job and the utilization thereof, as well as the ultimate quality of the product. The extraneous influences noted in the third category involve market conditions and the climate and personality of the job.

Market conditions may be described as bidding procedures, the price of labor and its general productivity, material costs, and like factors. The climate and personality of the job are related to conditions such as the degree of cooperation the plastering contractor receives from other trades and the general contractor, the weather, the progress of the total work, and the physical conditions under which plastering is required to proceed. It has been said — and with some truth — that the last category has more effect on the unpredictable portion of projected costs than does either the architect or the plastering contractor.

An important pecularity of the composition of plaster costs lies in the fact that labor constitutes a large portion of the cost, amounting in almost every case to more than half the total. The cost of material ranges from less than three tenths to eight tenths of the cost of labor. A matter also important in the projection of plaster costs is the general lack of reliable information on labor productivity. A study of 32 selected cases estimated by authoritative sources indicates that while material costs vary as much as 63 per cent from the median for all cases, labor cost estimates vary only 30 per cent. It is believed that this tends to demonstrate the greater sensitivity of material estimates due to more readily available specific information. Accurate material prices for a specific condition usually are easier to obtain than are labor time estimates.

Production cost analysis. The general production equation, stated in unit costs, is as applicable to lathing and plastering as it is to other aspects of the construction industry:

$$(1) \quad d = e + f + g$$

Wherein all units are the same as the units of d (in this case, square yards of finished plaster work), and where:

d = Unit cost of the product
e = Unit cost of labor

f = Unit cost of materials

g = Unit costs of those items not varying directly with the quantities of either labor or material such as, overhead, profit, the cost of capital, etc.

The items of cost comprising the term g tend to vary more with calendar time than with the magnitude of production.

Although of limited use in estimating, this equation is valuable in production cost analysis and permits rather complete scrutiny of the fundamental factors influencing these costs.

In addition to the terms of the general equation, there are a number of subterms which permit isolation of the effects of separate factors. These are:

k = *wage rate,* or the cost of labor per unit of labor, in terms of dollars per hour.

i = *the price of materials* per unit of weight or volume.

j = the unit cost of fixed charges or *overhead* in terms of dollars per calendar day. (Note, the calendar day is taken to be a unit of quantity representing those items of cost varying with time rather than quantity of product, such as the cost of capital, rent, permanent salaries, etc.)

x = *labor productivity,* or units of product per unit of labor in terms of yards of plaster per hour.

y = *material yield* or units of product per unit of material in yards per cubic foot (where the prepared mortar is considered as the material).

r = the *progress rate* or fixed cost yield in terms of units of product per calendar day.

s = *labor application rate* or total labor per calendar day, in man-hours per day.

t = *material consumption rate* or units of material used per calendar day in cubic feet per day.

Some of the ratios given above bear direct relationship to e, f, and g of equation (1):

$$(2)\ e = \frac{k}{x} \qquad (3)\ f = \frac{i}{y} \qquad (4)\ g = \frac{j}{r}$$

When the ratios listed above are given numerical values and substituted in equation (1) and applied to a specific case of production, some information can be had fairly quickly as to the relative importance of the several factors. It will be noted that the last five ratios: x, y, r, s, and t involve quantities only and are in no way related to prices. In this analysis these are of greatest interest since they represent factors more susceptible to the control of the architect and the plastering contractor than do the ratios involving price. There are three general expressions which state the relationship of the quantity ratios to each other:

$$(5)\ x = \frac{r}{s} \qquad (6)\ x = \frac{yt}{s} \qquad (7)\ y = \frac{r}{t}$$

To demonstrate the use of these formulas, let us assume that a lathing and plastering contractor estimates that a certain job of plastering will cost $2.02 per square yard. He estimates labor at $1.20, material at $0.56, and his overhead at $0.26, all per square yard. The contractor based his estimate on these data:

(k) The average of all wages, $3.00 per hour.

(x) The over-all average productivity of labor, 2.5 yards per hour. (The quantity of completed plasterwork divided by total man-hours employed.)

(i) Material prices average $0.785 per cubic foot of mortar.

(y) Material yield, 1.4 square yards of finished plaster per cubic foot of mortar.

(j) Overhead, $26.00 per day.

(r) The rate of production, 100 square yards of completed plasterwork per day.

(s) Average labor employment, 40 man-hours per day.

(t) Material consumption, 71.5 cubic feet of mortar per day.

For the purpose of simplification, we can assume that the contractor has considerable freedom with respect to specifications and job conditions. In this way we can more fully examine various opportunities open to the contractor to produce his job for more, or less, than his estimate.

Substituting price and quantity ratios in equation (1):

$$(8) \quad d = \frac{k}{x} + \frac{i}{y} + \frac{i}{r}$$

It can be seen in equation (8) that the price of labor and labor productivity are in the first term, the price of material and the material yield are in the second, and the price of overhead and the rate of progress are in the third. It should also be noted that the cost of plastering per yard varies directly with prices and inversely with the quantity rates. As mentioned before, the quantity rates — x, y, and r — are more sensitive to management control than are prices. The prices — k, i and j — vary in straight line relationship with d, d increasing as the prices increase. The terms involving only quantities — x, y, and r — however, vary in curvalinear relationship with d, with d decreasing at a decreasing rate, as x, y and r increase. (See Fig. 1.)

Productivity of labor. Suppose now the contractor discovers his labor productivity rate is not the same as his estimate. He had not changed the average number of labor hours applied per day and his material yield was as anticipated, making s and y constant in the equation. Although the plaster thickness remains as specified, he finds the job is producing only two yards of finished plaster per man-hour instead of the two and one half he had expected. This means, according to the first term of equation (8), that labor is now costing $1.50 per square yard instead of the estimated $1.20. This increases the cost of production by at least $0.30 per square yard. However, the influence of this decrease in productivity does not affect the labor item alone. It affects the overhead term as well because the anticipated progress per day cannot be maintained. To find the total difference this deficit of ½ yard per man-hour means, it is necessary to express g of the general equation in terms of x. This done, the equation reads

$$(9) \quad d = \frac{k}{x} + \frac{l}{y} + \frac{i}{xs}$$

Assuming that all terms except x — labor productivity — are constant at the values estimated by the contractor, the equation can be reduced to

$$(10) \quad d = \frac{3.62}{x} + .56$$

Substituting the new value of 2 for x in equation (10), we find that d now equals $2.38 per yard, or $0.36 per yard more than the contractor had estimated the plasterwork would cost. Substituting various values of x from 1.6 to 4.6 will show, as in Fig. 1, the cost of plaster per square yard in place to range from $1.35 to $2.82. Therefore, if by mechanization, or other means, the contractor is able to vary labor productivity from 1.6 to approximately three times, or 4.6 yards per hour per man, a saving of $1.47 per yard will result.

Material yield. Another case can be described by assuming that the contractor's labor productivity turned out to be what he expected, but that he decided to reduce the thickness of plaster originally intended for the job. He thereby increased the yield from 1.4 to 2.0 square yards of finished plaster per cubic foot of mortar supplied. It can be shown by calculations similar to the preceding example that theoretically this decision would reduce the cost of plastering to $1.43 per square yard. This is a saving of $0.59 per yard or approximately 29.2 per cent, for an increase in yield of 43 per cent.

As in the case of the labor productivity rate, a variation in material yield affects more than one term of the general equation (1). In fact, the yield (y), as it varies, affects all three terms if labor productivity (x), the amount of labor employed per day (s), and the amount of material consumed (t), are held constant while the progress rate (r), is allowed to vary in some relation to y. Relating x and r to y and substituting in equation (8), produces an equation expressing the full effect y as a function of d.

$$(11) \quad d = \frac{ks}{yt} + \frac{i}{y} + \frac{j}{yt}$$

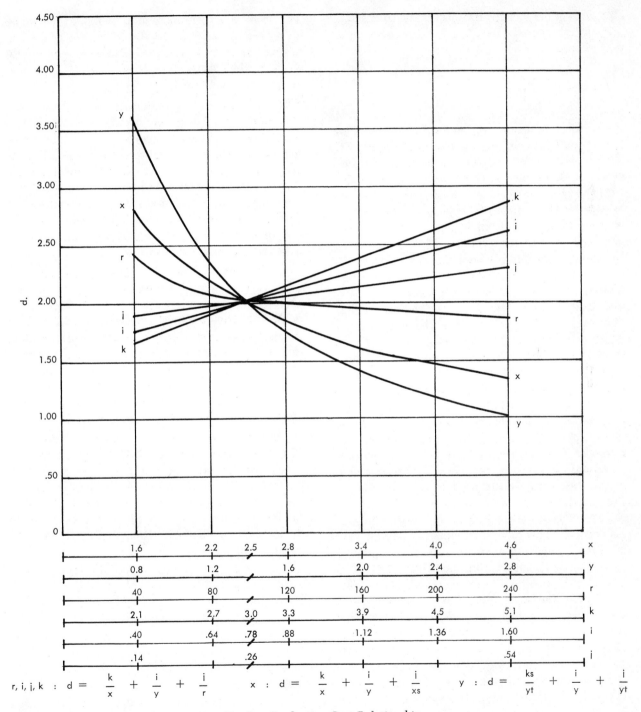

Fig. 1 — Production Cost Relationships

Substituting the numerical values of the contractor's original estimate for k, s, t, i and j reduces equation (11) to

$$(12) \quad d = \frac{2.83}{y}$$

By substituting a range of values for y in equation (12), it can be shown that the cost of plastering will vary downward from $3.52 to $1.01 per square yard as the yield is increased from .08 to 2.8 square yards of plaster per cubic foot of mortar. This approximates the range to be expected between two-coat plastering and a 2 inch solid plaster partition, and represents a cost reduction of 71 per cent for a material reduction of about the same amount.

It may be noted in Fig. 1, that the curve representing values of d for values of y through the range described above, indicates that the yield in finished plasterwork of a cubic foot of mortar has a greater effect on cost than labor productivity, or any other factor. This contrast, however, is more exaggerated in theory than in fact; for the form of the production cost equation used here is not sufficiently sensitive to compensate for the effect of that work such as straightening and finishing which is common to plaster of any thickness. It is important also to recognize that the contractor seldom has optional control of the thickness of plaster within so wide a range, this being usually fixed by specification.

Progress rate. The rate of progress of the job also has a significant influence on the unit cost of finished plasterwork. This rate (r in equation 8) can vary in several ways: by an increase in labor productivity (x); by an increase in yield (y), or by an increase in the number of men employed at one time (s). If the variation in r is due to a variation in x or y, the effect on unit cost (d) is similar to that represented on the chart by the curves for x and y. However, if material yield and labor productivity are unchanged and progress is speeded by adding hands to the job, only the overhead item of cost is affected (g in equation 1). The curve on the chart in Fig. 1 labeled r represents values of d for values

of r from 40 to 240 man-hours per day. It will be seen that by this method the contractor can range his cost from $2.41 downward to $1.87 per square yard. By increasing manpower six times, a reduction of 22.4 per cent in cost is effected.

Effect of prices. As mentioned previously, neither the contractor, the owner, nor the architect are in a position to influence labor or material prices to any great extent, as compared with the influence they can exert on quantities. Nevertheless, these are variable factors which do have a bearing on ultimate cost, and as such are of interest. On the chart in Fig. 1 we see the relationship between the unit cost of plasterwork and variations in the unit price of labor, material and overhead.

The curve labeled k represents the price of labor varying up and down from the $3.00 per hour that the contractor expected to pay. This factor is likely to have a slightly greater effect than other prices on unit cost over normal ranges of variation, due to the proportionately large share of the total cost usually contributed by labor. As the price of labor decreases 58.8 per cent, from $5.10 to $2.10 per hour, the cost of the product decreases 42 per cent, from $2.86 to $1.66 per square yard.

Similarly, as the price of material i decreases 75 per cent, from $1.60 to $0.40 per cubic yard, the cost of the product decreases 32.7 per cent, from $2.60 to $1.75 per square yard. And as the price of overhead decreases 75 per cent from $54.00 to $14.00 per calendar day, so the cost of the product decreases 17.4 per cent, from $2.30 to $1.90 per square yard.

Other studies can be made with the formulas given which will be of interest in varying degrees for different purposes. The reader may explore the various cost aspects of lath and plastering production to any extent he desires. When this has been done, undoubtedly the fact will remain that plastering production, if not lathing also, is largely a materials handling problem. Since the materials are relatively inexpensive in relation to cost of handling, the quantity handled and the efficiency with which it is accomplished is of major importance to the economics of their use in construction.

Economic effect of calendar time. As noted, an increase in the progress rate — which is to say a decrease in calendar time per job — does not have so dramatic an effect on the unit cost of plasterwork as does a variation in labor productivity or material yield. Nevertheless, it is a factor of great significance, the influence of which goes far beyond the unit production cost of plastering itself. Since the fixed charges are related strongly to calendar time, calendar conservation is of economic interest not only to the plastering contractor but to the general contractor and the building owner as well. To the contractor it is important because the possible variation in the total cost of the job due to a variation in calendar time can easily be larger than the profit margin in competitive work; and to the owner because the lack of possession of his building during the construction period denies him the return on his investment.

The period of calendar time consumed in lathing and plastering work is particularly critical with respect to the general schedule of construction, because usually in those areas of a building where this work is being done the space is completely occupied. Circulation is blocked, materials cannot be stored, and few other trades can work during this period. Although it may not be generally recognized in the competitive market, a fast plastering job is worth more money per yard to the general contractor and to the owner than a slower one of the same quality.

One way in which the effect of calendar time consumed by the lathing and plastering can be minimized in a general construction schedule, is in multi-function uses of the materials. When these trades are performing more than merely the function of finishing the walls of a building, the time allotted to them affects the total job progress rate more favorably. For example, when solid plaster partitions are used in lieu of partition work framed by other trades, the lather and the plasterer are subdividing the space at the same time they are finishing it. Thus they contribute more to total progress during the same calendar period. This is also true with plaster exterior curtain walls, membrane fireproofing, and many other uses of plasterwork.

Again, the economic value of telescoping the building schedule in this way is not always recognized or understood in competitive bidding and the plastering contractor is often not fully credited with this facility of his trade. Nevertheless, exploitation of this opportunity has a favorable influence on the over-all economics of building.

Operations of lathing and plastering. The foregoing analysis of cost factors is, of course, theoretical, and is meant to serve only as a guide to the general nature of plastering cost structure. Labor, being currently the major component of plastering costs, involves human beings and not machines. This condition limits the probabilities of correlation between general productivity experience and specific performance. As a statistic, labor productivity is not a completely satisfactory yardstick by which to measure the performance of persons, or particular teams of persons, in the several varied operations involved in lathing and plastering. First of all, these trades depend on proficiency for the quality of performance; therefore, the available skill varies with the individual workman according to his particular experience and talents. The average productivity rate, important though it is in the ultimate analysis of costs, tells the estimator very little about the difference in quality of one man's work from that of another, or how one will react to a job condition in relation to another. Moreover, since the actual productivity of an individual mechanic seldom varies directly with the yardage of completed plaster, verification of data for statistical purposes is very difficult. As will be seen below, only two of the five operations directly relate to finished area as labor quantity is concerned.

Lathing and plastering work can be divided into five fundamental operations, where in each case labor productivity varies with different units. These operations are:

(1) The *set-up*, which includes the mixing plant, material storage facilities, scaffold erection, moving, tearing down, and the cleaning up of the job.

(2) *Installation or preparation of the base,* which includes lathing, systems erection, special treatments for masonry, and concrete.

(3) The *production of mortar,* which includes materials handling, formulation, mixing, and delivery to the point of use.

(4) *Application or lay-on,* which is the operation of applying the material to the base, either manually or mechanically.

(5) *Straightening and finishing,* which includes rodding, darbying, troweling, and floating.

Not only does the labor productivity vary differentially in these five categories; so do other factors that affect costs. It can be seen that in the set-up, the cost of labor is related to the size of the job to some extent but not entirely. It costs nearly as much to set-up for a job that will employ four men for three days as it does if the job lasts a week or more.

To some extent the cost of scaffolding is related to the floor area of the space being plastered as well as to the number of times the scaffold must be moved. Take, for example, a clear area, rectangular in shape, 10 yards wide by 30 yards long, having a total ceiling area of 300 yards. Consider the alternate costs of scaffolding the whole area at one time against, say, three stages of 100 yards each. Two fundamental production operations are involved. One is the handling of the pieces in erecting or dismantling; the other is the transportation of the pieces from one place to another.

A simple calculation demonstrates the comparison. Assume the number of pieces vary directly with the area of the scaffolding and, for convenience, say there is one piece of scaffolding for each square yard of ceiling area. Now if the scaffolding is erected in three successive stages and finally re-moved from the building, a total of 600 pieces will have been handled, and each transported an average distance of 95 yards. If the entire area is scaffolded at once, exactly the same number of pieces have been handled but each has been transported an average of 45 yards. It will be noted that while there may be a savings in transportation costs, more scaffolding material is required for the single stage operation. This would be expected to produce an offsetting cost of some determinable amount.

The cost of a plaster base depends on the complexity of the system, and the number of accessories, as well as on the amount of yardage involved. The cost of mortar at the board depends as much, if not more, on the cost of delivery as on the cost of mixing; so that regardless of the yield, the cost of a cubic foot of mortar under one condition can be doubled or more in another. For example, mortar being delivered manually to a high scaffold from a remote mixing plant can require as many as eight or nine times the tending labor that would be required for the mechanical delivery of mortar to a point near the mixer. Also, the cost of mortar at the board varies, to some extent, with the quality of the mix and the materials used. However, the difference in cost between a sanded basecoat plaster mixed in proportions of one part gypsum to two parts sand, and one mixed in proportions of one to three, is considerably less than $0.10 per cubic foot, and even less than that per square yard of finished plaster.

The application of plaster to the base is fundamentally a materials handling operation. Its cost in both labor and material varies more directly with the volume and physical properties of the mortar than with the amount of surface area plastered. For example, the lighter weight mortars require less expenditure of energy per unit of volume to apply than denser mortars.

Application of those mortars of high plasticity and good working characteristics can also be expected to require less labor than stiff or sticky plasters, but by far the greatest factor in the cost of application is the total quantity of mortar handled. As noted previously, the productivity of labor of application, when measured in terms of square yards of finished plaster per man-hour, is most affected by plaster thickness. When plastering machines are used, a similar relationship between volume of mortar and productivity exists.

The cost of straightening and finishing, like the cost of the plaster base, is related more directly to the amount of surface area than are the other operations. Even here, however, there are interfering factors. The number of angles or other interruptions in plane, and the size of the space to be plastered, can be equally as important as the quantity of surface area. In large spaces of simple surface, the time required to straighten and finish is more closely related to the quantity of surface than are smaller, more complicated spaces. For example, contrast hotel or hospital bedrooms of 400 square feet or less that include window reveals, dropped beams and closets, with the condition prevailing in a clear store space of 10,000 square feet or more. In the latter, the theoretical production cost formula explained elsewhere in this section might be applied with considerable accuracy in its simplest form. In the former, a very complex and expanded formula would be required to analyze production costs in terms of plastered area.

III. COSTS OF LATH AND PLASTER IN PLACE

As explained in Section II of this chapter, during the preliminary phases of the design of a building the relationships of economic factors in construction are an important consideration. This section will provide a means whereby the order of costs of various lathing and plastering systems and assemblies can be ascertained by comparison during the advanced design period, at the time specific materials and methods are being selected.

The tabulation and publication of lathing and plastering costs, directly in terms of dollars per unit, appears to have little, if any, value. The number of variables influencing the in-place cost of plaster is large enough to cause wide price variations from one job to another within a relatively small geographical area. Shipping costs of materials, size of shipment, local labor rates, productivity, individual organization conditions, and similar factors will be reflected in the going general price of lathing and plastering. With some effort these variations can be calculated and used for estimating purposes. However, a number of other considerations will influence the cost of specific work, that are neither so general nor so easily calculated. For example, we can expect a square yard of plaster placed on the twentieth floor of an office building will cost more than one on the first floor of a school, because of the additional transportation required to deliver mortar to the point of use. But *how much* more? A nationwide survey of lathing and plastering contractors conducted for this study, revealed that as a result of this single factor, price variations of 4 per cent to 6 per cent are not uncommon. The size and shape of the individual rooms also affect the cost of lathing and plastering. Also, local in-place costs are influenced by the availability of skilled labor, labor productivity, accepted standards of quality, local preferences for specific materials or assemblies, and the quality of the relationship to be anticipated between the plastering and lathing contractor and the general contractor, or the architect and the owner. With regard to the last factor, lathing and plastering contractors have reported that it has been necessary to increase their bid price as much as 10 per cent as a result of adverse previous experience with particular architects and general contractors who are unfair, unrealistic, or negligent in the conduct of work. If we add the cost variables attending these job conditions to those of a more general nature that are taken into account in averaged price statistics, the variation becomes too broad to be useful in evaluating design selections. For this reason the cost information presented in the tables that follow makes no attempt to supply in-place prices. Rather, they are meant to establish a more useful comparison of costs for various systems and materials which can be readily related to the performance data found in other sections of this book.

Quantities — units of measurement. Depending upon the character of the work, the units of measurement used in estimating lathing and plastering quantities are generally stated in square yards or in lineal feet. This tabulation indicates the units that are used most frequently:

Lathing and plastering — general	Sq. Yds. of finished surface
Columns and beams	Lin. Feet Or Sq. Feet of finished surface Per Lin. Ft.
Trim, casings, beads, etc.	Lin. Feet.
Metal base	Lin. Feet.
Cornerite, strip lath	Lin. Feet.
Channels, furring	Lin. Feet.
Metal studs	Lin. Feet.

Plaster coverage or yield. The amount of material required to cover a surface depends upon the type of cementitious material, aggregate, amount of mixing water used, base to which plaster is applied, thickness of plaster required, and method by which the plaster is applied. A table of yields for various plasters and the amount of coverage that can be expected over different bases is included in Chapter 3.

Lathing and plastering materials. Table I lists various basic lathing and plastering materials, their sizes, their weights, and the manner in which they are packaged and sold. It is suggested that, as items are priced locally, the right-hand column of this table be filled in and maintained for cost reference.

LATHING AND PLASTERING COST INDEX

Labor. The amount of labor required to place any given amount of lath and plaster varies with the quality of workmanship required, the materials be-

ing used, the specific type of assembly fabricated, the job mechanic's effort and other factors discussed elsewhere in this chapter. Productivity figures are often quoted for "standard" or "average" quality work.

The unqualified use of such data frequently can be misleading. The amount of labor actually required to place lath and plaster to a considerable extent is determined by the degree of perfection demanded in the final product. A finished lathing and plastering job that is considered "standard" in one region might be classified "fair" to "poor" in another, or when judged by different observers.

The amount of plaster that can be applied in a given time varies according to the method used for placing it. It is generally thought that the mechanical placement of plaster significantly increases labor productivity. One leading exponent of this method has noted that under average conditions from 50 per cent to 100 per cent more plaster can be placed per man-day by machine than by hand.

Preliminary selection and cost estimation of lathing and plastering systems and assemblies. The series of tables that follow have been compiled to provide an "order of costs," for purposes of comparison, of the most frequently used lathing and plastering systems and assemblies. Costs are presented in index form rather than as prices. If reliable local price information is available on one or more assemblies, a unit price can be ascertained for other systems in the index. The chart in Fig. 2 and the explanation accompanying it describe the procedure for making this calculation. In most cases, the unit prices that are established by use of the index will be found adequate for budget estimating purposes, and generally will fall within 10 per cent of average going prices in a particular locality. Strong local preference for, or familiarity with, a particular system usually will result in the lowering of the local index value for that system, but generally will not affect the over-all order of costs.

Table I
Lathing and Plastering Materials

Material	Size	Weight or Gage	Packaged	Unit of Quantity	Local Cost
Gypsum Lath*					
Plain	16"x48"				
	⅜" Thick	14#/Yd²	6/Bdl.	M.S.F.	$_____
	½" Thick	19#/Yd²	6/Bdl.	M.S.F.	$_____
Perforated	16"x48"				
	⅜" Thick	14#/Yd²	6/Bdl.	M.S.F.	$_____
	½" Thick	19#/Yd²	6/Bdl.	M.S.F.	$_____
Foil Backed	16"x48"				
	⅜" Thick	14#/Yd²	6/Bdl.	M.S.F.	$_____
	½" Thick	19#/Yd²	6/Bdl.	M.S.F.	$_____
Long Length					
Plain	24" Wide	19#/Yd²	----	M.S.F.	$_____
	½" Thick				
	up to				
Foil Backed	12' Long	19#/Yd²	----	M.S.F.	$_____
Metal Lath					
Diamond Mesh					
Copper Bearing Painted	27"x96"	2.5#/Yd²	10/Bdl.	100 Yd²	$_____
	24"x96"	3.4#/Yd²	9/Bdl.	100 Yd²	$_____
Galvanized	27"x96"	3.4#/Yd²	10/Bdl.	100 Yd²	$_____
	24"x96"		9/Bdl.	100 Yd²	
Ribbed-Expanded					
⅛" Flat-Rib	24"x96"	2.75#/Yd²	10/Bdl.	100 Yd²	$_____
	or				
	27"x96"	3.4#/Yd²	10/Bdl.	100 Yd²	$_____
⅜" Rib	24"x96"	3.4#/Yd²	10/Bdl.	100 Yd²	$_____
	or				
	27"x96"	4.0#/Yd²	10/Bdl.	100 Yd²	$_____
¾" Rib	24"	0.60#/Ft²	6/Bdl.	100 Yd²	$_____
	or 29" Wide	0.75#/Ft²	10/Bdl.	100 Yd²	$_____
	8', 10' or				
	12' Long				
Sheet Lath	24"x96"	4.5#/Yd²	9/Bdl.	100 Yd²	$_____
	or	5, 6.3 and	6/Bdl.		
		7.56#/Yd²	10/Bdl.		
	27"x96"	4.5#/Yd²			

* Standard for West Coast Region — 16 1/5" x 48" Packaged 5/Bdl.

Table I (continued)

Material	Size	Weight or Gage	Packaged	Unit of Quantity	Local Cost
Stucco Mesh					
Copper Bearing Painted	24"x96"	1.8#/Yd²	10/Bdl.	100 Yd²	$_____
	27"x96"	or			
	or				
	48"x96"	3.6#/Yd²	5 and 10/Bdl.	100 Yd²	$_____
Lathing Accessories**					
Base Screeds (Galvanized)					
Plain					
Standard Flange Expanded Flange	10' Long	26 Ga.	50 Pc/Ctn	M.L.F.	$_____
Curved Point	10'	26 Ga.	50 Pc/Ctn	M.L.F.	$_____
Casing Beads (Galvanized)					
Quarter Round					
Short Flange	½", ¾", ⅞"	24 Ga.	80 or 60 Pcs/Ctn	M.L.F.	$_____
Expanded Flange	½", ¾"	24 Ga.	7' or 10' Long	M.L.F.	$_____
Square					
Short Flange	½", ¾", ⅞"	24 Ga.	80 or 60 Pcs/Ctn	M.L.F.	$_____
Expanded Flange	½", ¾"	24 Ga.	7' or 10' Long	M.L.F.	$_____
Modified Square					
Short Flange	½", ¾", ⅞"	24 Ga.	80 or 60 Pcs/Ctn	M.L.F.	$_____
Expanded Flange	½", ¾"	24 Ga.	7' or 10' Long	M.L.F.	$_____
Channels — Cold-Rolled					
¾"		0.30#/Lf	20/Bdl.	M.L.F.	$_____
1½"	16' or 20' Long	0.47#/Lf	10/Bdl.	M.L.F.	$_____
2"		0.59#/Lf	10/Bdl.	M.L.F.	$_____
Corner Beads (Galvanized)					
Small Nose					
Standard Flange	7', 8', 9', 10'		560', 640',	M.L.F.	$_____
Wide Flange (2½")	or	26 Ga.	540', 600',	M.L.F.	$_____
Expanded Flange	12' Long		or 720' Per Ctn	M.L.F.	$_____

** Packages are listed as examples only since practice varies between manufacturers.

Table I (continued)

Material	Size	Weight or Gage	Packaged	Unit of Quantity	Local Cost
¾″ Bullnose					
Standard Flange	Similar to	26 Ga.	Similar to	M.L.F.	$_____
Wide Flange (2½″)	Small Nose		Small Nose	M.L.F.	$_____
Expanded Flange	Corner Beads		Corner Beads	M.L.F.	$_____
1½″ Bullnose	Similar to	26 Ga.	Similar to	M.L.F.	$_____
	Small Nose		Small Nose		
	Corner Beads		Corner Beads		
Expansion Joints					
½″ Grounds			24 Pc/Ctn	M.L.F.	$_____
¾″ Grounds	10′ Long			M.L.F.	$_____
⅞″ Grounds				M.L.F.	$_____
Cornerite (Expanded)					
2″x2″	96″ Long	2.5#/Yd²	75 Pc/Ctn	M.L.F.	$_____
3″x3″	96″ Long	2.5#/Yd.²	75 Pc/Ctn	M.L.F.	$_____
Metal Base and Accessories					
2½″	10′ Long	18 and 20 Ga.	10-26/Bdl.	M.L.F.	$_____
3″	10′ Long	18 and 20 Ga.	10-26/Bdl.	M.L.F.	$_____
Channel Floor Runner	10′ Long		100/Bdl.	M.L.F.	$_____
"L" and "Z" Type Ceiling Runners	10′ Long	Varies	25/Bdl.	M.L.F.	$_____
"Prong" Type Ceiling Runners	10′ Long	Varies	6/Bdl.	M.L.F.	$_____
Metal Studs and Track					
1⅝″			10 Pc/Bdl.	M.L.F.	$_____
2½″			10 Pc/Bdl.	M.L.F.	$_____
3¼″	Lengths As		10 Pc/Bdl.	M.L.F.	$_____
4″	Required	Varies	10 Pc/Bdl.	M.L.F.	$_____
6″			6 Pc/Bdl.	M.L.F.	$_____
Picture Moulding					
Concealed (Galvanized)	10′	26 Ga.	50 Pc/Ctn	M.L.F.	$_____
Strip Lath Expanded					
4″	96″ Long	2.5#/Yd²	75 Pc/Ctn	M.L.F.	$_____
6″	96″ Long	2.5#/Yd²	75 Pc/Ctn	M.L.F.	$_____

Table I (continued)

Material	Size	Weight or Gage	Packaged	Unit of Quantity	Local Cost
Aggregates					
Lightweight	——	——	4 cf. bg.	cf., bg.	$_____
Sand	——	——	——	Ton	$_____
Cementitious Materials					
Basecoat Plasters					
Gypsum (Neat)	——	——	100# Sack	Ton	$_____
Gypsum-Wood Fiber	——	——	100# Sack	Ton	$_____
Gypsum (Lightweight					
Aggregate) Ready-Mix	——	——	80# Sack	Ton	$_____
Gypsum Bond Plaster	——	——	100# Sack	Ton	$_____
Fibered Hydrated Lime	——	——	50# Sack	Ton	$_____
Finish Plasters					
Gypsum Gauging Plaster	——	——	100# Sack	Ton	$_____
Gypsum Gaug. High Strength	——	——	100# Sack	Ton	$_____
Gypsum Trowel Finish	——	——	100# Sack	Ton	$_____
Keene's Cement	——	——	100# Sack	Ton	$_____
Colored Finish					
Interior	——	——	100# Sack	Ton	$_____
Exterior	——	——	100# Sack	Ton	$_____
Finishing Hydrated Lime					
Unfibered	——	——	50# Sack	Ton	$_____

The data included in the tables have been compiled from the results of a nationwide survey of lathing and plastering contractors that was conducted on a selected sample basis. The results were checked and to some extent adjusted by averaging authoritative published estimating statistics.

Use of the tables. Unless otherwise specifically indicated, the order of costs is based upon the following constant factors:

Partitions are complete systems, plastered on both sides and have a 2½″ metal base on each side.

In taking off quantities consider the area of one side only.

Ceiling-wall furring. Structural components of the building have not been considered. The index value shown includes only those materials and methods employed by the lathing and plastering trades. The rating does include the attachment of hangers and furring devices.

Plaster.

a. Gypsum — A gypsum-sand plaster (1:2½) applied ½″ thick over gypsum lath

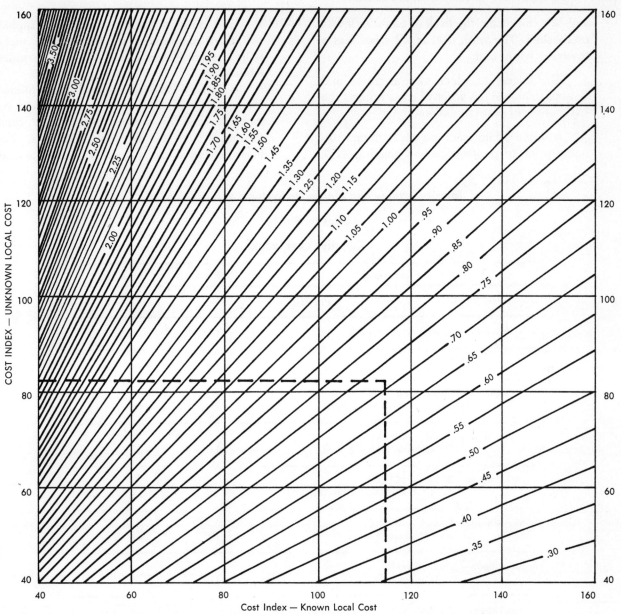

EXAMPLE: The cost of a 2″ Studless Metal Lath Solid Partition in a given locality is $550. per 100 Sq. Yds. and its Index Value is 114. To determine the cost of a suspended ceiling having an Index Value of 82 (1½″R.C. @ 3′0″O.C.; ¾″F.C. @ 13½″O.C.; 3.4 #M.L.) in this same locality:
1. Enter the graph above at a Cost Index of 114 on the Known Local Cost scale.
2. Enter the graph at a Cost Index of 82 on the Unknown Local Cost scale.
3. These lines intersect between the .70 & .75 Lines of the Translation Factor scale, giving a Translation Factor of approx. .72.
4. Using the formula: Known Local Cost X Trans. Factor = Unknown Local Cost. The suspended ceiling described above could be expected to cost approximately 550 X .72 = $380. per 100 sq. yds.

Fig. 2 — Local Cost Translation Factor

and ¾″ thick from the back of metal lath was established. The finish coat in all cases was a troweled white coat.

The degree to which various mixes and finishes influence the order of costs follows the basic order of cost tabulations.

b. Lime — Lime-sand plaster with or without gypsum or portland cement gauging. (1:3,

1:4 lime putty to sand by volume). Applied ¾″ thick measured from the back of metal lath. The finish coat in all cases is a troweled white coat.

c. Lime — Portland cement-sand plaster. Mixed 1:1:6, 2:1:9, lime putty to portland cement to sand by volume applied ¾″ thick measured from the back of metal lath. The finish coat in all cases is a troweled white coat.

Interior Lathing and Plastering Systems and Assemblies

Gypsum Plaster

Relative Cost Index

System or Assembly	Cost Index	Local Cost
Partitions		
2″ Solid. Long Length Gypsum Lath	100	$_____
2″ Solid Studless. ⅜″ Rib Lath @ 3.4#	to	$_____
2″ Solid. ¾″ Channel Studs — 16″ O.C. 3.4# Diamond Mesh Metal Lath	126	$_____
Wood Studs — 2″ x 4″ — 16″ O.C. ⅜″ Gypsum Lath — Nailed	110	$_____
Wood Studs — 2″ x 4″ — 16″ O.C. ⅜″ Gypsum Lath — Clip Attached	to	$_____
Wood Studs — 2″ x 4″ — 16″ O.C. 3.4# Diamond Mesh Lath	135	$_____
Steel Studs — (2½″) 16″ O.C. ⅜″ Gypsum Lath	114	$_____
Steel Studs — (2½″) 16″ O.C. 3.4# Diamond Mesh Lath	to	$_____
Steel Studs — (3¼″) 16″ O.C. ⅜″ Gypsum Lath	137	$_____
Steel Studs — (3¼″) 16″ O.C. 3.4# Diamond Mesh Lath		$_____

System or Assembly	Cost Index	Local Cost
Gypsum Tile — 3″	118	$_____
Lightweight Concrete Partition Block — 4″	142	$_____

Contact Ceiling Systems (Cost of Joists Not Included)

System or Assembly	Cost Index	Local Cost
Wood Joists — 16″ O.C. ⅜″ Gypsum Lath — Nailed	42	$_____
Wood Joists — 16″ O.C. ⅜″ Gypsum Lath — Clip Attached	to	$_____
Wood Joists — 16″ O.C. 3.4# Diamond Mesh Lath	55	$_____
Steel Joists — 24″ O.C. ⅜″ Rib Lath Tied to Joist	57	$_____
Steel Joists — 24″ O.C. ¾″ Channels 16″ O.C. Tied to Joists ⅜″ Gypsum Lath — Clip Attached	to	$_____
Steel Joists — 24″ O.C. ¾″ Channels 16″ O.C. Tied to Joists 3.4# Diamond Mesh Lath	70	$_____

Radiant Heat Systems (Cost of Joists, Tubing Not Included)

System or Assembly	Cost Index	Local Cost
Wood Joists — 16″ O.C. Tubing Placed *Below* Lath ⅜″ Gypsum Lath — Nailed Plaster (⅜″ Min. Cover From Bottom of Tube)	57 to	$_____
Wood Joists — 16″ O.C. Tubing Placed *Below* Lath 3.4# Diamond Mesh Lath Plaster (⅜″ Min. Cover From Bottom of Tube)	74	$_____
Wood Joists — 16″ O.C. Tubing Placed *Above* Lath 3.4# Diamond Mesh Lath (Tubing Embedded at Least ½ Dia. in Plaster Above Lath)	57 to 74	$_____

System or Assembly	Cost Index	Local Cost

Suspended Ceiling Systems

System or Assembly	Cost Index	Local Cost

1½″ Main Runner Channels — 3′-0″ O.C.
   ¾″ Furring Channels — 13½″ O.C.
   3.4# Diamond Mesh Lath
	71	$_____

1½″ Main Runner Channels — 3′-0″ O.C.
   ¾″ Furring Channels — 16″ O.C.
   ⅜″ Plain Gypsum Lath
	to	$_____

1½″ Main Runner Channels — 3′-0″ O.C.
   ¾″ Furring Channels — 24″ O.C.
   ⅜″ Rib Lath 3.4#
	80	$_____

If Holes must be drilled in concrete or tile ceilings in order to attach hangers, increase the cost index 6 points.

If ¾″ furring channels are spaced on centers other than 13½″ revise the cost index as follows:

12″ O.C. Spacing............................	Deduct 2 Points
16″ O.C. Spacing............................	Deduct 4 Points
24″ O.C. Spacing............................	Deduct 6 Points

Furred Wall Systems

System or Assembly	Cost Index	Local Cost

¾″ Furring Channels — 16″ O.C.
   3.4# Diamond Mesh Lath
   2½″ Metal Base
	79	$_____

	to	

¾″ Furring Channels — 16″ O.C.
   ⅜″ Gypsum Lath
   2½″ Metal Base
	84	$_____

Fireproofing Dropped Beams

System or Assembly	Cost Index	Local Cost
⅜″ Channel Furring Bent Around Beam and Tied To Ceiling Furring. Beam Projects Below Ceiling Line. 3.4# Metal Lath and ¾″ Plaster.	110	$_____

System or Assembly	Cost Index	Local Cost
Fireproofing Free Standing Columns		
Self-Furring Metal Lath and ¾″ Plaster	81	$_____
⅜″ Gypsum Lath Surrounding Column-tied. ½″ Plaster.	to	$_____
¾″ Furring Channels, 3.4# Metal Lath, ¾″ Plaster.	109	$_____

Interior Plaster

Alternate Specifications

Gypsum Plaster

Basecoat Plasters
If lightweight plaster is specified in lieu of sanded plaster, increase the cost index as follows:

⅞″ Grounds...................................	4 Points
⅝″ Grounds...................................	3 Points
½″ Grounds...................................	2 Points

If gypsum-wood fiber plaster is specified in lieu of gypsum-sand plaster, increase the cost index as follows:

⅞″ Grounds...................................	8 Points
½″ Grounds...................................	6 Points

If the thickness of the basecoat plaster is increased beyond standard thickness, for each additional ¼″ of plaster increase the cost index as follows:

Sanded Plaster...............................	6 Points
Lightweight Plaster........................	8 Points
Wood Fiber Plaster........................	12 Points

Finish Plasters
If a finish coat other than a troweled lime white coat is used, revise the cost index by the following:

½″ Acoustic Plaster...............Add	6 Points
Lime-Keene's-Sand (No Color) Float...........Subtract	4 Points
Lime-Keene's-Sand (Integral Color) Float...........Add	4 Points
Gypsum Trowel Finish.........Add	3 Points

Interior Plaster (continued)

Bond Plaster

The cost index for 3-coat gypsum plaster over roughened concrete or masonry

(Scratch coat: bond plaster-neat
Brown coat: gypsum-sand
Finish coat: lime white float)
⅝″ Grounds.................................... 34 Points

Interior Lathing and Plastering

Systems and Assemblies

Lime or Lime-Portland Cement Plaster

System or Assembly	Cost Index	Local Cost
Partitions		
2″ Solid Studless. ⅜″ Rib Lath @ 3.4#		$_____
2″ Solid ¾″ Channel Studs — 16″ o.c. 3.4# Diamond Mesh Metal Lath		$_____
Wood Studs — 2″x4″ — 16″ o.c. 3.4# Diamond Mesh Lath	°	$_____
Steel Studs —(2½″) 16″ o.c. 3.4# Diamond Mesh Lath		$_____
Steel Studs — (3¼″) 16″ o.c. 3.4# Diamond Mesh Lath		$_____
Lightweight Concrete Partition Block — 4″		$_____
Contact Ceiling Systems (Cost of Joists not Included)		
Wood Joists — 16″ o.c. 3.4# Diamond Mesh Lath		$_____
Steel Joists — 24″ o.c. ⅜″ Rib Lath Tied to Joists	°	$_____
Steel Joists — 24″ o.c. ¾″ Channels 16″ o.c. Tied to Joists 3.4# Diamond Mesh Lath		$_____

System or Assembly	Cost Index	Local Cost

Radiant Heating Systems (Cost of Joists and Tubing not included)

Wood Joist — 16″ o.c.

      Tubing placed *below* lath.

      3.4# Diamond Mesh Lath.

      Plaster Basecoat applied in three oper-
          ations as Scratch, Fill-In, and
          Brown Coats.

      Finish Coat Contains Burlap   ✿
        Troweled in during finishing. $_____

Suspended Ceiling Systems

1½″ Main Runner Channels — 3′-0″ o.c.

  ¾″ Furring Channels — 13½″ o.c.

  3.4# Diamond Mesh Lath $_____

                                          ✿

1½″ Main Runner Channels — 3′-0″ o.c.

  ¾″ Furring Channels — 24″ o.c.

  ⅜″ Rib Lath @ 3.4# $_____

Furred Wall Systems

  ¾″ Furring Channels — 16″ o.c.

  3.4# Diamond Mesh Lath   ✿

  2½″ Metal Base $_____

✿ Relative cost indices not presently available.

Exterior Lathing and Plastering Systems and Assemblies

Relative Cost Index

	Cost Index	Local Cost

Wood Framing
  3 Coat Lime-Portland Cement-Sand
  Plaster
  3.4# Metal Lath
  Sand Float Finish
	76	$_____

Masonry Back-Up
  3 Coat Lime-Portland Cement-Sand
  Plaster
  Sand Float Finish
	47	$_____

Alternate Specifications

If a white cement float finish is desired, add 5 points to cost index.

If a job-mixed colored finish is desired, add 2 points to cost index.

If mill prepared colored finish is desired, add 6 points to cost index.

If a rough wet cast surface is desired, add 11 points to cost index.

If a brushed or stippled finish is used in lieu of a float finish, add 3 points to cost index.

If a smooth trowel finish is used in lieu of a float finish, add 6 points to cost index.

CHAPTER 8

ACOUSTICAL AND THERMAL
CHARACTERISTICS OF PLASTERWORK
AND RADIANT HEATING

I. ACOUSTICS

Acoustics is that branch of physics which treats of the production, transmission and effects of sound. Architectural acoustics deals more specifically with the relationship of the auditor to sound and noise in the man-made, physical environment. It enables the designer to study this relationship and to offer solutions towards the development of an acoustical environment which is in the context of architecture.

Plaster as an architectural material is distinctive in that it adapts readily not only to all forms of building construction, but to the many requirements of acoustical planning and design as well. It can be made porous for use as a sound-absorbing surface material and, conversely, can be made extremely dense in order to reduce the transmission of sound energy through a structural assembly. Due to the monolithic, plastic nature of plaster, it is unre-

stricted by the geometric grid and modular nature of most acoustical systems.

Hard plaster finishes are among the most efficient reflectors; they are capable of reflecting up to 97 per cent of the sound energy incident at their surfaces.[1] This ability to reflect sound is an important acoustic property that is often overlooked in favor of the more dramatized "acoustical plasters," so called because of their sound absorbing properties.

A SURVEY OF FUNDAMENTALS

Basically all problems of acoustics can be reduced to the simple relationship of wanted sound versus unwanted sound (noise).[2] A primary acoustic requirement is to provide an environment free from the disturbances of unwanted sound where auditory communications are exchanged without strain or distraction. This requirement is fulfilled either by reducing the degree of noise or by amplifying the sound needed for communication.

Sound exerts an influence on the everyday living processes of work, play and rest; noise distracts and disturbs us while we rest, causing some amount of discomfort.[3] In some industries the noise levels are high, causing a direct loss in worker efficiency and even affecting the health of workers. On the other hand, absence of noise can disturb too. When we become accustomed to common sounds and they are removed, the effect is noticeable and the environment becomes unfamiliar.

Sound waves. Sound energy is described as pressure waves in an elastic medium. These pressure waves consist of alternating compressions and rarefactions. If unrestricted, sound will proceed uniformly in all directions outward from its source, diminishing in magnitude inversely as the square of its distance from the source. Generally, sounds are produced in air by the vibration of a solid material which, acting as a diaphragm, is oscillated rapidly. The vibrations of this diaphragm are imparted to the air which reacts to the same back-and-forth motions. The number of these motions or cycles per unit of time (seconds) is called *frequency.* [4, 5]

Wave length. The wave length of a sound is the distance the sound wave travels in each complete cycle or vibration of the sound source. It can easily be shown that the wave length will vary with frequency and is equal to the velocity of sound (relatively constant at 1,120 feet per second) divided by the frequency. This is an important relationship in the design of reflecting surfaces such as for auditoriums, and speech rooms.[6]

Intensity. The intensity of sound is the rate at which sound energy or acoustic power is being transmitted when measured at any point in the medium. The unit of measure for intensity is the *decibel,* usually expressed as *db.* The sound intensity values most commonly used in acoustical studies, range from the feeblest sound the ear can hear to the loudest sound not causing the sensation of pain.

These two sound levels are called *threshold of audibility* and *threshold of feeling.* The mathematical relationship here is in the ratio of one to one trillion. This range of intensity is so broad as to make simple calculation difficult. In order to bring this within comprehension, the unit *decibel* was derived. It is the ratio between two amounts of power or sound energy. The number of decibels denoting the ratio of any two sound intensities is defined as 10 times the logarithm to the base 10 of that ratio.

The zero or reference level used with this system of sound intensity measurement has been arbitrarily assigned a standard value of 10^{-16} watts per square centimeter.[3] This is a measure of power approximating the intensity of the feeblest sound that can be heard. The painful limit is reached at about 120 db. It is important to bear in mind that this relationship is logarithmic, and not linear. If the intensity of a sound is increased by 10-fold above this zero level, the resulting level is 10 db; an increase of 100 fold is 20 db; 1,000-fold is 30 db; 1,000,000-fold is 60 db; and so on.[7] Fig. 1 shows the relation of decibel scale to absolute scale, and also includes a graphic illustration of the audio spectrum.[8]

Acoustic effects of sound waves. We have already discussed the theory of sound with respect to the motion of sound in air. In architectural acoustics it is necessary to study the effects produced by sound energy waves on striking the boundaries of an enclosed space. The total effect on a partition, for example, is shown by the diagram in Fig. 2. Sound energy generated from a source, and encountering a solid material, will be partly reflected, refracted, partly absorbed and partly transmitted by the material; all parts accounting for the total energy distribution. In selecting surface materials the architect must know how much sound will be absorbed and reflected, and in selecting structural materials, how much sound will get through them.[9]

In general, acoustical design work is divided into two functions:

(1) The study of sound wave propagation in an enclosed space or room; essentially the proportion-

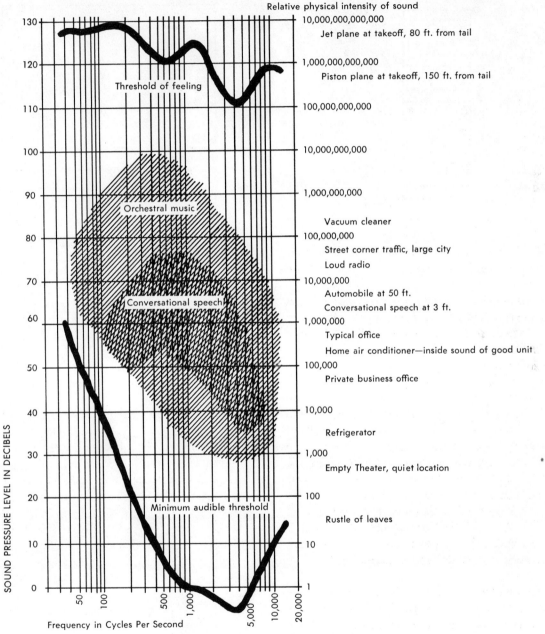

From *Man's World of Sound*, Copyright © 1958 by John R. Pierce and Edward E. David, Jr. Reprinted by permission of Doubleday & Company, Inc.

Fig. 1 — Decibel Levels of Common Sounds

ing of reflective and absorptive surface material to achieve an optimum reverberation time. Two considerations are involved in this study: the design of spaces requiring the hearing of speech and music; and noise reduction in spaces where disturbances are created by the reflection of unwanted sounds.

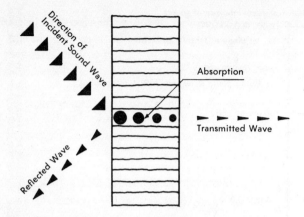

Fig. 2 — Action of Sound on Striking a Solid Medium[10]

(2) The transmission of sound through walls, floors and ceilings, and methods for its control and isolation.

Reverberation. Experiments have determined that noise problems in a room can be directly attributed to the reflection of sound from walls, floors, ceilings and objects within it. This condition of reflecting sounds in a room is known as *reverberation*. The time it takes for an original sound intensity to drop to a certain level is called *reverberation time*. If allowed to progress unimpeded these reflections will tend to emphasize the original sound, especially if the sound is a continuous one. In such a room a listener will not only hear the direct sound from the source point, but also the many rapid reflections from the room's boundaries. The combined pressure of the direct and reflected sound at his ear will be greater than that of the direct sound alone. Fig. 3 illustrates with four diagrams, how a single sound wave reflection can develop into multiple reflections.[11]

Because reverberation time in an enclosed space is a key factor in the acoustical design of a room, a more specific definition is required: "The reverberation time for a given frequency is the time required for the average sound pressure level, originally in a steady state, to decrease 60 db (to one millionth of its original pressure) after the source is stopped."[12] There is a definite relationship between reverbera-

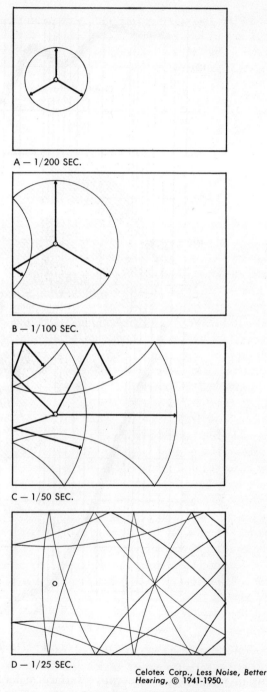

A — 1/200 SEC.

B — 1/100 SEC.

C — 1/50 SEC.

D — 1/25 SEC.

Celotex Corp., *Less Noise, Better Hearing*, © 1941-1950.

Fig. 3 — Reverberation: Multiple Reflection of a Single Wave Front in a Closed Room

tion time, the volume, and total absorption of room surfaces including absorption of objects within the room. This is mathematically expressed by the Sabine formula:[13]

$$t_{60} = \frac{0.049V}{a} \text{ seconds.}$$

where;

t_{60} = Reverberation Time (sec.)
V   = Volume of room (cu. ft.)
a   = Total absorption of room (sabins)

Sound absorption. If the volume of the space is known and the desired reverberation time has been determined, the total absorption units required can be calculated. This total absorption involves both the areas and the absorption coefficients of all the room surfaces and finishings, and is measured in sound absorbing units. One sound absorbing unit is defined as one square foot of a surface having an absorption coefficient of 100 per cent (perfect absorption). An open window of one square foot area is equivalent to one sound absorbing unit because all sound that reaches it passes on to the outdoors. So far as the room is concerned, the open window has an absorption coefficient of 100 per cent. If a surface having a 50 per cent absorption coefficient were substituted for the open window, each square foot would furnish only half a unit, and it would require two square feet to furnish one unit. The number of sound absorbing units furnished by any surface is equal to its area in square feet multiplied by its absorption coefficient.

The total absorption in a room is equal to the sum of the number of units furnished by each of the interior surfaces, plus the number of units furnished by objects such as chairs or the members of an audience.[14]

Sound reflection. The reflection of sound in a room is the primary means by which sound can be distributed uniformly to all parts. This is an important factor in auditorium design. The control of such distribution depends upon the proportioning of re-

flective and absorptive surfaces, their location in the room, and their orientation with respect to the source. In the same manner, reverberation time also depends upon this proportioning of surfaces. The reverberation time should vary between one half and two seconds, the actual time being determined by the room use (speech or music) and volume. This standard of acceptable range was developed empirically through analysis of existing auditoriums of known acoustical performance. In the case of music, it is usually desirable to extend the reverberation time to allow the blending of orchestral tones. The hearing of speech, however, depends more on the speaker's articulation and the accuracy of the reception by the listener which would be impaired by the overlapping of sounds occurring in rooms with the higher reverberation times.[15]

The effects of loudness and reverberation oppose each other. A lower reverberation time which improves audibility of speech, is accompanied by a diminished loudness which impairs audibility. Usually, this consideration is not important in smaller rooms. In larger rooms it is necessary to obtain an optimum time of reverberation. That is, the time which, if either increased or decreased, will be accompanied by such a change in loudness that the two effects will just compensate. The largest rooms nearly always require the use of electronic devices to amplify the sound, even at optimum reverberation times.[16]

Reverberation will vary with frequency, so that calculations to obtain the optimum time must be based on several frequencies. Charts have been devised to show these optimum reverberation times for various types of rooms. Again, these are based on the evaluation of existing structures with known acoustical acceptability.

It should be noted that the use of certain shapes and space arrangements can lead to serious acoustical defects. Some of the major pitfalls are these:

(1) *Excessive reverberations* result in overlapping and blurring of sounds.

(2) *Focusing.* Domes, vaults and generally any concave surface will tend to direct sound to a focal

point. If this point occurs at the audience level, distortion and overemphasis of sound develops. Other symptoms of this defect are whispering galleries where the focal point is above the audience and echo effects are created. These shapes can be destroyed or broken up by means of banners, clouds, suspended panels, and other devices. Another solution is to give the focusing surfaces heavy sound absorbing treatment.

(3) *Flutter*. Sound is reflected back and forth rapidly between two parallel walls in a rectangular enclosure with walls of approximately equal dimensions. Such a defect is identified by a noticeable fluttering distortion of certain sounds, such as an apparent quivering of voice.

Acoustical or sound absorptive materials. "Acoustical materials" is a term to which a special definition is applied by some groups to restrict its application to those materials serving only the acoustic function of sound absorption. In this sense, the term may be defined as describing those materials which have the property of absorbing a substantial fraction of the energy of sound waves which strike their surfaces. The primary function of such materials in noise control is to counteract the undesirable effects of sound reflection which otherwise would be produced by the harder surfaces which they cover or replace. There are three types of absorbents: porous materials, resonant panels, and cavity resonators. Absorbent materials most widely used are of the porous type. Others are specialized and therefore are limited to specific applications.

A porous material has openings in the surface through which the sound can enter and be absorbed by friction between vibrating air particles and the walls of the pores. The dissipated sound wave energy is thus transformed into heat.[17] The significance of the heat energy produced may be shown by reference to an illustration used by Mr. Robert B. Newman (Bolt, Beranek and Newman, Inc., Boston, Mass.) in a talk before a Building Research Institute conference on metal curtain walls: "There is no danger of heating up the material very much. Someone has done a calculation which shows that if

80,000 people at a football game shout at the top of their lungs for one hour, they will generate just enough acoustic energy to fry one egg. It is not a fire hazard."

For material to be classified as porous, it is generally considered that it must be capable of absorbing a minimum of 45 per cent of the sound wave energy incident at its surface. Thus an arbitrary limit is set with a coefficient of .45. This measurement or sound absorption coefficient represents the fraction of energy absorbed when a sound wave is reflected. These values are generally determined in tests at frequencies of 125, 250, 500, 1,000, 2,000, and 4,000 cycles per second. However, these frequencies may vary with testing agencies. An average of the four intermediate values is then taken to give the Noise Reduction Coefficient (NRC) which is recorded to the nearest multiple of .05. This average value does not generally indicate the effectiveness of a material throughout the frequency range, but is a practical index for comparing materials. Most manufacturers publish tables which show the range of absorption and frequency of their products. The architect should consult such charts, when available, in preference to using the NRC rating alone.

The designer must first determine the required area of absorption units (required number of sabins calculated by the reverberation formula.) Then he prescribes the area available for application of an acoustical material. This will set the limits for an absorption coefficient. In addition, the frequency spectrum of existing noise or sound producing sources should be known. Most acoustical materials are better absorbers in the higher frequency range than in the lower. If a high degree of absorption at lower frequencies is required, a specialized construction is usually necessary.

Sound absorbing plaster.[18] These plasters are usually referred to as acoustical plasters or plastics. Usually they are a specialized factory formulation which, when mixed with water and applied on walls and ceilings, will form a highly porous surface. For these materials Federal Specification SS-A-111 is the generally recognized performance specification. The components of most acoustical plaster mixtures are binder material, lightweight aggregate, and air entraining agent.

Gypsum, lime and certain types of clay are the most common binder materials. Vermiculite, perlite and pumice are commonly used as aggregates. Many plasters use a foaming or air entraining agent which produces minute air bubbles in the wet plaster. Upon application, the bubbles coalesce to form many interconnected pores that absorb sound. Lightweight aggregates contribute to acoustic efficiency by the tiny voids left between the aggregate and binder, and those within the aggregate itself.

Although sound absorption is the primary function of acoustical plaster, several other factors will influence the use of this material.

Since the plaster surface can conform to virtually any contour, it is possible to shape surfaces to create special sound distribution and absorption patterns. The construction of sound baffles, and the modeling of surface detail are examples of acoustical solutions. A wide variety of textures and surface finishes may be produced by varying the tool treatment or application methods. Sound absorbing plasters can have interesting textures, and can provide uniformity to large and irregular surface areas. Sand blasting techniques can provide such surface textures. This process involves embedding of sand rather than sand blasting in the usual sense of scouring or erosion.

Where the material is used on exterior walls and top floor ceiling areas, the relatively good thermal properties of acoustical plaster will favorably influence the heat transfer calculations for heating design. The conductivities (k) range in value from .50 to .65. The average value of batt or blanket type insulation is .27, and for gypsum-sand plaster 5.60.

Although generally acoustical plasters are used as a finish on walls and ceilings, their contribution to fire protection is threefold, depending on the particular type of plaster: prevention of flame spread, retarding of heat transmission, and ability to remain in place in the presence of fire. Most acoustical plasters exhibit excellent performance for all three purposes, particularly when used in combination with other plasters. (See Chapter 9.)

Strength is important only to the extent that the material must support itself and remain in place. Acoustical plasters, as a group, are not selected for service requiring great strength or surface hardness. Structural soundness of the base materials and bond between finish and base coats determines the limits of over-all strength performance.

Maintenance and painting. Preserving the acoustical life of a material is an important economic factor in building maintenance programs. The sound absorption properties of the material should not be substantially reduced as a result of cleaning and painting. Improper painting can reduce absorption values by as much as 25 to 50 per cent.

To retain their light reflectivity, acoustical plasters, like other absorbent materials, require periodic cleaning. With some, this can be accomplished by scrubbing with water and mild soap, vacuum cleaning (with brush attachments) and wallpaper type cleaners. The methods used depend upon the particular material involved. Some materials will soften upon contact with water; certain others are relatively friable and will tend to crumble if wallpaper type cleaners are used. To avoid such damage, manufacturers' directions should be followed regarding all maintenance procedures.

The factors determining type and method of painting depend upon the characteristics of surface structure. The perforated plasters can be brush-painted with a minimum of paint bridging at the openings. In spray applications, paint tends to enter the larger openings and seal the porous material within. Nonperforated type materials must be spray-painted, otherwise the surface porosity will be lowered. It is better to apply several light coats than a single heavy one. In all cases painting should be done in accordance with the acoustical plaster manufacturers' recommendations.

Types of acoustical plaster. Because the many acoustical plasters commercially available vary considerably in binder material, aggregate, chemical agents, application and finishing. A survey of a majority of these plasters indicates classification into four basic groups established on the basis of binder material type: gypsum, lime-Keene's, lime, and clay. Within these groups physical and performance characteristics will vary. The manufacturers' descriptive and technical data should be consulted for details relating to a particular product.

(1) *Gypsum base.* This acoustical plaster is produced by mixing special gypsum binders with either vermiculite, perlite or pumice aggregates. It develops its acoustic performance in the setting of the gypsum, leaving voids between particles of the lightweight aggregates. Some plasters employ chemical air entraining agents to create an open cellular construction.

Most acoustical plasters require the addition of water only at the job, and machine mixing is usually recommended. Additional water is sometimes required if the material is hand mixed. The length of mixing time is determined by checking the weight of a sample (usually a 12-quart bucket) until the desired aeration or fluffing is attained.

The material is applied over standard gypsum basecoats. Full scratch and brown coats of gypsum plaster over metal lath, gypsum lath or masonry, will serve as a base for the acoustical finish. The procedures for these basecoats are similar to those prescribed in Chapter 4 for regular plaster finishes. The basecoat must be sufficiently dry to provide suction for bond. In some instances, cross scoring is necessary for a mechanical bond, but usually a rough darby finish will suffice.

The acoustical finish application involves two coats. The first is applied ¼ inch to ⅜ inch thick, allowed to set and partially dry overnight. The final coat is applied to bring the total thickness to ½ inch. To obtain surface continuity, areas should be completed in one operation. Machine spray application is not recommended for this type of plaster.

Final performance characteristics are acquired in the mechanical opening of the surface by trowel or float. In addition, a stipple brush texture may be applied. Troweling should be minimized to avoid uneven textures and over-densification of the surface.

For trowel and float finishes, cleaning is done with vacuum equipment. Painting should be done with spray equipment, using water-thinned non-sealing paints.

(2) *Lime-Keene's base.* The lime-Keene's acoustical plaster is similar to the gypsum base type with certain exceptions. It is composed of a lime and Keene's cement binder material in combination with a lightweight aggregate. Lime-Keene's acoustical plaster, when applied over a portland cement lime basecoat, may be used in areas of moderate humidity. This plaster has a surface of high durability that resists abrasion, but it must be opened mechanically. The surface is treated by stippling, perforation or floating. Machine application or use over monolithic concrete is not usually recommended.

(3) *Lime base.* All lime acoustical plasters available today are sold under proprietary names. Some lime acoustical plasters are manufactured with vermiculite or perlite as the predominating aggregates. To obtain the required porosity, many producers combine a chemical foaming agent with the lime. Others make use of a mineral fiber with the lightweight aggregate.

Lime plaster primarily differs from the other plasters in that over a period the surface becomes appreciably hard while the interior material remains soft. This surface hardness necessitates mechanical perforation for maximum acoustical performance. The durable finish is highly receptive to repeated decoration with no undue loss in efficiency. The excellent moisture resistance allows use in moderate to high humidity areas.

Mixing is similar to gypsum base acoustical plaster, and hand application is required.

Brush stippling and mechanical perforation (nail stippler) is required. The stippling process can be completed soon after the final coat has been applied. Perforation is best accomplished when a crust has formed on the surface. In this way a clean sharp perforation is made without tearing or crumbling the material.

As previously mentioned, this acoustical plaster has relatively high abrasion resistance. It is not appreciably affected by repeated painting, including brush applications. The surface is water resistant so that most types of cleaning are possible.

(4) *Clay-adhesive base* generally consists of non-setting clay binder materials with adhesive properties combined with lightweight aggregate, usually vermiculite or perlite. This plaster or plastic is designed for either hand or machine application and acquires acoustical properties by the porosity and surface fissuring that result from drying.

The material should be mixed with water only by hand or machine.

This material may be applied to any clean, firm surface such as plaster basecoats, monolithic concrete, masonry, galvanized metal, and oil painted surfaces. The base and finish coats should be applied in accordance with the manufacturers' specifications.

Most of these materials can be cleaned with vacuum equipment having a soft brush. Brush painting is not recommended. The surface may be refinished with a thinly sprayed application of the same plaster, or it may be spray painted in accordance with manufacturers' directions.

Thickness vs. sound absorption. Data currently available are insufficient for conclusively analyzing the relationship between thickness and sound absorption. However, in the porous nonmetallic acoustical materials, an increase in thickness will be accompanied by greater sound absorption values up to a point where further gains are uneconomical. The graphs in Fig. 4 illustrate this. Five thicknesses ranging from ¼ inch to 1 inch are plotted for two plasters (A & B). In both instances it is apparent that little additional absorption value can be gained with thicknesses beyond ½ inch. This factor accounts for the standardization of the ½ inch application. The graphs further indicate that the function of thickness varies over the frequency range.[19]

In Fig. 5, the composite average values of 14 acoustical plasters (½ inch thickness) have been plotted as tested and reported by the respective

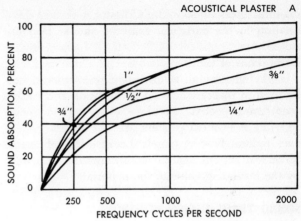

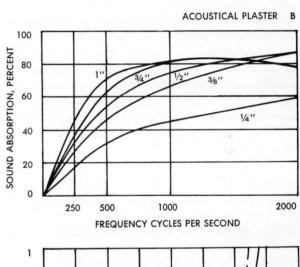

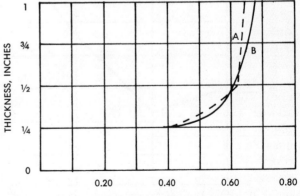

Fig. 4 — Thickness Vs. Sound Absorption in Acoustical Plasters

manufacturers. In selecting a plaster, technical data relating to the particular material should be consulted.

Limitations of use

(1) In general, acoustical plasters should not be used in places where heavy abrasion and rough usage are expected.

(2) Acoustical plasters are not recommended over radiant heating panels, because the efficiency of such a system would be substantially impaired by the insulating value of the material.

SOUND TRANSMISSION CONTROL

The subject of sound transmission encompasses the method by which sound travels through enclosure materials. Fig. 6 illustrates the reduction in intensity of sound passing through a wall. There are many economical combinations of materials and methods of construction which can substantially reduce this transmission of sound. Many of them em-

ploy lath and plaster. Once the source and cause of the unwanted noise and the amount of noise that can be tolerated are determined, the proper construction and materials can be selected to reduce the transmission to a desired level.

Means by which sound is transmitted. Sound can be transmitted only through a solid, liquid, or gaseous medium. It cannot be transmitted through a vacuum. In a building, solid bodies such as walls or ceilings act as diaphragms and are set in motion by sound wave vibrations. In turn, they radiate these vibrations to other mediums (air or solid). The transmission of noise into or within a building may occur in several ways.

(1) *Transmission of air-borne sounds.* Sound waves are generated in the air and progress until interrupted by a solid body, such as a wall. The waves then cause vibration, and sound energy is radiated from the opposite side.

(2) *Transmission of solid-borne sounds.* In this instance, transmission is through a solid or

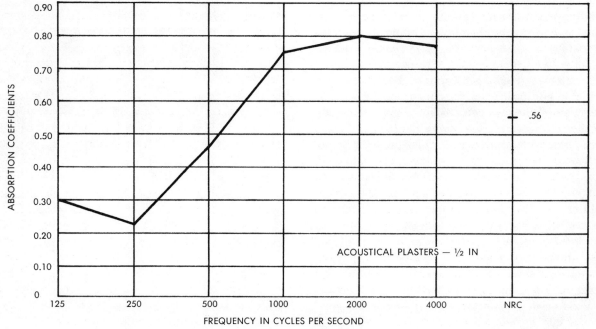

By permission from *Handbook of Noise Control*, Edited by C. M. Harris, Copyright 1957. McGraw-Hill Book Co.

Fig. 5 — Average Absorption of Acoustical Plasters ½" Thick

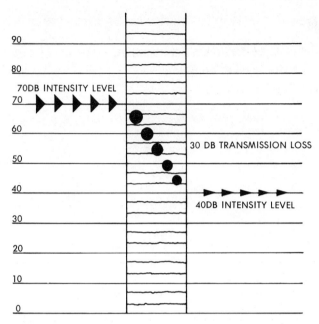

Celotex Corp., Less Noise, Better Hearing. © 1941-1950.

Fig.6 — Reduction in Intensity Level of Sound Passing Through a Wall Having a 30 DB Transmission Loss

liquid medium. Mechanical equipment, building movement, and vehicles are some of the causes of structural vibration. Impact noises are produced by the presence of sound generating bodies in direct contact with the structure. These vibrations can transmit sound to all parts·of a building, particularly where continuity of structure exists.

(3) *Direct transmission entirely by air.* Sound will travel from one space to another — for example, through open windows, porous materials, and cracks. This is significant in the design of high transmission loss barriers where cracks or openings, caused by faulty construction or planning, can nullify the expenditure required for the assembly.

Measurement of sound transmission. Transmission loss is defined as the ratio in decibels of the total acoustic energy that is directed against one side of a partition to the energy transmitted through it. (See Fig. 7.) It is abbreviated T.L. Transmission loss is completely independent of the acoustical properties of the rooms on either side, and varies

with the frequency of incident sound. It has been observed that the lower frequencies are more easily transmitted through a wall or ceiling. For this reason, in testing partitions and floor panels, measurements usually are made at nine standard frequencies. For convenience, an average of these various frequencies is denoted, and whenever a single rating is given for a particular construction it usually refers to this average value.

Prevailing noise problems must be recognized before selecting a particular wall or floor construction. These problems may originate either on the site or in surrounding areas, and may result from sources such as factories, traffic, or aircraft. To insure proper functioning of the contemplated building, a reasonably accurate survey of the existing noise frequency and intensity should be made so that, where necessary, measures for noise reduction or isolation can be incorporated in the design.

Fig. 1 gives the intensity levels of some of the more common sounds. Table I classifies partitions in degrees from poor to excellent.

Masking effect. Up to here, it has been assumed that sound passing through a barrier enters a completely quiet space. In practice this rarely occurs, because there is almost always some sound present. It may be the sound of distant traffic or noise from a ventilating duct. The sounds already present have an appreciable effect on the transmitted sounds. For example, in considering the case of two adjacent apartments with a common partition, let a rating of 40 db be assigned to the partition; that is to say, any sound in one apartment will be reduced 40 db upon passing through the common wall. If a radio is playing at 60 db in one apartment, it will be heard at an intensity of 20 db in an adjacent room if that room is perfectly quiet. However, a 30 db noise level in the adjacent room will effectively cancel the 20 db coming through the partition. Experiments indicate that one sound must be at least 10 db louder than another prevailing sound to drown it out.[20]

Effect of openings. Published values of transmission loss are based on tests performed on panel

Table I.

Classification of Sound Insulating Properties of Partitions According to Their Average Transmission Loss. A Noise Level of Approximately 30 db Is Assumed on the Listening Side in Each Case.

Transmission Loss of Wall	Hearing Conditions	Rating
30 db. or less	Normal speech can be understood quite easily and distinctly through the wall.	Poor
30 to 35 db.	Loud speech can be understood fairly well. Normal speech can be heard but not easily understood.	Fair
35 to 40 db.	Loud speech can be heard, but is not easily intelligible. Normal speech can be heard only faintly, if at all.	Good
40 to 45 db.	Loud speech can be faintly heard but not understood. Normal speech is inaudible.	Very good — recommended for dividing walls between apartments.
45 db. or greater	Very loud sounds, such as loud singing, brass musical instruments, or a radio at full volume can be heard only faintly, or not at all.	Excellent — recommended for band rooms, music practice rooms, radio and sound studios.

Source: "Less Noise — Better Hearing," The Celotex Corporation

constructions which have no openings. Since airborne sounds pass through voids and joints in a material, the transmission characteristics of the solid enclosure are qualified by the extent of openings in a sound barrier. If a door or window having a low transmission loss is placed in a partition of high efficiency, the over-all transmission loss of the combination will be intermediate between the two values, depending on the areas of the door or window in relation to that of the partition. If the door is of loose fit, the resulting crack will further decrease the over-all efficiency. Other factors which can contribute to a reduction in value are loose-fitting pipes, back-to-back medicine cabinets, electrical outlets, duct work, and generally loose construction.

Mr. Robert B. Newman illustrated the effects of openings on sound transmission through walls in a symposium on sound transmission during the conference on Metal Curtain Walls conducted by BRI in Washington, D. C., during September 1955.[17] This is a summary of his illustration:

A 100 square foot wall specimen having a transmission loss of 40 db (and a transmission coefficient of .0001) will transmit only .0001 of the energy striking one side by reradiation from the opposite side. A hole in the panel will have a coefficient of at least 1.0. Therefore, a .01 square foot hole in this panel will transmit as much energy as will the remainder of the panel. Mr. Newman further stated that as this hole is enlarged, the transmission loss characteristics of the construction tends to become insignificant.

Mass law. One of the simplest types of sound retardant construction is a nonporous, homogeneous partition which has the same physical properties throughout. Typical examples of homogeneous partitions are brick walls, concrete walls and floors, solid concrete and solid gypsum block, and solid plaster partitions. An example of a non-homogeneous partition is the wood stud and plaster partition. At a given frequency, the transmission loss for a homogeneous partition increases with the mass per unit of area. This empirical law is called the *Mass Law,* and is represented by the straight line as shown in Fig. 8. In theory, when the mass doubles, the average transmission loss is increased by 6 db. Experiment has determined the actual increase to be approximately 4.4 db. This relationship, as seen in the chart, holds for most types of construction. The partition systems which fall either above or below the curve are discussed in the following pages. Fig. 7 compares various types of construction.

Stiffness effect. A transmission loss can also be expected in a very stiff lightweight panel if it is mounted so that it is rigidly fixed at all edges. The transmission loss will be greatest in the lower frequency range. It is difficult, however, to construct this panel so that the stiffness will effect a transmission loss in the audible frequency range.

Resonance effects. When struck, most panels will vibrate for a certain period at their own natural frequencies. When the sound incident on a wall is the same frequency as one of the natural frequencies of the wall, the wall will resonate and vibrate at a much larger amplitude than at other frequencies. This results, in some instances, in almost 100 per cent transmission of sound at the natural frequency. If effects of natural frequency are to be avoided, it is desirable to provide the lowest natural frequency possible. This condition can be met by partitions of large mass and small stiffness. Hard

plaster meets these conditions because in the presence of average noises its natural frequencies are either too high or too low to become a problem.

Porosity. Materials of a porous nature (that is, having interconnecting cells or passageways), are generally poor sound insulators because they allow much of the sound to pass unobstructed. For this reason, lightweight hollow concrete blocks are usually unsatisfactory unless the pores are sealed. An appreciable effect (5 db) is achieved by painting the block with two coats of cement paint. If ½ inch of plaster is applied to both sides, the resulting value approaches that predicted by the mass law. This is illustrated by the chart in Fig. 8.

There is a general misconception that sound absorbing materials are sound insulating in the direct sense, and that they substantially reduce transmission through them. To some, "sound absorbing" suggests that sound energy, on passing into such a material, is largely swallowed up and disappears. The fact that absorption is not a measure of transmission loss is forcibly illustrated by the extreme example of the open window, which is 100 per cent absorbing but also 100 per cent transmitting.

Damping effect. In addition to what has been described above, in a panel there is always a certain amount of internal damping. Steel has very little internal damping; wood and concrete have considerably more; and some kinds of rubber and fiberboard have large degrees of damping. When struck, a panel with small damping vibrates at a natural frequency for a relatively long time, while a highly damped panel (sheet of lead) produces a full thud and stops vibrating almost immediately. This principle applies in both absorption of sound and reduction of sound transmission.

Multiple panels. Many wall and floor constructions are made of multiple panels such as double wood stud construction, brick cavity walls, and double channel stud plaster construction.

Separate panel systems take advantage of complete isolation between the surfaces and the spring effect of the air space. Sound energy striking and

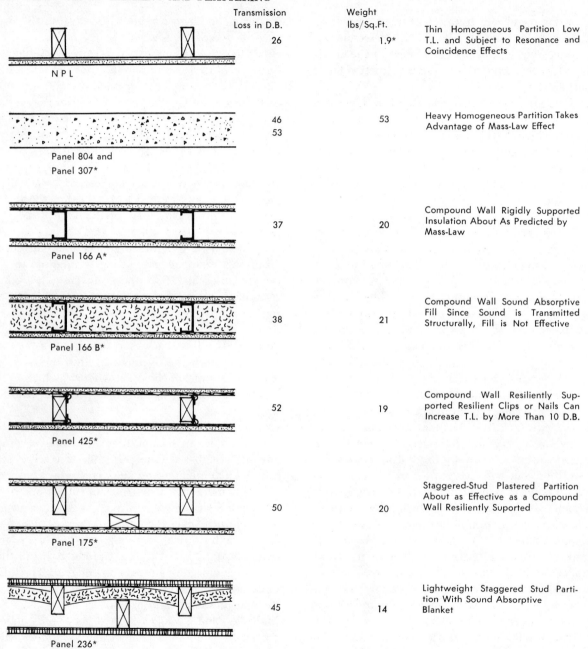

	Transmission Loss in D.B.	Weight lbs/Sq.Ft.	
N P L	26	1.9*	Thin Homogeneous Partition Low T.L. and Subject to Resonance and Coincidence Effects
Panel 804 and Panel 307*	46 53	53	Heavy Homogeneous Partition Takes Advantage of Mass-Law Effect
Panel 166 A*	37	20	Compound Wall Rigidly Supported Insulation About As Predicted by Mass-Law
Panel 166 B*	38	21	Compound Wall Sound Absorptive Fill Since Sound is Transmitted Structurally, Fill is Not Effective
Panel 425*	52	19	Compound Wall Resiliently Supported Resilient Clips or Nails Can Increase T.L. by More Than 10 D.B.
Panel 175*	50	20	Staggered-Stud Plastered Partition About as Effective as a Compound Wall Resiliently Suported
Panel 236*	45	14	Lightweight Staggered Stud Partition With Sound Absorptive Blanket

* Panel Numbers Refer to
Superficial Weight of Sheet (I.E. Excluding Studding)
Sound Insulation of Walls & Floors
U.S.D.C.   NBS.   BMS   REPT. 144

Panel labeled NPL frm: Ashton, G. H., *The Sound Insulation of Partitions*, National Physical Laboratory, London, 1948.
All others by permission from *Handbook of Noise Control*, Edited by C. M. Harris, Copyright 1957. McGraw-Hill Book Co.

Fig. 7 — Various Types of Partitions Which Illustrate Principles of Sound Insulation

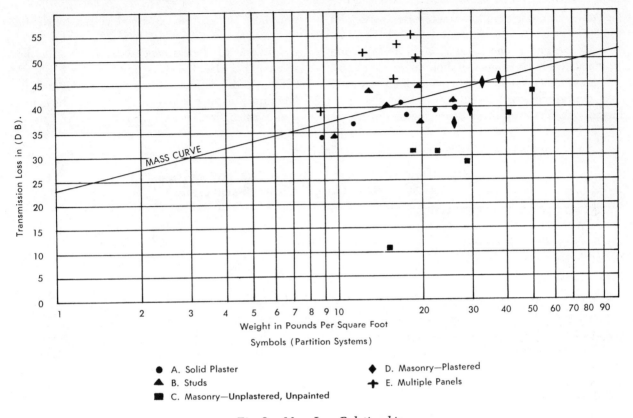

Symbols (Partition Systems)

● A. Solid Plaster   ◆ D. Masonry—Plastered
▲ B. Studs   ✚ E. Multiple Panels
■ C. Masonry—Unplastered, Unpainted

Fig. 8 — Mass Law Relationship

vibrating one panel will not immediately reproduce these vibrations in the opposite panel. Three stages of energy loss occur as sound passes through such a system: the vibration of the first panel, damping effect of the air space, and vibration of the second panel. To obtain maximum sound transmission loss, it is necessary to eliminate any rigid contact between the two panels.

Another form of independent panel system is produced by the use of flexible clips or hangers for panel attachment. An example is the use of spring clips to attach plaster and its base to either side of a metal or wood stud construction. This partition is very satisfactory because it has a high transmission loss rating with a relatively low mass. Such a combination is desirable in current construction practices.[21]

Testing authorities. The primary source of data currently available is provided by agencies which have been sponsored to test and record the values of specific test panels.

Two types of tests for acoustic properties are made at various standard frequencies: the test for determining sound absorption performance of surface materials; and the test for determining the sound transmission reduction through a panel, wall, floor and ceiling assembly.

The most comprehensive sound transmission data currently available to the designer are published by the National Bureau of Standards in its Building Materials and Structures Report BMS 144. These ratings are used in this manual, unless otherwise indicated. (See Table II for comparative ratings of partitions.) Transmission test data have also been produced by the Armour Research Foundation; Geiger and Hamme; Lane; U. S. Testing; and National Research Council Laboratories.

Field tests on completed buildings indicate that performance is usually lower than that predicted by laboratory investigation with similar assemblies. This can be explained in part by the facts that laboratory test panels are solidly constructed, tightly and rigidly fastened at the edges; the maximum panel size tested is approximately 8 feet x 9 feet;[22] the job conditions and workmanship of laboratory caliber are difficult to reproduce in actual construction.

Table II.

Representative Partition Systems — Comparative Table
(Thickness-Weight-Average Transmission Loss)

Description	Plaster	Lath	Thickness (Inches)	Weight (Lbs./Sq. Ft.)	Transmission Loss (DB)
A. Solid Plaster					
1. Studless	Gypsum-Perlite	Metal Lath (Exp.)	2″	8.8	33*
2. Studless	Gypsum-Perlite	Gypsum Lath	2″	10.9	37*
3. Studless	Gypsum-Sand	Metal Lath (Exp.)	2″	18.4	38*
4. Channel Stud	Gypsum-Sand	Metal Lath (Exp.) ¾″ Cold-Rolled Channels @ 12″ o.c.	2½″	22.4	39*
5. Studless	Gypsum-Sand	⅜″ Gypsum Lath	3″	25.4	40*
6. Studless	Gypsum-Sand	2 Layers ⅜″ Gypsum Lath	2½″	18.1	41*
7. Channel Stud	Gypsum-Vermiculite	Metal Lath (Exp.)	2″	11.2	40**
8. Studless	Gypsum-Vermiculite	Gypsum Lath (½″)	2½″	10.8	39**
B. Stud (Wood & Metal)					
1. 2″x4″ Studs @ 16″ o.c.	½″ Gypsum-Vermiculite	⅜″ Gypsum Lath	5⅜″	9.6	33*
2. 3¼″ Hollow Steel Stud @ 16″ o.c.	¾″ Gypsum-Sand	Metal Lath (Exp.)	4¾″	19.1	40*
3. 2″x4″ Studs @ 16″ o.c.	½″ Gypsum-Sand	⅜″ Gypsum Lath	5⅜″	15.2	41*
4. 3¼″ Hollow Steel Stud @ 24″ o.c.	¾″ Gypsum-Sand	Metal Lath (Rib)	4¾″	26.8	46**
5. 3¼″ Hollow Steel Stud @ 16″ o.c.	½″ Gypsum-Sand	⅜″ Gypsum—Held with Clips	5¼″	13.7	43*
6. 2″x4″ Studs @ 16″ o.c.	⅞″ Lime-Sand	Metal (Exp.)	5⅜″	19.8	44*

* National Bureau of Standards — Building Materials and Structure Report #144
** Armour Research Foundation, Riverbank, Illinois

Description	Plaster	Lath	Thickness (Inches)	Weight (Lbs./Sq. Ft.)	Transmission Loss (DB)
C. Masonry Block					
(Unplastered, Unpainted)					
1. 4″ Hollow Pumice			3⅝″	15.5	11*
2. 8″ Hollow Cinder			7⅝″	28.8	28.3**
3. 6″ Hollow Expanded Shale			5⅝″	22.8	31.3**
4. 4″ Hollow Cinder			3⅝″	19.2	32.6**
5. 6″ Solid Cinder			5⅝″	40.2	34.6**
6. 8″ Hollow Dense			7⅝″	49.2	44.2**
D. Masonry Block — Plastered					
1. 4″ Hollow Pumice	½ ″ Gypsum-Sand		4⅝″	25.3	37*
2. 4″ Hollow Cinder	⅝″ Gypsum-Sand		4⅞″	29.7	39*
3. 3″ Hollow Cinder	⅝″ Gypsum-Sand		3⅞″	32.2	45*
4. 4″ Hollow Cinder	⅝″ Gypsum-Sand		4⅞″	35.8	46*
E. Multiple Panel and Resilient Assemblies					
1. ¾ ″ Staggered Channel @ 16″ o.c. Set on Cork Strip Base.	½ ″ Gypsum-Perlite	⅜ ″ Gypsum—Held with Clips and held from opposing studs by ⅜″ sponge rubber dots.	2¾ ″	8.6	39*
2. 2½ ″ Staggered Hollow Steel Stud	½ ″ Gypsum-Sand	⅜ ″ Perforated Gypsum — Held by Clips	5½ ″	16.5	46**
3. 2″x4″ Staggered Wood Stud @ 16″ o.c. (Studs set flat one side)	¾ ″ Gypsum-Sand	Metal (Exp.)	6¾ ″	19.8	50*
4. 2″x4″ Wood Stud @ 16″ o.c. (Resilient Clips)	½ ″ Gypsum-Sand	⅜ ″ Gypsum	6⅛″	13.1	52*
5. 2 Rows ¾ ″ Steel Channels @ 12″ o.c. Stiffened by Horizontal 1″ Channel at mid-point of Panel. (Entire Panel set on 1″ Cork Strip Base.	¾ ″ Gypsum-Sand	Metal (Exp.)	4½ ″	17.2	53*

* National Bureau of Standards — Building Materials and Structure Report #144
** Armour Research Foundation, Riverbank, Illinois

	Description	Plaster	Lath	Thickness (Inches)	Weight (Lbs./Sq. Ft.)	Transmission Loss (DB)
6.	3¼″ Hollow Steel Studs @ 16″ o.c. (Resilient Clips)	¾″ Gypsum-Sand	Metal Lath (Exp.) Wired Ties to ¼″ Metal Rods — Wire tied to Resilient Clips.	5¾″	19.0	55**

II. THERMAL CHARACTERISTICS

Ever since two of the elements of human existence, heat and shelter, were combined in a rudimentary house, the amount of attention to thermal matters required of those concerned with building has steadily increased. A state has been reached now where this subject may not be ignored in any phase of the building process.

So long as the structural concern for thermal problems was limited to providing fireplaces for cooking and enough protection from the cold to preserve life, the ancient art of plastering remained relatively unaffected. However, new responsibilities have been placed on plaster in the form of thermal functions, to the extent that some knowledge of the mechanical subjects is required to effectively utilize the material in modern construction.

While neither the general subject of heat transfer nor the history of its influence on the building arts can be treated here, we shall discuss those thermal aspects of plaster which are essential to its proper use and treatment. There is no intention to propose the substitution of plaster materials for insulating materials. However, lath and plaster construction is capable of sufficient thermal performance to warrant consideration when used in conjunction with these materials.

This discussion will be limited to these pertinent topics: Requirements of thermal insulation in buildings in relation to lath and plaster; the general principles of heat transfer; plaster materials as insulators; nonmetallic and reflective materials; and moisture control and its effect on lath and plaster.

Heat transfer. Heat is a form of energy that is transferred when a temperature difference exists. The difference represents a potential which causes the transfer. Heat always flows from a warmer to a colder zone and may be transmitted by one or all of three processes: conduction, convection, and radiation. The transfer of heat in building construction usually involves all three processes.

Conduction is the process by which heat is transferred in solid bodies, and under certain conditions, from solid to fluid bodies. Although the mechanism is more precisely described in terms of molecular action, it may suffice for this purpose to say that heat is transferred by the touching of one particle of material to the next. If an object or material is heated on one side, the opposite side eventually will attain the same temperature by conduction.[23]

Convection is the process by which heat is transferred in fluid bodies. Convection is not a simple heat flow; it involves conduction as well as diffusion and mixing. One aspect of convection is a flow of heat from a warm surface to cooler air in contact with it, or from warm air to a cooler surface, the heated air tending to rise and the cooled air to fall. This rising and falling makes possible a physical transportation of heat. Fig. 9 illustrates how air motion in an enclosed space such as a wall cavity can transfer heat from the warm side to the cold side.[24]

Radiation is the transmission of energy by means of electromagnetic wave of very long wave length. Radiant energy of any wave length may, when absorbed, become thermal energy, and result in an increase in the temperature of the absorbing body. Radiant energy travels at the speed of light in a straight line and is not affected by the temperature or currents of the air through which it passes.

The reflectivity of materials plays an important part in the control of heat transfer by this method.[25]

Thermal insulation. All materials offer some resistance to the flow of heat by conduction and this resistance in any given material is directly proportional to the thickness (reflective materials are an exception). It is interesting to note that no matter how thick a material, if there is a temperature differential between the surfaces, eventually heat transfer will effect a state of equilibrium. The primary thermal objective in the design of buildings is to slow up the process sufficiently to allow the mechanical system (heating or cooling) to compensate at minimum output for the loss or gain. In addition, for human comfort it is desirable to maintain a certain range of interior surface temperatures which is also related to the heat transfer rate through exterior walls.

These principles are analogous to the heat gain and loss of the human body. If a person remains outdoors in winter with inadequate clothing, he becomes readily conscious of discomfort. A great differential between body temperature and the outside air temperature causes heat to be lost rapidly. The greater the temperature difference the greater the

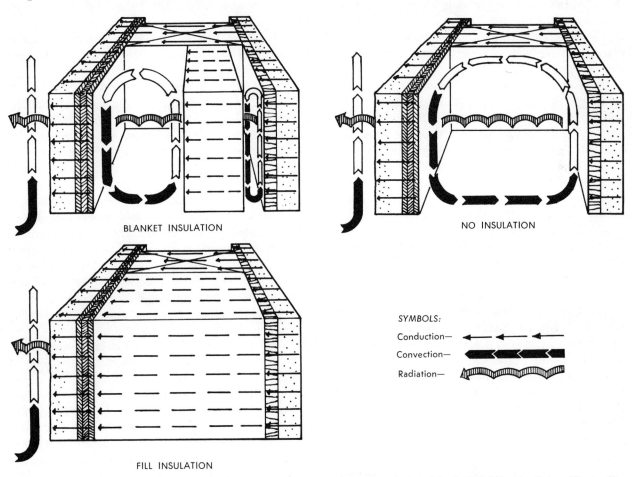

BLANKET INSULATION

NO INSULATION

FILL INSULATION

SYMBOLS:

Conduction—

Convection—

Radiation—

Rogers, T. S., *Design of Insulated Buildings for Various Climates*, New York © 1951, F. W. Dodge Corp.

Fig. 9 — Three Methods of Heat Transfer Through Building Sections

rate of heat flow, and the degree of comfort depends on this rate. Only when the body maintains a thermal balance (that is the ability to produce heat as fast as it is lost at a normal rate) does one experience the satisfaction of comfort. This balance is accomplished by insulating the body with proper clothing and thus retarding the rate of heat transfer.

So far only the temperature differential aspect of body discomfort has been considered. It should be added that solar radiation, wind characteristics, humidity, and other factors in varying degrees will have considerable influence. (Under warm weather conditions the same principles apply with the direction of heat flow reversed.)[26]

The study and theory of thermal insulation is essentially an extension of these principles. As pointed out, the primary interest in heat transfer is in the control of human comfort. In other times, when buildings were constructed without benefit of insulation, the entire load was put on the heating unit. Heating units were sized to handle the enormous losses, and even then were sometimes inadequate. A belief continues to prevail that when economy is no obstacle, the best solution in combating heat loss is to provide more heat. The prevalence of this fallacy can be attributed to a popular misunderstanding of heat flow rates. In uninsulated structures, depending on exterior conditions, the inside surface temperatures of exterior walls, floors, and ceilings can vary considerably from the inside air temperatures. This difference in surface air temperature will have a direct effect on radiation to or from the occupants, with a corresponding effect on their comfort which is independent of the ambient temperature. The distance one stands from these surfaces determines the rate of heat loss or gain. In effect, a pronounced discomfort zone is created at the building perimeter when the surface to air temperature differential is high.[27]

In addition, surface temperature variations in plasterwork contribute to pattern soiling and shadowing. These defects are discussed in greater detail in Chapter 6, and elsewhere in this chapter under "Radiant Heating."

Economics of insulation. Once minimum comfort conditions have been satisfied, economy becomes the important consideration in the use of insulation. Insulating materials probably lead the building material field in providing the greatest financial return on the initial installation investment. These savings are realized in the conservation of fuel (winter) and power for air-conditioning equipment (summer).

In determining the most economical thickness of insulation to use in any particular construction, it is helpful to understand the relationship between thickness and heat transmission. Here is an example that illustrates this:

An uninsulated wood frame wall consisting of wood siding, sheathing, 4 inch studding, lath and plaster will transfer heat at the rate of .25 BTU per hour per square foot of exposed surface, a "U" factor of 0.25. The corresponding factor for the first 1 inch of insulation added to the wall will be 0.13, a reduction in heat transfer of 48 per cent; for the second inch, .087, a reduction of 17 per cent; for the third inch, .066, a reduction of 8.4 per cent. In theory, about 20 added inches of insulating material would be required to duplicate the effectiveness of the first inch. This principle of diminishing returns is an important factor in the economics of insulation. It is generally thought that the most economical thickness to install is that amount which will effect a fuel or power savings giving 20 per cent annual return on the original investment. The initial cost of insulation may, as a result of the reduced design loads, in part be offset by the lower cost of a heating or cooling unit.[28]

The design procedures involved in heat transfer calculations and thermal transmission coefficients of building assemblies are not confined to the use of lath and plaster, and for that reason are not discussed. Anyone interested in more detailed information of this kind may consult the *Heating, Ventilating, Air-Conditioning Guide* (latest edition) and other reference works, some of which are listed in the notes at the end of this chapter.

Thermal characteristics of plaster. Sometimes insulating materials are classified according to the temperature ranges within which they are expected to perform. Usually a material will exhibit thermal properties that make it better suited for use in one range than in another. The low range involves temperatures up to 212 degrees F.; the moderate temperature range is from 212 degrees F. to 1,000 degrees F.; and the high temperature range is above 1,000 degrees F. A general rule, to which there are significant exceptions, implies that the more specialized an insulating material, the more efficient. Many materials, however, can be employed in two or more of these ranges. For this purpose only the first group comprising those materials commonly used in building construction need be considered.

Still or trapped air is an excellent insulator.[29] Materials of cellular or porous construction are more efficient retarders of heat flow by conduction than denser materials. The relative effectiveness of a material as an insulator is related to the amount of trapped air contained in a given thickness.

This characteristic in plaster can be controlled to some degree by fairly simple methods, in the use of lightweight aggregates and air entraining agents. Cellular materials like perlite, vermiculite, and pumice trap air in relatively large enclosures. These enclosures are found either within the aggregate or between the aggregate and binder particles; whereas air entrainment produces widely distributed individual cells containing varying quantities of air.

The degree of insulating effectiveness of a lightweight aggregate plaster is directly related to the ratio of cementitious material to aggregate. The most common proportions are a 1:2, 1:3 and 1:2½ mill mix, using a gypsum binder with perlite or vermiculite. The conductivity values (k) for these four insulating plasters are shown in Table III.

Although lower thermal conductivities are available in these plasters when greater amounts of the lightweight aggregate are used, other desirable features (primarily durability) may be sacrificed. This can be illustrated by noting in Table III that the acoustical plasters which are not usually selected for use in locations requiring high surface durability have higher heat flow resistances than harder lightweight plasters.

Thickness also contributes to thermal effectiveness. Although plaster of greater thickness will give the higher performance, due to the requirements of other functions and economic considerations, plaster thickness ordinarily is limited to ½ inch to ¾ inch, with a corresponding limit on the thermal rating. In view of these factors, insulating plaster usually is regarded as supplementary to another layer of more specialized material.

It must be noted here, however, that conventional plaster thickness acts as a limitation of insulating value only at the lower temperatures. Fire resistance properties of plaster (moderate to high temperature uses) provide effective barriers to heat transmission, within the normal thickness and time ranges. However, gypsum plaster is not a stable material when continuously exposed to high temperature. Recent developments in curtain wall construction have made use of a perlite or vermiculite plaster core. This use has many interesting aspects and no doubt will increase in prevalence with the continued increase in the use of metal curtain walls in building construction. The plaster core, or backup, provides fire resistance to lightweight exterior walls without the weight penalty of masonry filler construction. At the same time the plaster also provides the principal thermal insulation for the low temperature range.

For curtain wall work (see the section on curtain walls in Chapter 5) the proportions of portland cement to aggregate vary from 1:3 to 1:6, depending upon particular strength, weight and thermal requirements.

Machine placed portland cement-perlite plaster (1:4 mix by volume) will have a dry density of 50 pcf, thermal conductivity (k) of 1.4, and compressive strength of 1,000 psi.[30] It can be seen that machine application results in greater compressive strength, but at the expense of thermal values.

Insulating materials in general and their use with plasterwork. In addition to classifying insulation materials according to the temperature ranges in which they work, in building construction they are often grouped according to physical structure, such as "loose fill," "blankets," "batts," "rigid board," and so on. Reflective insulation is considered in a class by itself, because of its special nature.

The use of some insulation material in conjunction with the plaster is usually required to prevent pattern soiling or shadowing of the interior surface. Experiments have shown that the rate of dirt accumulation on a surface is inversely proportional to surface temperature. Therefore, any variation in temperature over a surface will produce a corresponding difference in dirt accumulation which ultimately shows up as a noticeable difference in color. For example, in an uninsulated frame wall the pattern established by the studs behind the plaster will show on the plaster face after a short time. This results from a difference in surface temperature created by the differing heat transfer rates of the studs and the spaces between them. This difference in transfer rate can be controlled by the proper amount of insulation reducing surface temperature differences to the point where staining will not occur within the normal cleaning and painting period.[31]
Materials classified by reflectivity. The reflective behavior of heat energy (radiation), with respect to surfaces, involves consideration of the heat source temperature. The heat radiating from high temperature (incandescent) sources such as the sun, behaves differently than radiation from the low temperature sources common within buildings. The two types of radiation are sometimes referred to as *white heat* and *black heat*. There is further discussion of heat reflection in this chapter, under "Radiant Heat."

In its reflecting performance, the first type (white heat) behaves much like light. Light colors reflect light, but dark colors absorb it. Heat waves from incandescent sources are similarly reflected and absorbed in approximate relation to color. White stucco exterior surfaces and white gravel roofs are highly efficient as heat reflectors of solar radiation; testimony to this is found in the prevalence of white stucco throughout the warmer climates of the world.

In addition, surface texture is important. Smooth surfaces are better reflectors.

The reflection of black heat occurs without regard to color, but is sensitive to surface brightness. The term *reflective insulators* refers to a group of metallic materials which are identified by their surface brightness. Aluminum is commonly used as a reflective heat insulator. In order to achieve rated performance, several conditions must be satisfied concerning the installation of aluminum foil.

Metallic reflective materials must always be used in conjunction with an adjoining air space, or heat transfer will occur by means of conduction. The effectiveness of the air space is greatest at ¾ inches or more, and successive reflective spaces increase values proportionately. Rate of heat transfer does not depend on which side of an air space the foil is installed. However, these materials often serve as a vapor barrier and are therefore installed on the warm side of the construction.[32]

Reflectivity also depends on orientation (horizontal, diagonal, vertical position) and on the direction of heat flow (winter, summer). Quantities of heat required and the rate of heat transfer vary with these conditions, thus calculations should be made for each particular variation. Regular gypsum lath with a lamination of aluminum foil on one face is produced in standard and long lengths. This combination material serves to reflect heat and resist the transfer of moisture (vapor barrier) in addition to its use as a plaster base. Reflective lath usually is applied directly to wood studs and joists, or to wood furring in the case of masonry and steel construction.

Fig. 10 demonstrates how foil-backed gypsum lath and plaster finish coats provide a heat barrier against flow in either direction. This performance is explained by the poor emissivity of the foil. Reflective materials work regardless of which side first receives the heat. The face opposite an enclosed air space either reflects most of the heat radiating toward it, or retards by slow emissivity the heat coming the other way.

Some precautions which should be taken regarding installation are these: Aluminum foil should

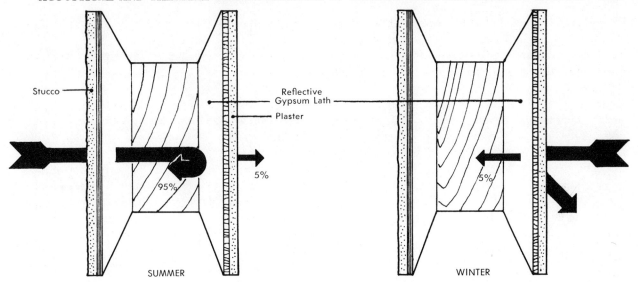

Rogers, T. S., *Design of Insulated Buildings For Various Climates*, New York © 1951, F. W. Dodge Corp.

Fig. 10 — Effectiveness of Aluminum Foil Regardless of Heat Transfer Direction

never come into contact with wet plaster where the alkaline reaction can destroy the thin metal. Foil or sheet metal reflective material should not be used on the cold side of construction. Reflective material should not be attached directly to conductive metallic supports or framing members.

Moisture control. Plaster, plaster base materials, insulation, and structural elements are all subject to varying degrees of damage from repeated exposure to water. This applies not only to water in its free state, but as well to water vapor, ice and frost. The major effects on plaster are efflorescence, deterioration and soiling.

The results of tests on insulating materials show that a water content up to 10 per cent by dry weight will not substantially lower the thermal resistance. Technical data are available for the reduced effectiveness of insulating materials relative to moisture content.[33]

The detrimental influences which water exerts on materials usually occur in the cavities of the structure behind the finished surface. Detection is often delayed until considerable damage has resulted. For this reason, effective control measures must be taken during the design and construction stages of building. The summarization that follows regarding water vapor characteristics and methods of control is intended to provide such information as may be helpful in preventing moisture damage to plaster work and other parts of the structure.

Since water vapor is a gas it can pass through porous materials, cracks and joints even though they may be water resistant. In many respects the requirements for vapor resistance are more stringent than those for water. Water vapor moves as a result of a vapor pressure differential. The difference in vapor pressure between the inside and outside of a confined space is the motivating force for passage of moisture through the material. This flow generally occurs in a direction from higher to lower temperature zones.

A maximum amount of vapor can be retained in a given space at any given temperature. This saturated condition is referred to as a state of 100 per cent *relative humidity*. The higher the temperature, the more vapor it takes to reach saturation. The temperature which corresponds to 100 per cent saturation is called the *dew point,* and this is the point beyond which precipitation can occur. Thus, when a mixture of air and vapor is cooled, the relative humidity progressively increases as the temperature drops, until saturation is reached at the dew point temperature. If the temperature is further reduced, vapor leaves the mixture as condensation. If the surface temperature of any area is below the dew point of the air and vapor mixture surrounding it, the air in contact with that area will be cooled to the dew point, and condensation will form.

In uninsulated construction, condensation will occur at the juncture of warm and cool zones, often the interior surface finish. By adding insulation material this juncture of warm and cool is moved into the construction, usually somewhere within the insulation. If relative humidity of the air and surface-to-air temperature differentials are known, the approximate location of potential condensation trouble zones can be determined. As water vapor progresses through the wall section towards the colder surface its temperature is lowered until it reaches saturation. The region of the wall at which this temperature is reached is called the *dew point zone* where, theoretically, condensation should occur. Condensation, however, usually forms against the nearest surface intercepting the flow of vapor, such as the interior surface of the sheathing.[34]

If an air space is provided between the insulation and the condensing surface, moisture will not easily be absorbed by the insulation and carried back to the lath and plaster. The porosity of the exterior surface material is important to the dissipation of moisture in the wall cavity. Research has shown that where the movement of vapor is relatively unobstructed, condensation is greatly reduced.[35] Portland cement plaster (stucco) is remarkably permeable to the passage of vapor. Thus it facilitates the escape of air-borne moisture to the outdoors while at the same time it prevents the intrusion of water from outside. Similarly, the building paper usually employed as backing material for stucco work is vapor permeable, although water resistant. **Vapor control.** In considering materials for the control of water vapor, the most important single prop-

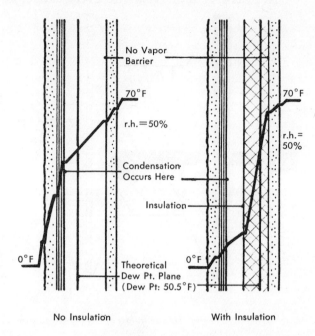

Rogers, T. S., *Design of Insulated Buildings For Various Climates*, New York © 1951, F. W. Dodge Corp.

Fig. 11 — Dew Point Temperature Zone

erty is vapor permeability; that is, the property of a material that allows the passage of water vapor. Vapor barrier materials are rated in terms of the permeance unit, *perm*. This unit is defined as a vapor transmission rate of one grain of water vapor through one square foot of material per hour when the vapor pressure difference is equal to one inch of mercury. A material having a vapor transmission rate of one perm or less as a property of the substance, is designated by the symbol (μ), and is based on unit thickness (*perm-inch*).

Whenever it is necessary to deal with materials of a stated or implied thickness other than unit thickness to which (μ) refers, then use is made of the permeance coefficient M, where $M = \mu/1$. These units are further defined in ASTM C355.

There are several methods for successfully preventing condensation: The proper location and installation of an effective vapor barrier material, ventilation of the structural cavity to decrease relative humidity, and control of moisture producing sources.

Vapor barriers. Materials usually classified as membranes are sheet metal, metallic foils, plastic films, bituminous papers, felts, and paint films. These materials will effectively restrict the movement of water vapor from a zone of high vapor pressure to one of lesser vapor pressure. Most have permeance values of one perm or less. The effectiveness of membranes is reduced by breaks, pinholes or improperly butted joints.

Table V lists various plasters, building materials and vapor barriers with their corresponding water vapor permeance ratings.

Once a particular material is selected, its final performance depends upon its location in the structural assembly and the care with which it is installed. When a vapor barrier is used it must always be installed on the warm side (inside) of the construction. By placing a vapor barrier between the interior finish and the insulation, a temperature is maintained at the level required to prevent condensation against the barrier.

In installation precaution should be taken to insure that materials are tight fitting and are not damaged. In spite of the most rigid controls the greater percentage of vapor passing the barrier will be through joints unless the material itself has been damaged.

Ventilation. A means of eliminating moisture in structural cavities is to lower the relative humidity of the air within the space. This is best accomplished by ventilating the cavity. The ventilation must be on the cold side so as not to offset the performance of insulation. In floor and roof construction, protected openings are made in soffits, overhangs, and facias. The area requirements for these openings cannot be predicted by precise calculations, but building codes and certain government agencies have set down minimum requirements. Wall and curtain wall elements are most difficult to ventilate because of the nature of their construction and climate exposure. Openings must be designed to keep water out but to allow air and water vapor to pass freely.

Another method is to reduce or control moisture at the source. Present-day living habits contribute to increased concentration of humidity within buildings. There tends to be more vapor producing elements per cubic foot of interior space. In housing and similar construction these vapor producing sources are controlled by exhausting moisture to the exterior with ventilating fans.

Dehumidifying and mechanical ventilation equipment properly located will accurately control relative humidities to a degree where structural and surface condensation become negligible. Higher costs, however, usually prohibit the use of such equipment except in special circumstances where the severity of the problem or the benefits derived are sufficient to warrant extraordinary measures.

III. USE OF PLASTER IN RADIANT HEATING SYSTEMS

Radiant heating was used extensively by the ancient Romans as a means of providing heat for large public buildings. In the Far East the rudimentary system can still be observed in Korea where radiant floors are used in practically all buildings. These historical methods, however, are crude and relatively inefficient compared to present systems. The development and refinement of heating elements such as hot-water pipes and electric resistor cables have given us a variety of efficient systems and a greater choice of locating heating panels. The comparatively small heating elements can be placed within a plaster panel or a concrete slab. During the past several decades enough radiant heating installations have been made, research completed, and material published to dispel the novelty once associated with this type of system. The theory and procedures of radiant heating are now an established part of the vocabulary of the architectural and engineering professions and of the construction industry.

Plaster has been used so extensively in conjunction with such systems that it has become the accepted surface material for radiant heating systems installed in walls and ceilings. This section will discuss the advantages, limitations, procedures, and methods of using plaster with radiant heating.

Table III.

THERMAL INSULATION

Conductivities (k) and Conductances (c) of Plaster and Lath

Material	Description	Thickness (In.)	Conductivity k	Conductance c	Source
Plaster	Gypsum, neat wood-fibered		3.15		a
	Gypsum-sand, 1:2 mix		5.51		a
	Gypsum-sand, 1:3 mix		5.60		a
	Gypsum-vermiculite, 1:2 mix		1.74		a
	Gypsum-vermiculite, 1:3 mix		1.42		a
	Gypsum-perlite, 1:2 mix		1.42		b
	Gypsum-perlite, 1:3 mix		1.12		b
	Portland cement plaster		8.00		c
	Vermiculite concrete, 1:4 mix		.97		d
	Vermiculite concrete, 1:6 mix		.76		d
	Perlite concrete, 1:4 mix		.77		b
	Perlite concrete, 1:6 mix		.58		b
	Gypsum lath and plaster	½″ plaster		2.4	e
	Metal lath and plaster	¾″ plaster		4.40	e
	Acoustical plasters (average)		.55-.65		f
Lath	Gypsum lath	⅜″		4.11	a
	Gypsum lath	½″		3.00	a

Source: a — Gypsum Association; b — Perlite Institute; c — Portland Cement Association; d — Vermiculite Institute; e — *Heating, Ventilating, Air-Conditioning Guide,* 1958; f — Manufacturers' Technical Literature.

Table IV

Coefficients of Over-All Heat Transmission (u) for Various Walls

Wall Construction		Plain Wall No Plaster	½-in. Plaster on		
			Wall Direct	¾-in. Furring	
				⅜-in. Plaster-Board	½-in. Rigid Insulation
Concrete Masonry Cores not filled	8-in. Sand and gravel or limestone	0.53	0.49	0.31	0.22
	8-in. Cinder	0.37	0.35	0.25	0.19
	8-in. Expanded slag or clay	0.33	0.32	0.23	0.18
	12-in. Sand and gravel or limestone	0.49	0.45	0.30	0.22
	12-in. Cinder	0.35	0.33	0.24	0.18
	12-in. Expanded slag or clay	0.32	0.31	0.23	0.18

Wall Construction		Plain Wall No Plaster	½-in. Plaster on		
			Wall Direct	¾-in. Furring	
				⅜-in. Plaster-Board	½-in. Rigid Insulation
Cores filled with cork or equal	8-in. Sand and gravel or limestone	0.39	0.37	0.26	0.19
	8-in. Cinder	0.20	0.19	0.16	0.13
	8-in. Expanded slag or clay	0.17	0.17	0.14	0.12
	12-in. Sand and gravel or limestone	....	....	....	....
	12-in. Cinder	0.20	0.19	0.15	0.13
	12-in. Expanded slag or clay	0.15	0.14	0.12	0.11
Cast-in-Place Concrete	6½-in. Wall	0.76	0.68	0.38	0.26
	8-in. Wall	0.69	0.62	0.36	0.25
4-in. Face Brick Plus:	4-in. Common brick	0.50	0.46	0.30	0.22
	4-in. Clay tile	0.45	0.42	0.28	0.21
	4-in. Hollow sand and gravel unit	0.53	0.49	0.31	0.23
	4-in. Solid sand and gravel unit	0.65	0.59	0.35	0.24
	4-in. Hollow cinder unit	0.45	0.42	0.28	0.21
	4-in. Solid cinder unit	0.49	0.46	0.30	0.22
	4-in. Hollow expanded clay or slag	0.43	0.41	0.27	0.20
	4-in. Solid expanded clay or slag	0.45	0.42	0.28	0.21
	1-in. Wood sheathing, paper 2x4 studs (wood lath and plaster)	....	0.27	0.27	0.20
4-in. Common Brick Plus:	4-in. Clay tile	0.39	0.37	0.26	0.19
	4-in. Hollow sand and gravel unit	0.45	0.42	0.28	0.21
	4-in. Solid sand and gravel unit	0.52	0.49	0.31	0.22
	4-in. Hollow cinder unit	0.39	0.37	0.26	0.19
	4-in. Solid cinder unit	0.42	0.39	0.27	0.20
	4-in. Hollow expanded clay or slag	0.37	0.35	0.25	0.19
	4-in. Solid expanded clay or slag	0.39	0.37	0.26	0.19
	Wood sheathing, paper, 2x4 studs (wood lath and plaster)	....	0.25	0.25	0.19
Wood Construction	Wood siding, 1-in. wood sheathing, 2x4 studs (wood lath and plaster)	....	0.25	0.24	0.19
Clay Tile Walls:	6-in. No exterior finish	0.43	0.40	0.27	0.20
	8-in. No exterior finish	0.41	0.38	0.26	0.20
	10-in. No exterior finish	0.40	0.38	0.26	0.20
	6-in. Stucco exterior	0.41	0.39	0.27	0.20
	8-in. Stucco exterior	0.40	0.37	0.26	0.20
	10-in. Stucco exterior	0.39	0.37	0.26	0.19

Wall Construction		Plain Wall No Plaster	½-in. Plaster on		
			Wall Direct	¾-in. Furring	
				⅜-in. Plaster-Board	½-in. Rigid Insulation
Cavity	9-in. Wall of two 4-in. sand and gravel or limestone units	0.35	0.33	0.24	0.18
Walls: Built in two	9-in. Wall of two 4-in. lightweight units	0.28	0.27	0.20	0.16
units with a 1 inch or larger air space	9-in. Wall of 4-in. face brick and 4-in.				
between.	lightweight unit	0.33	0.31	0.22	0.18
Cavity not filled.	13-in. Wall of 4-in. face brick and 8-in.				
	lightweight unit	0.26	0.25	0.19	0.16
	13-in. Wall of 4-in. lightweight unit and				
	8-in. lightweight unit	0.23	0.23	0.18	0.15

Source: Portland Cement Association. *How to Calculate Heat Transmission Coefficients and Vapor Condensation Temperatures of Concrete Masonry Walls, 1946.*

Table V.

Vapor Permeance of Lathing and Plastering Materials

Permeance values in grains per square foot per hour per inch of mercury pressure

Material	Vapor Permeance (P-Perms)	Vapor Resistance (I/P-Rep)
Plaster Materials		
Gypsum lath with aluminum foil backing	0.09-0.39	2.56-11.5
Plaster base and plaster, ¾″	14.7	0.08
Plaster, wood lath	11.0	0.09
Plaster, fiberboard or gypsum lath	19.7-20.	0.05
Plaster, 3 coats of lead and oil paint	3.68-3.84	0.26-0.27
Plaster, 2 coats of aluminum paint	1.15	0.87

Source: Rogers, T. S. Design of insulated buildings for various climates. Ratings compiled from data by L. V. Teesdale, L. G. Miller, J. D. Babbitt and Forest Products Laboratory, U.S.D.A.

Much information is currently available on the theory and design of various radiant heating systems. A selected bibliography is included at the end of this chapter that will serve as a guide for those interested in acquiring more detailed information on the theoretical and technical aspects. Discussion of the theory of radiant heating will be limited to the location and selection of materials, the establishment of standards of comfort, and the successful installation of plaster as one component of the system.

Definition of radiant heat. Thermal radiation is the transmission of energy by means of electromagnetic waves of very long wave length. Radiant energy of any wave length may, when absorbed, become thermal energy and result in an increase in the temperature of the absorbing body.[36] Radiant energy travels in a straight line at the speed of light and is not affected by the temperature or currents of the air through which it passes.

Comfort. Radiant heating provides comfort by reducing the amount of heat loss from the body due to radiation. In convection methods of heating, the reduction in body heat loss is effected by maintaining higher temperatures of the surrounding air.

The term *Mean Radiant Temperature* (MRT) is used in radiant heating to designate one of the basic design considerations. It can be described as the point where a balance in temperature occurs between the warmest and coolest surfaces of a room. Exact standards of comfort for all persons are difficult, if not impossible, to state. Adlam,[37] on the basis of laboratory research, does set values. While apparently conservative, they serve as a point of departure in designing radiant heating systems. From his experience it was found that a feeling of comfort was generally acknowledged when the temperature of the skin and surface of clothing was 81 degrees F. In order to balance the total heat losses from the body and maintain this temperature, the relationship of an air temperature of 68 degrees F. and an MRT of 72 degrees was found to be the most satisfactory.

Panel temperatures. Considerable controversy exists regarding the maximum panel temperature that can be used without producing discomfort to the occupants of a room and without damaging the panel materials. These are the recommendations most frequently found in technical literature on the subject:

Table VI.

Surface Temperatures Generally Recommended for Radiant Panel Systems

Type of Panel	Average Surface Temperature, °F.
Plaster Ceiling(A)	110-115
Plaster Walls	110-120(B)
Floors	85
Floors (borders, aisles)	110-120

(A) 8 to 10 foot ceiling height.
(B) 115°F. maximum recommended for gypsum plaster.

There are abundant claims of successful installations that run contrary to these figures. The opportunity for such conflict arises largely from the fact that absolute comfort values have not been established. In a forum discussion series held at Pratt Institute this observation was made by participating engineers, architects, and other professional people: "It is obvious then that more exact information is required concerning (A) the comfortable surface temperatures for human beings as well as (B) the safe temperatures for floor and ceiling materials. The gradual process of accumulating these data by various means represents a necessary phase through which any developing technology must go; in the meantime, the results

of accepted practice indicate that there is little reason to doubt that existing recommendations for panel temperature limitations — while not ideally precise — are reasonably accurate and cautiously low."[38]

Plaster panels — design considerations. Plaster panels are readily adaptable to most radiant heating systems being used at the present time. They have been used successfully with hot water, warm air, and electrical heat sources. The heating medium has been distributed in small elements such as pipes and electrical wires embedded in the plaster; in large elements such as 1½ inch pipes; in fin-tube elements placed above the plaster panel for combination radiation and convection of heat; and in warm air plenum systems where the plaster serves as part of the duct enclosure.

Plaster — materials and practices. In general, radiant heating presents no special plastering problems from the standpoint of selection of materials, preparation, and application procedures. The same methods outlined in Chapters 3 and 4 are used.

Gypsum, lime, and portland cement are all used as cementitious materials and possess the same advantages and limitations for radiant panel use that are acknowledged in common plastering practice and discussed elsewhere. The same considerations hold for metal lath, gypsum lath, and aggregates, except those particular limitations which are discussed below.

Certain special application techniques have been developed, particularly with respect to systems using embedded hot water coils. These will be outlined in that part of this chapter dealing with the various methods of heating the plaster panel. Before making final material selection or specifying preparation and application methods, the designer should refer to these discussions of various heating systems.

Following are recommendations on the use of lathing and plastering materials:

In radiant panel heating systems where gypsum products are employed, the surface temperature should not exceed 115 degrees F. and the temperature of the heat conductors in direct contact with the gypsum should not exceed 125 degrees F. These temperatures are necessitated by the fact that the process of calcination of the gypsum begins at approximately 125 degrees F. In practice, this limitation is not particularly restrictive since other general considerations, such as maximum panel temperature allowed for comfort and the uniform surface temperature required to prevent pattern soiling, more often govern design temperatures. Usually, these design temperatures will be less than the maximums specified for gypsum products.

The maximum design temperature for lime plaster is theoretically 1,725 degrees F., at which point lime will calcine. Due to comfort restrictions, there is rarely cause for such high temperatures unless the panel surface is an appropriate distance away, as might be the case in a high ceiling.

Gypsum products should not be used in radiant cooling systems because condensation can occur within the panel with resulting harmful effects to the physical properties of the material. Similar restrictions do not apply in the same degree to the use of lime and portland cement plasters. Lightweight aggregates and acoustical plasters and plastics are not generally used in radiant heating systems due to their greater thermal resistance.

In systems employing electric cables embedded in plaster over metal lath, a 3/8 inch scratch coat of plaster should be applied before attaching the heating units.

Radiant energy travels in a straight line at the speed of light. Using this principle with plaster panels that can be formed to any shape or slope, it is possible to concentrate heat on any given point or surface where higher temperatures are desired, much in the manner of controlled reflectivity in acoustics. While the use of this design information is generally reserved for special situations, it should be considered in all instances where heated surfaces of a room are not parallel to other planes. This is done in order to avoid an unwanted concentration of radiant energy at one point and an absence of radiant energy at another.

Surface finish and color. It can be seen that the control, or lack of control, of rays is related as closely to the surface finish as it is to the angle or shape of the heating panel. Contrary to general belief, all rays are not necessarily emitted at right angles to the surface of the panel. This would be true only in a perfectly smooth surface. In the case of rougher textures, rays are emitted along lines normal to every facet of the surface protrusions, regardless of their size or orientation. The rays are therefore projected in all directions. They can, in fact, travel parallel to the surface.

The radiation from a heated panel depends not only on the temperature, but also on the nature of the surface. Certain substances that radiate and absorb more energy than others are said to have greater *emissivity*. The consideration of this property of materials should serve as one basis in selecting materials to be used.[39]

Because of the variety of colors and surface textures available in plaster, the designer can obtain an efficient radiating panel as well as a surface that meets other requirements.

Panel temperature. The recommended panel temperature for wall and ceiling radiant panels could be in the range of 110 to 120 degrees F. without causing discomfort to the occupants or possible damage to the materials. On the other hand, floor installations are generally designed for a maximum surface temperature of 85 to 90 degrees F. Therefore, a higher BTU output per unit of surface area can be more readily obtained in either ceiling or wall panels without adversely affecting the comfort of the occupants of the room. This statement is from the technical literature of one large manufacturer of coils designed for use in either floor, ceiling or wall: "Ratings above 65 B.T.U./sq. ft./hr. should not be used for low ceiling or wall panels, nor ratings above 40 B.T.U./sq. ft./hr. for floors in continuously occupied rooms."[41]

"The comfort limit for a ceiling is less crucial (than floor or wall surfaces), since occupants never come into direct contact with its surface. However,

Table VII.

Relative Emissivities of Various Materials and Surfaces[40]

Material	(E)*	Colored Paints and Surfaces	(E)*
Dull Black Matt Finish	1.00	Matt Black Paint	1.00
Plaster (Rough) Unpainted	0.94	Grey Paint	0.99
Plaster (Smooth) Unpainted	0.92	White Paint	0.95
Plaster (Papered)	0.94	Ivory Paint	0.94
Stonework	0.94	Green Paint	0.91
Brickwork	0.95	Aluminum Paint	0.54
Concrete (Rough)	0.95	Bronze Paint	0.48
Concrete (Smooth)	0.92	Plain White Paper on Black Surface	1.00
Woodwork (Waxed)	0.91	Plain White Paper on Copper Surface	1.00
Woodwork (Rough)	0.95	Plain Copper Dull Finish	0.20
Woodwork (Painted)	0.93	Polished Copper	0.11
Glass (Plain)	0.90	Polished Steel	0.10
Linoleum (Unpolished)	0.90	Polished Aluminum	0.05
Iron (Painted)	0.93		
Glazed Tile	0.90		
Unglazed Tile	0.94		
White Marble	0.85		
Asbestos Board	0.92		
Asbestos Tiles (Polished)	0.85		

*Emissivity: Relative amount of energy radiated from surfaces of the same temperature.

an unpleasant awareness of active radiation may result from certain combinations of high ceiling temperatures and low ceiling heights, and many engineers hold that the maximum surface temperature which an occupant finds comfortable increases proportionately with the height of the room."[42]

In rooms with higher ceilings the uniform panel temperature can be increased, with resulting BTU output to balance the heat loss of the room without creating uncomfortable awareness of the heat source. Plaster containing either gypsum or lime-portland cement binders can be used without concern in all instances where the plaster is not subjected to temperatures higher than 125 degrees F. Above this temperature, it is recommended only lime-portland cement plaster be used. Successful installations of lime-portland cement plaster radiant panels have been reported where the surface temperature was as high as 180 degrees F., although the incidence of conditions requiring temperatures in this range is relatively small.

Radiant panels transfer heat to the surrounding air by convection, and to solid objects by radiation. Compared to wall and floor surfaces, ceiling surfaces transfer the greatest percentage of heat by radiation, and are therefore the truest radiant systems (see Table VIII). For most installations, particularly in residences, the ceiling is considered an ideal location, since there is less likelihood of later alterations obstructing the output of heat.

Table VIII.

Effect of Radiant Panel Location on Method of Heat Transfer

Surface	Convection Transfer	Radiant Transfer
Ceiling	35%	65%
Wall	48%	52%
Floor	52%	48%

Location of plaster radiant panels. Either the walls or the ceilings of a room finished in plaster can be used as the radiant surface of the heating system. While specific design factors, some of which will be outlined later, may influence the choice of panel location, there are certain considerations that remain constant in all systems.

Thermal lag. The most frequently heard criticism of radiant heating systems, particularly in structural floor panels, is the lack of sensitivity to rapid temperature change. In contrast to warm air, hot water, or steam systems (which heat primarily by convection), radiant systems do not begin pouring heat into the room the moment an indoor thermostat "feels" the need. Nor will a radiant system cease to transmit heat after the source has been retarded. The basic cause of this behavior in radiant systems is related to the thermal capacity of the radiant panel.

An analogy can be made between these characteristics of radiant panels and a sponge placed in a shallow pan of water. Before any water will appear on the face of the sponge and begin to evaporate, the sponge must first become saturated. Conversely, evaporation will continue from the sponge after the original water supply has disappeared

from the pan. The lag thus demonstrated is proportional to the water-carrying capacity of the sponge.

Since thermal capacity, or the ability to "soak up" heat, is largely related to mass and density, any reduction in the thickness of panel material reduces the time required for the panel to respond to demanded changes in temperature. Plaster panels, usually less than 1 inch thick, with heating elements often as close as ⅜ inch from the panel surface, provide a relatively sensitive response to temperature needs. The influence of response of the more massive panels required in floor construction, plus the effect of floor coverings, was discussed at the forum series on radiant heating held at the Pratt Institute's School of Architecture.

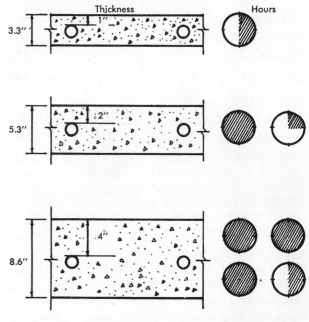

Radiant Heating — Radiant Cooling: A Forum Series, Bulletin No. 1, 1954, Pratt Institute.

Fig. 12 — Relationship of Thermal Response to Thickness of Slab

In Fig. 12 it can be seen that the time of response of the thinner slab is one-seventh that of the thicker one, even though it is approximately one-third as thick.

The sensitivity of floor panels to response is further diminished when floor coverings are considered. Table IX shows the equivalent concrete thickness of various finish flooring materials.[43]

Table IX.

Floor Coverings and Equivalent Thicknesses of Concrete For Heating Calculations

Floor Covering	Equivalent Thickness of Concrete (inches)
1″ Wood Floor	8
Carpet (Average) No Base Pad	5.8
Carpet Rubber Base Pad	7.0
Carpet Felt Base Pad	10.3
Asphalt Tile	0.5

In addition to the importance of using a thin slab to minimize the adverse effects of thermal lag, a number of other design measures must be considered. Among these factors are proper thermostatic control, zoning, insulation, and piping layout. **Thermal insulation.** Because radiant panels will emit rays equally from either face, it is necessary to reduce the heat loss from the non-functional side of the panel by installing as much insulation as is economically practicable. In building situations where a radiant ceiling is installed below an occupied space, the practice of trying to heat the ceiling of one room and the floor of another with a single heating source, is open to question. The supply of adequate heat to both spaces is complicated by the difference in recommended surface temperatures between floors and ceilings; by the possible difference in heating requirements in both spaces; and by the problem of placing the heating elements in the proper position with relation to both spaces.

Expansion and contraction in radiant plaster panels. Uncontrolled expansion and contraction are contributing causes of cracking in plaster, as has been shown in Chapter 6. Radiant panels represent additional considerations only to the extent that the plaster slab is subject to greater temperature variation, with a resulting increase in linear movement. Recommendations for unrestrained panel edges, division of large areas by expansion joints, and recognition of the relationship of panel configuration to expansion characteristics remain unchanged.

Drying and curing plaster panels. All plasters contain a greater amount of water for mixing and application than is needed to complete the chemical action that occurs in the setting or hardening of the material. The only way this excess "mixing water" can be removed from the plaster is by evaporation. Conditions must be maintained that will allow the moisture to be evaporated into the finished room and then removed by ventilation. During the plastering operations and the drying of the plaster the room temperature should be maintained between 55 and 70 degrees F. It should not exceed 90 degrees F. or the outside air temperature (whichever is higher) until the plaster has set and is thoroughly dry.[44]

The radiant heating system should never be used to accelerate the drying of plaster. All heat that is required to maintain the recommended room temperatures should be supplied by temporary heaters that will uniformly distribute warm air. During the drying and curing period, plaster is particularly sensitive to thermally induced dimensional change. Unless the heat in the room is evenly distributed the possibility of thermal shock and resultant cracking is increased, and the chances of a dryout are greater due to accelerated evaporation in the vicinity of the heating unit.

Starting a radiant heating system after the plaster is dry. In order to avoid thermal shock it is recommended that heat be introduced into the slab gradually until its design temperature is reached. While minor variations will be found in common practice, the following method has been used extensively without mishap, and is therefore considered by most authorities as acceptable:

(1) Operate the heating system for at least 24 hours at that temperature maintained by temporary heating methods during the plastering and drying operations.

(2) Increase the operating temperature of the system in increments of 5 degrees F. every 24 hours until final operating temperatures are reached.

The same procedure should be observed when the system is being turned off and the temperature of the atmosphere is below that of the inside of the building.

Pattern soiling and shadowing. The major causes for the occurrence of shadows and soiling on radiant panels is more often due to faulty design or execution of the work than to inherent characteristics. Since dust and other air-borne impurities are attracted to cold surfaces more readily than they are to warm surfaces, significant differences in surface temperature are to be avoided. Shadow marking is caused by convection currents and temperature differences.[45]

Properly designed radiant plaster panels should present no problems in this respect. The surface temperatures of the panel are several degrees above the surrounding air, and the convection currents created by radiant systems are fewer and weaker than those found where other conventional heating systems are used.

Difficulties may be encountered, however, if the heating conductors are widely spaced and operated at high temperatures in order to produce an *average* allowable, but not uniformly distributed, surface temperature. Fig. 13 illustrates the amplitude of temperature differences on the surface of a plaster panel caused by variations in operating temperatures and coil spacing.

The values shown for the relationship of tube spacing, total panel output, and surface temperature wave amplitude, resulted from research by the American Society of Heating and Ventilating Engineers.[46] In this series of tests, the panels were constructed of metal lath and plaster on wood joists. Hot water radiant coils, placed above the lath, were firmly embedded in the plaster. The

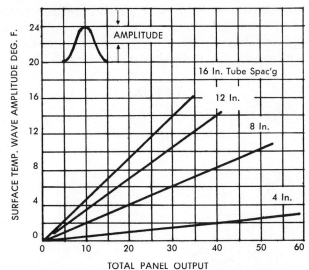

Reproduced by permission from *Further Studies of the Thermal Characteristics of Plaster Panels*, by L. F. Schutrum and C. M. Humphreys in the ASHVE Journal, Section of Heating, Piping and Air Conditioning, June 1953, Fig. 6, p.125.

Fig. 13 — Relationship of Tube Spacing to Surface Temperature

temperature was found to be highest directly beneath the heating element and lowest at mid-point between the coils. The amplitude values shown in Fig. 13 represent this temperature difference.

T. S. Rogers, in *Design of Insulated Buildings for Various Climates*, says that where ". . . the [surface] temperature differences are slight, it may take four to five years or more for any visible evidence of ghost markings [shadowing] to appear. When walls and ceilings are cleaned or repainted within this period, the problem is not troublesome. However, wide temperature differences cause dust patterns to develop in a single heating season.[47*]

The minimum property requirements of the Federal Housing Administration set 6.5 degrees F. as the maximum surface temperature difference that can be used without presenting a serious problem. Rogers has observed that even smaller variations are apt to show noticeable dust patterns.[48]

* T. S. Rogers finds from experience that relatively minor temperature differences will cause noticeable dust patterns to show and the dustiness of the air is an important factor.

Painting and decorating radiant plaster panels. The procedures for painting and decorating these panels differ only slightly from those recommended in Chapter 6. Certain limitations on the choice of decorating materials are imposed by the technical requirements of radiant heating. It has been pointed out (Table VII) that the emissivity of a radiant panel is not directly related to the color value (dark to light). But it is related to the degree of gloss of the paint (dull surfaces generally have greater emissivity than those that are glossy). For this reason metallic paints such as bronze or aluminum should not be used. The Invisible Panel Warming Association of England further recommends "That the finish of warming panels should not be more glossy than 'eggshell gloss.' Heat radiation from glossy surfaces is less effective than from flat or dull surfaces, and with glossy surfaces there is a tendency for discoloration and dusting. Discoloration will most certainly occur on other than flat finishes if the surface temperature is allowed to exceed 105 degrees F., and in no circumstances should the surface temperature be allowed to exceed 110 degrees F. The general surface temperature for moderate weather is 95 degrees F. . . . varnishes must never be used; they will discolour."[49]

Application of paint. It is generally agreed the heating system should be operated for a time and then cooled prior to decoration. It is recommended that in no case the system be in operation during painting and decorating, or be used to accelerate the final drying of the surface. The Gypsum Association recommends that the heating system be operated at the design panel temperature for at least 24 hours prior to the application of decorating materials. In addition, it states that where textures or tinted finishing plasters or decorations are used, they should be allowed to set and dry thoroughly before heating is resumed.

* Although a difference in definition of *pipes* and *tubes* is acknowledged, they will be used interchangeably in the text; the use of one term will not connote exclusion of the other unless so stated.

In this respect, English specifications seem more stringent than those used in the United States. The specification of the Invisible Panel Warming Association states that no decoration should be attempted for at least one week after the heating system has been in operation. After the panel has been turned off and allowed to cool, dry distempers (sizing or priming) may be applied. "At least three weeks should be allowed for water paint distempers and two months for paints and enamels."[50]

"Unless otherwise specified a minimum of twenty-four hours is required for each coat to become thoroughly dry before the application of the next coat, and heat should not be turned on between the application of the various coats and until four days after the application of the final coat. In specific instances longer periods are required."[51]

Plaster as panel material in various heating systems. The foregoing discussion has dealt with general considerations concerning the use of plaster in radiant heating. We have noted that several mediums (hot water, air and electricity) could be used to provide heat for the radiant panels. Specific attention must be given to these variations.

Hot water systems. Pipes or tubing embedded in the plaster panel are most frequently used as conductors in hot water radiant systems. A secondary method makes use of fin-type convectors placed above, or behind, the plaster panel.

Pipe and tubing installations. Copper, brass, wrought iron, and steel pipes and tubes,* formed into coils or grids are the most frequently used materials in hot water radiant systems. The coils or grids are placed either above or below the lath prior to the application of plaster. Practical considerations usually require that larger pipes (more than ¾ inch I.D.) be placed above the lath; smaller sizes can be installed either above or below. Regardless of their size, if the pipes or tubes are placed below the lath, it is recommended that the plaster be at least ⅜ inch from the radiant surface to the bottom of the conductor. (See Fig. 14.)

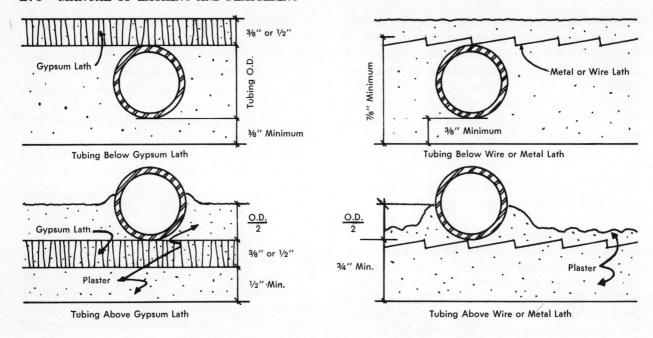

Fig. 14 — Recommended Thickness of Plaster With Tubes or Pipes Embedded Above and Below the Lath

It will be noted that where the tubing is placed below the lath the thickness of plaster is determined primarily by the outside diameter of the tubing. The cost of the lathing and plastering will be unnecessarily high if an exceptionally thick plaster slab is required; and thermal lag, of which thickness is a direct function, will increase.

It is interesting, when discussing the size of tubes, to see the results of tests that were made to determine the relationship of tube size and tube spacing to panel output. In Table X, it can be seen that the panel conductance is not, for all practical purposes, affected by the size of the tube; the output is inversely proportional to the spacing of the tubes.[52]

While from Table X there appears to be no substantial advantage in the use of smaller size tubing, in practice the selection must be influenced by other factors. These include pressure drop, maximum permissible temperature difference between the entering and leaving water, and uniformity of

Table X.

Panel Output at Various Tube Spacings and Tube Sizes

(B.T.U./Hour/Sq. ft. of panel/°F*)

Tube Diameter (O.D.)	Spacing		
	4″	6″	9″
⅜″	2.32	1.50	1.07
½″	2.30	1.55	1.11
¾″	2.48	1.60	1.15

* Temperature difference between water in coils and panel surface temperature.

panel surface temperature. Such factors combine to indicate an optimum for any particular installation. **Tube patterns.** Two basic patterns are used in coil radiant heating: grid, and continuous.

Of the two, the grid provides more even water temperatures while varying in water pressure and velocity. On the other hand, the continuous pattern produces more constant pressures with varying water temperatures. When a continuous coil system is used the hottest part of the coil usually is placed near the exterior wall, where the largest amount of heat is required. Adlam recommends the use of the continuous coil ". . . because it insures constant circulation through its entire length. With

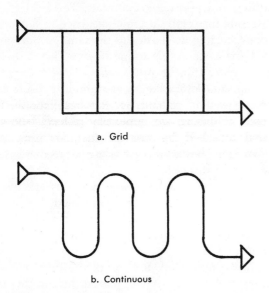

Fig. 15 – Tube Patterns Grid and Continuous

the grid type coil there is greater rigidity and any unequal expansion in the pipes forming the grid creates a greater risk of cracking the plaster."[53] One manufacturer of wrought iron piping lists these advantages and disadvantages of the continuous coil:

(1) Little less expensive than grid coils because random lengths of pipe are used more easily and generally less welding is involved. The economies realized through less welding, however, often are counteracted by the labor involved to bend continuous coils.

(2) There is greater frictional loss in a continuous coil, and therefore the use is generally restricted to small areas.

(3) A compromise between the two systems often leads to the most satisfactory solution. (See Fig. 16.)

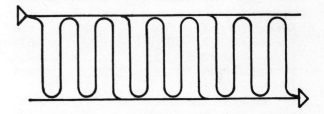

Fig. 16 – Combination Grid and Continuous Coil

Expansion and contraction. In the design and operation of a radiant heating system, where coils are to be embedded in the plaster, every effort must be made to minimize the stresses in the panel during the expansion and contraction of the coils. It must be borne in mind that where the coefficient of expansion of the pipe is equal to, or greater than, that of the plaster, when heat is first introduced into the system, the pipe will expand more rapidly than will the plaster surrounding it. Where the coefficient of expansion of the tube is less than that of the plaster this consideration, though still of great importance, is minimized and often longer coils can be used.

In plaster construction, care should be used in laying out the coils to avoid placing hot supply lines next to cooler returns. If this caution is not heeded, pattern soiling or shadowing of the surface can be expected, even if the plaster slab is not damaged by the temperature differential.

One proposal for countering the effects of expansion and contraction suggests that hot water be circulated through the coils intermittently during the application of the plaster basecoat in order to destroy the bond between the coils and the plaster. It is generally agreed, however, that any benefits that might be derived from this method are nullified by other considerations. The air space created around the piping will reduce the thermal conductance of the panel and increase the thermal lag.

Table XI.

Coefficients of Linear Expansion

(inches/inch/°F) x 10–6

Plaster

Gypsum-Sand 1:2	6.50
Gypsum-Sand 1:3	6.75
Gypsum-Wood Fiber	9.30
(A) Gypsum-Perlite 1:2	7.35
(A) Gypsum-Perlite 1:3	7.30
(A) Gypsum-Vermiculite 1:2	8.35
(A) Gypsum-Vermiculite 1:3	8.60

Pipes and Tubes

Copper	9.3
Brass	10.8
Wrought Iron	6.7
Steel (soft)	6.2

Others

Portland Cement Concrete	7.9

(A) Not generally recommended for radiant heating due to thermal insulating properties.

Attachment of coils. Many convenient methods have been developed to facilitate placement and attachment of coils. A light wood frame or cradle may be used to hold the tube at desired spacings, after which it is temporarily braced on the ceiling so that one man can fasten the coil in place.

Published standards recommend that the tubing be supported by the joists, furring channels or runners, and never by the lath. Tubing is attached by means of tie wire, staples, straps or other devices similar to those shown in Fig. 17. Reference should be made to the design tables of Chapter 5 for allowable loadings of supporting members.

Care should be taken during the installation of tubes to prevent leaks or damage caused by denting or squeezing. Grids and coils should not be placed directly against steel joists or other steel framing members, because of the heat loss that will occur from conduction.

Lathing and plastering materials. The lathing and plastering materials and methods used in hot water radiant heating are basically the same as those outlined for general plastering work. They are discussed more fully in other parts of this manual.

Gypsum lath. Plain or perforated gypsum lath can be used in radiant heating installations. The coils of tubing are generally placed below the lath and attached by one of the methods previously shown. Lime basecoat plasters are not recommended for use over this lath.

In those instances where the coils are placed above gypsum lath, it is recommended that the tubes be covered or partially covered with plaster. This is done to increase conduction to the radiant surface.

Metal lath. Coils are installed either above or below metal lath. When placed below the lath there must be at least ⅜ inch from the face of the plaster to the bottom of the tubing. (See Fig. 14.) Back-plastering of panels where the tubes are placed above the lath is desirable but often not

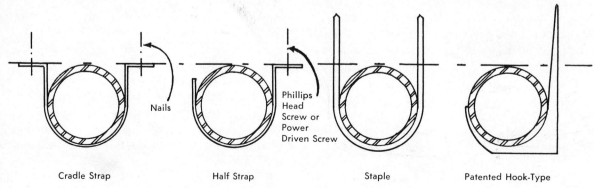

Cradle Strap   Half Strap   Staple   Patented Hook-Type

Fig. 17 — Devices Used for the Attachment of Tubes

practicable. A generally preferred method is to apply the scratch coat with sufficient force to embed each tube at least 50 per cent. Several advantages are claimed for placing the coils above the lath, including a saving in labor materials. In the photographs (Fig. 18), it is shown that the workmen applying plaster to the ceiling where the coils were placed below the lath must use short, choppy strokes in order to fill the spaces between the coils. On the other hand, the workman applying plaster on the lath installed under the coils does so in a normal sweeping manner.

These specifications for use in radiant heating are published by the Metal Lath Manufacturers Association:

"The application of metal lath to a radiant panel ceiling is exactly the same as for ordinary ceilings. Diamond mesh metal lath should be nailed to wood joists with 1½", 11 gauge, barbed roofing nails with 7/16" heads, spaced not more than 6" apart. Longer nails should be used with 3/8" rib-lath so that there is at least 1⅜" penetration into wood joists. For suspended ceilings, metal lath should be attached to the furring channels with 18 gage galvanized annealed wires at intervals of not more than 6".[54]

Plaster and plastering. The Gypsum Association recommends that all lathing and plastering be done in accordance with the applicable provisions of ASA No. A42.1, "Standard Specifications for Gypsum Plastering," and ASA No. A42.4, "Standard Specifications for Interior Lathing and Furring."[55] It further recommends observance of these check points and job practices:

"Before applying gypsum products the construction method should be carefully examined to make certain that the weight of heating elements is carried by permanent attachment to the structural framing members.

"Prior to applying gypsum products above or below the circulating elements, the system should be checked for leaks and operating efficiency.

"Grounds for plaster should be thoroughly checked to insure a minimum plaster cover of 3/8" over the outside of the heating elements.

"Where more than ½" basecoat thickness is required over the face of gypsum lath, the plastering shall be done by a minimum three coat method, including the finish. In this case the scratch coat shall be thoroughly cross-raked and shall set and dry at least over night before applying the brown coat. Very thick applications shall be in four coats, including finish. Thicker than usual basecoat applications require longer drying time before finish coat application. To avoid "shadowing" under pipes the basecoat shall be dry or almost dry before finish coat application. If bone dry, the basecoat may be wetted, if necessary, to reduce suction for finish application."[56]

The Finishing Lime Association of Ohio reports excellent results from installations using a specification developed primarily for radiant coil ceiling panels. Note that this specification allows maximum water temperatures of 180 degrees or more.[57] (See Fig. 19.)

Lathing and Attachment of Tubing: Expanded metal lath is applied to the ceiling joists after which the tubing is attached below the lath by metal clips fastened to the joists.
Number of Coats-Proportions: Four coats are required in this specification: scratch, fill-in, brown, and finish. The basecoats are all double scratched and contain hair or fiber. The proportions for the basecoats are as follows:

	Lime	*Portland Cement*			*Sand*
Scratch	1	to	1	to	4
Fill-in	1	to	1	to	4
Brown	1	to	1	to	3

Finish Coat: The finish or white coat consists of 1 part lime, 3 parts sand, and 1 part gauging plaster. It is applied 3/16" to ¼" thick, laid on evenly and, before setting, burlap (running 7 meshes to the inch) is laid on dry. The burlap is then trowelled into the finish coat until it can no longer be seen. Additional sand is added to the white coat at time of mixing if a sand finish is desired.

Radiant cooling. Just as hot panels can *radiate* heat to a room and its occupants, so a cool panel can *absorb* heat from them. Thus, the circulation of

Fig. 18 — (A) *Plastering Coils Above Lath* (B) *Plastering Coils Below Lath*

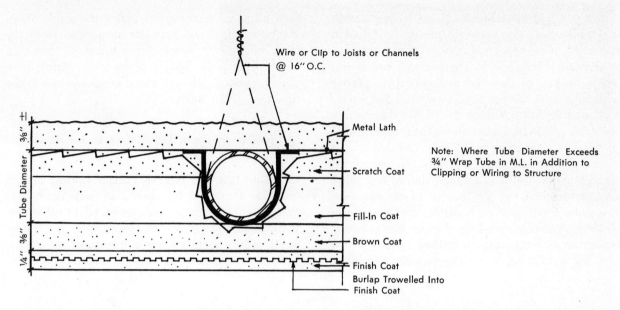

Fig. 19 — Radiant Panel Using Lime — Portland Cement Plaster

cool water through radiant coils would seem a reasonable method for cooling a building during the summer. While theoretically correct, this principle has not found widespread use, for one important reason: Unless supplementary means are used to reduce the moisture content in a room, it is difficult to obtain any cooling effect from the panels without reducing the surface temperature below the dew point of the space. The result is an accumulation of condensation within and on the surface of the panel.

A sensible approach taken during recent years recognizes the limitations of radiant cooling. This approach provides a limited amount of air conditioning in order to create a moisture-temperature relationship within a space, and it is conducive to economical use of the radiant system. This type of combination cooling system not only provides a considerable saving of space, compared to conventional air conditioning systems, but at the same time reduces the operating costs. It is reported that in the Alcoa Building in Pittsburgh, where a combination radiant cooling-air conditioning system was

used, the cost of the system was approximately half the estimated cost of one that did not make use of radiant cooling.[58]

The use of lath and plaster in radiant cooling is similar to that in radiant heating. In either case, the same methods for installing materials are recommended. The single exception that should be mentioned concerns the formulation of plaster. Where plaster is to be used in connection with a radiant heating-cooling system, materials such as lime and portland cement that are not susceptible to damage by moisture should be selected.

Enclosed convector panels. Short, fin-tube convectors placed in the spaces between ceiling joists are another hot water radiant system that can be used with plaster ceiling panels.

The sections of tubing are manufactured in lengths that are arranged to fit between joists 12 inches, 16 inches, or 24 inches o.c. They consist of aluminum fins bonded to a ⅝ inch diameter copper tube. To be fully effective, each joist space must contain at least one section of tubing. Thus the air in each joist space will be heated, after which the ceiling will become a radiant panel by convection and conduction. The units are placed on 2 foot 6 inch to 10 foot centers and operate at a water temperature of 215 degrees F. There is only one limitation in the use of these heating units with plaster ceilings. That is, the coil must be operated at a temperature that will not cause the plaster directly beneath the unit to be heated above the recommended maximum temperatures previously discussed.

Warm air radiant panels. Warm air circulated through plaster wall and ceiling plenums is another method for obtaining the benefits of radiant heat. This radiant system is particularly advantageous in buildings that require a high degree of ventilation. While the air circulated for radiant heating is not used for ventilation, it is a simple matter to intro-

then attached to the joists. After the guide strips are installed, pencil rods are suspended from the joists by wires or screw-type hangers so that they are flush with the bottom of the guide strips. Usually, the pencil rods are placed perpendicular to the direction of the joists.

After the rods have been secured in place, lath and plaster are applied in conformance with normal recommended procedures.

Note that this type of radiant heating system provides a method for control of each room, and that it is relatively simple compared to other systems. Stack dampers can be installed in the supply ducts of any room where temperatures other than over-all design temperatures are desired. Complete

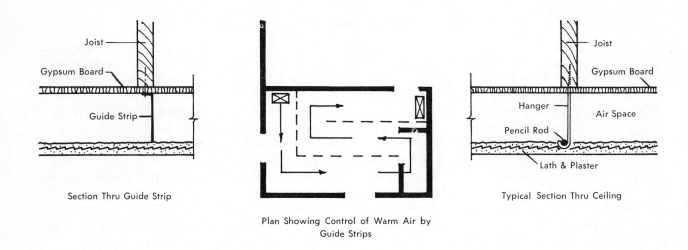

Section Thru Guide Strip

Plan Showing Control of Warm Air by Guide Strips

Typical Section Thru Ceiling

Fig. 20 — Warm Air Panel Heating

duce convected conditioned air into the rooms of the building.

One method of constructing a warm air radiant panel is described thus: ⅜ inch gypsum board is first attached to the bottom of the joists; the joints between sheets are then covered with paper tape. Galvanized iron guide strips 3¼ inches deep are

technical information on warm air panel systems can be obtained from the National Warm Air Heating and Air Conditioning Association.[59]

Electric conductor radiant heating. Within recent years several thousand radiant heating systems have been installed where insulated resistance wires were embedded in the plaster on ceilings and walls. The

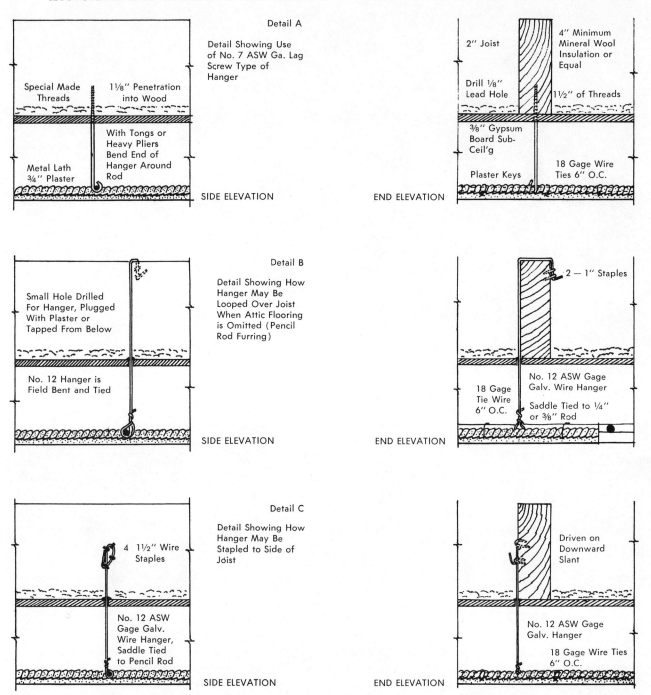

Detail A

Detail Showing Use of No. 7 ASW Ga. Lag Screw Type of Hanger

Special Made Threads

1⅛" Penetration into Wood

With Tongs or Heavy Pliers Bend End of Hanger Around Rod

Metal Lath ¾" Plaster

SIDE ELEVATION

2" Joist

Drill ⅛" Lead Hole

4" Minimum Mineral Wool Insulation or Equal

1½" of Threads

⅜" Gypsum Board Sub-Ceil'g

Plaster Keys

18 Gage Wire Ties 6" O.C.

END ELEVATION

Detail B

Detail Showing How Hanger May Be Looped Over Joist When Attic Flooring is Omitted (Pencil Rod Furring)

Small Hole Drilled For Hanger, Plugged With Plaster or Tapped From Below

No. 12 Hanger is Field Bent and Tied

SIDE ELEVATION

2 — 1" Staples

18 Gage Tie Wire 6" O.C.

No. 12 ASW Gage Galv. Wire Hanger

Saddle Tied to ¼" or ⅜" Rod

END ELEVATION

Detail C

Detail Showing How Hanger May Be Stapled to Side of Joist

4 1½" Wire Staples

No. 12 ASW Gage Galv. Wire Hanger, Saddle Tied to Pencil Rod

SIDE ELEVATION

Driven on Downward Slant

No. 12 ASW Gage Galv. Hanger

18 Gage Wire Ties 6" O.C.

END ELEVATION

Fig. 21 — Details of Warm Air Panel Ceilings[60]

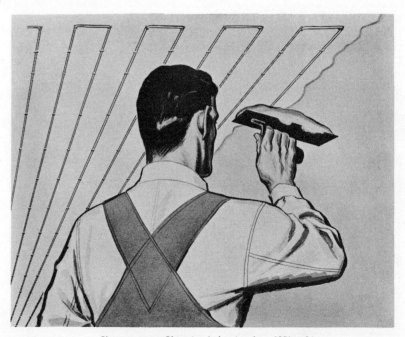

Photos courtesy *Plastering Industries*, Aug. 1956, p.34.

Fig. 22 — (A) Attachment of Heating Cable to Gypsum Lath (B) Scratch Coat being Applied Over Cables, Electric Heating Panels

most widespread use of this system will be found in those areas where electric power rates are relatively low and where the annual heating load is moderate.

The electric conductors are approximately ⅛ inch in diameter and are connected to non-heating leads. Cables are available in a variety of watt sizes. Most cables have an output of 2.75 watts per lineal foot, a figure readily converted into BTU/lineal foot.[61] (1 watt = 3.143 BTU/hr.)

The minimum thickness recommended for plaster over electric heating cables is ½ inch.[62]

The specification literature published by some manufacturers of electric heating cables allow the heat to be turned on after a minimum waiting period in order to facilitate drying of the plaster. While such a practice may be successful in some instances, previous discussion of the proper methods for drying and curing indicate that the practice is unnecessarily risky.

CHAPTER 9

FIRE RESISTANCE IN BUILDING CONSTRUCTION

From the standpoint of occupant safety and the protection of structures and their contents from damage or destruction, it would seem desirable to make all buildings absolutely fireproof. Practically, however, completely fireproof buildings are virtually non-existent. Instead, calculated risks are taken which result in feasible buildings having a reasonable and appropriate degree of fire safety.

The inherent risks in all types of construction and occupancy have been analyzed by organizations and officials who are responsible for minimizing the loss of life and property due to fire. These inherent risks are then adjusted so that they fall within reasonable limits of safety through building code requirements and recommendations of fire insurance underwriters and other authoritative agencies.

Finally, the designer is responsible not only for integrating those fire protection measures required by law and necessary from the standpoint of insurance economics, but also for incorporating any supplementary measures needed to compensate for con-

ditions arising out of the specific design with which he is concerned.

While the information in this chapter is intended primarily for use by the designer, it is also of a sufficiently general nature to permit integration with other criteria during the early stages of the design process.

The latter part of this chapter describes lath and plaster membrane fireproofing, a particularly efficient and flexible means at the designer's disposal of providing a necessary degree of fire safety.

BUILDING CODE REQUIREMENTS

In building fires, most deaths are caused by exposure to flame and hot or toxic gases, suffocation by smoke, deprivation of oxygen, and panic. Restrictions and limitations applicable to fire safety included in local building codes are designed primarily to prevent the spread of fire from one area to another, and to limit use of potentially dangerous flammable surface materials, thereby safeguarding public health and welfare.

To a considerable degree, local code requirements are based on these model codes:

Basic Building Code, published by the Building Officials Conference of America, Inc.

National Building Code, recommended by the National Board of Fire Underwriters.

Southern Standard Building Code, published by the Southern Building Code Congress.

Uniform Building Code, published by the International Conference of Building Officials.

These model codes base their requirements upon fire resistance tests and flame-spread data provided by testing facilities such as those maintained by the National Bureau of Standards, Underwriters' Laboratories, Inc., Ohio State University and the University of California.

Standardized testing methods and free exchange of data among these organizations and others such as the National Fire Protection Association result in a uniformly high degree of knowledge on the subject. These organizations have minimized inconsistencies in their published information.

A certain degree of latitude in adapting this information to local requirements is necessary, although local code authorities sometimes exercise such freedom of interpretation that a confusion of terms and apparent inconsistencies result. However, if the designer has a general knowledge of the fundamental principles of fire safety and the usual relationship between them, these obstacles to a general method of code analysis may be surmounted to a large degree.

In general, criteria used by code authorities to establish fire safety requirements fall into these categories:

Occupancy classification with respect to hazard:

Quantity of combustible contents contained in a building.

Construction classification with respect to hazard:

Size of areas undivided by fire barriers.

Building height.

Proximity to adjacent buildings and property lines.

Fire limits or zones.

Combustibility of structural and surface materials.

Degree of fire resistance of structural elements.

Occupancy classification. The fire hazard to life inherent in a particular occupancy is evaluated in terms of the number and concentration of occupants; whether or not the occupants are able-bodied and free, or confined or restrained; and the amount and degree of combustibility of fixed and movable building contents. Larger places of public assembly, and institutions such as asylums and prisons, usually are rigidly restricted as to fire resistance requirements. Though not so restricted, residential occupancies such as hotels, apartment houses and private dwellings, according to the National Bureau of Standards, actually suffer the greatest total life loss. Although, compared to public assembly occupancies, this classification generally contains relatively small amounts of combustible contents and occupant concentrations, the hazard involved — particularly at night when the occupants are asleep — is apparently great.[1]

Studies are sponsored by various national organizations in an attempt to establish a rational basis for ascertaining the effect of certain occupancies on fire resistance requirements for structural elements. These studies indicate that there is a definite relation between the amount of combustible contents in a building and the intensity and duration of a resulting fire. This relationship has been studied in buildings having the main structural elements of incombustible materials with fire resistance sufficient to preserve their integrity in a fire consuming all the combustible contents. These studies included burn-out tests performed with various concentrations of combustibles having calorific values in the range of wood and paper (7,000 to 8,000 BTU per pound) and arranged to represent certain categories of occupancy. Fire intensity (temperature) and duration (hours) were measured for various loadings of combustible materials in terms of pounds per square foot of the total floor area of various typical space subdivisions.

Fire severity (a measure of intensity and duration, expressed in terms of exposure time equivalent to that encountered in the standard fire test) was related to fire load (average weight of combustibles per square foot floor area) approximately as follows:

Table I.

Fire Load (Combustible Contents) Related to Fire Severity[2]

Average Weight of Combustibles in Pounds Per Square Foot Floor Area (including wood trim and floors)	Fire Severity (Hours)
5	½
7½	¾
10	1
15	1½
20	2
30	3
40	4½
50	6
60	7½

NOTE: *Wood, paper, cotton, wool, silk, straw, grain, sugar, and the like, are taken at actual weights. Animal and vegetable oils, fats, waxes, petroleum products, asphalt, alcohol, napthalene, and similar substances are taken at twice their actual weights. When combustibles vary greatly from wood or paper, or where they are stored in incombustible containers, a correspondingly corrected weight should be used in estimating expected fire severity.*

Results of surveys to determine average weight of combustible contents associated with space divisions common to certain occupancies are summarized in Table II. Fire load may be equated to fire severity to indicate the areas in each group that require special consideration.

Generally, fire resistance ratings specified by building codes have been calculated to counterbalance fire severity, thus precluding the necessity for such calculation by the designer. In many instances, however, the estimated fire severity for various areas common to a building type may be useful in determining the relative locations in plan. Isolation of certain high-hazard areas often proves economically advantageous. This same advantage may be extended to apply in the case of a building containing two or more occupancies of varying hazard. Where effective separation of high and low hazard is not accomplished, the entire building may be rated according to the highest risk present.

Because of their vital anti-panic function in a fire, exits, stair towers, corridors and other circulation areas, while generally low in combustible contents, are always given preferred consideration.

Construction classification. To insure that the established minimum requirements for fire safety are met in all buildings, codes place several series of limitations, or "construction classifications" on their size, location, and construction methods, which generally become more restrictive as the occupancy hazard increases. Generally, there are five individual categories, variously titled "fireproof," "fire resistant construction," "all steel construction," "heavy timber" or "mill construction," and "wood frame." Most codes use designations such as Type I, II, III, etc., or Class A, B, C, etc., proceeding from the least to the greatest risk.

Each construction classification places limitations on size of areas not divided with respect to fire, height, proximity to adjacent buildings, fire limits or zones in which the classification is permitted, building materials with respect to fire hazard, and degree of fire resistance of structural elements.

Standardized procedures have been developed to measure the degree of fire resistance of structural assemblies, and the hazard involved in the use of certain surface materials.

Fire resistance ratings of construction assemblies. Fire resistance ratings specified by most codes are based on tests performed by the National Bureau of Standards, Underwriters' Laboratories, Inc., and other authorities according to the "Standard Methods of Fire Tests of Building Construction & Materials" (ASTM E-119). The test involves subjecting a construction sample to heat and flame in a test furnace which is regulated according to a standard time-temperature curve. Various types of testing furnaces are used for wall and partition assemblies, floor and ceiling assemblies, columns and similar construction elements and assemblies.

At periodic intervals, a standard measuring procedure is used to read temperatures at various locations on the test specimen. The test is continued until either the fire resistance rating sought is obtained or failure occurs. Failure may result from structural collapse or by temperature transmission beyond the allowable limits.

The second part of the test exposes a duplicate specimen for a certain period in the furnace, withdrawing it, and immediately applying a stream of water from a fire hose. In lieu of this, the endurance specimen may be subjected to the hose stream test. The hose stream is not always necessary, and is not required on constructions rated less than one hour.

Most published ratings list endurance periods that have been rounded off to the next lower hour or half hour. Although endurance periods of many constructions are longer than four hours, time in excess of four hours is not ordinarily indicated in published tabulations because this is the maximum period required by most codes. The fire resistance rating tabulation which appears at the end of this chapter is explained in a later section.

Flame spread ratings for surface materials. From the standpoint of loss of life, many disastrous fires have occurred in buildings generally regarded as structurally fire-safe but which contained highly combustible finish materials. Combustible contents and interior finishes vary as to the speed with which they will ignite. If there is sufficient fuel and air to develop the necessary temperatures, many will ignite very rapidly and a stage may be reached where all combustible surfaces burst into flame. This condition, known as *flash-over*, is a critical factor in life hazard.

Rapid spread of fire throughout a building can deny opportunity for escape. An example is the fire in the LaSalle Hotel in Chicago, where 61 persons were burned by flame or suffocated by smoke. Flashover conditions were produced in certain areas by a highly combustible finish material over which flame

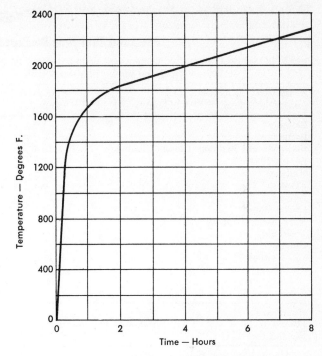

ASTM-119: Standard Method of Fire Tests of Building Construction and Materials.

Fig. 1 — Standard Time — Temperature Curve

spread so rapidly that the general panic prevented the escape of many occupants. Although the fire was confined to the lower floors, smoke produced by burning surfaces traveled to the upper stories through shaftways, causing many deaths by suffocation. Subsequent examination disclosed that the building had sustained only relatively minor structural damage.

With a view to preventing the recurrence of such disasters, several tests have been developed to determine the fire hazard classification of various finish materials. The most widely accepted test is defined by ASTM E-84, commonly called the *Tunnel Test*. It is designed to measure flame spread, fuel contributed, and toxicity and amount of smoke developed. This test applies to flame propagation characteristics of surface materials when used as tested, whereas fire resistance ratings apply to the comparative protection afforded by various construction assemblies.

Table II.

Fire Load That May Be Expected in Various Occupancies[3]

FIRE LOAD = Combustible contents (in pounds per sq. ft. of total floor area) consisting of movable property, combustible floor, and exposed combustible woodwork.

APARTMENT AND RESIDENCES (Based on survey of 17 buildings)	FIRE LOAD (Pounds)
Basement	1.0
Bathroom	7.0
Bedroom and Bedroom Closets Combined	10.4
Dining Room	7.2
Hallway	10.5
Kitchen	6.8
Library	13.0
Living Room	8.1
Store Room (Apt. Bldg.)	7.2
Vestibule	9.6
Closets	
Clothes	19.4
Linen	36.1
Kitchen	39.2
Entire Apartment or Residence	8.8

HOSPITALS
(Based on a survey of St. Elizabeth's Hospital buildings, Washington, D.C.)

1. Medical-Surgical Bldg.

  a. *Administrative*

Administrative Office	8.1
Doctor's Office	8.6
Waiting Rooms	3.2
Nurses' Offices and Rooms	5.0
Nurses' Training School	4.0
Nurses' Infirmary	3.0
Library and Conference	7.7

  b. *Service*

Corridors	2.65
Heating and Mechanical	.51
Refrigeration	3.75
Kitchen	.53
Laundry	5.00
Janitor's Closet and Supplies	.90
Stores	5.7
Lockers and Toilets	1.4

  c. *Clinical*

Surgery	1.80
Minor Surgery and Casts	3.2
Therapy and Laboratories	4.4
Clinics	3.9
Dormitories	2.5
Rooms, Single	2.3
Rooms, Disturbed Patients	2.90
Day and Waiting Rooms	3.20
Porches, Patients'	1.30
Sterilizers and Clothing Stores	5.40
Pharmacy, Dispensary and Stores	7.70

Diet Kitchens and Patients' Dining Rooms	3.60
Lavatories, etc.	1.90

2. Neuro-Psychiatric Continued Treatment Building

  a. *Administrative*

Administrative Offices and Records	5.0
Waiting Room	3.2

  b. *Service*

Corridors	2.4
Heating and Mechanical	1.0
Laundry Rooms and Clothes Storage	1.3
Janitor's Closet and Supplies	4.3
Storage Room	2.1
Lockers, Toilets, and Barber Shop	.2

  c. *Clinical*

Treatment Room	2.5
Dormitories	1.5
Single Rooms	2.1
Sitting Rooms and Porches	.8
Patients' Clothing	.5
Lavatories, Bath, etc.	.1

3. Tuberculosis Infirmary Bldg.

  a. *Administrative*

Administrative Office and Records	3.5
Doctors' Offices	2.9
Attendants' Offices	3.7
Waiting Rooms	1.4

  b. *Service*

Corridors	1.2
Mechanical Services Incinerator	.5
Kitchen and Dining Rooms	1.7
Janitor's Closets and Supplies	6.5
Barber Shops, Lockers and Toilets	1.4

  c. *Clinical*

Treatment Room and Medical	1.7
Dormitories	2.8
Single Bedrooms	3.7
Rooms for Disturbed	3.7
Porches (Patients')	1.3
Sterilizers and Clothing	4.0
Lavatories, Baths, etc.	0.5

SCHOOLS
(Based on Survey of 57 schools in the District of Columbia, Chevy Chase, Maryland, and Bethesda, Maryland.)

Auditorium	5.54
Art Room	9.8
Bookkeeping	12.0
Mechanical Drawing	10.6
Typewriting	11.0

Table II.

Fire Load That May Be Expected in Various Occupancies[3]

Geography	7.5	Storerooms	
Music	6.7	Janitor's	38.3
Physics Lecture	11.4	Lumber	45.7
Typical Classroom	6.9	Paint	19.7
Gymnasium	7.4	Paper	103.3
Biology Laboratory	8.4	Text Books	173.6
Chemistry Laboratory	8.4	Woodworking Shop	9.4
Physics Laboratory	7.3		
Library Reading Room	11.1	OFFICES	
Library Stack Room	35.9	(Based on survey of 37 offices.)	
Lunch Room	6.7		
Offices		Office (only)	7.9
File Room	39.0	Office and Reception Room	6.6
Home Economics	17.3	Office and Light Files	10.9
Publications	16.5	Files (Heavy)	42.9
Teachers'	11.5	Law Office and Libary	18.8
		Library	27.5

Table III.

Typical Flame Spread Classifications of Various Building Materials

Standards of Measurement:	
Red Oak (untreated)	100
Asbestos Cement Board	0
Walnut-Faced Plywood	171-260
Douglas Fir Plywood (untreated)	100-169
White Pine (untreated)	74.8
Redwood	65-80
Fibrous Glass	10-20
Mineral Acoustical Tile	10-20
Vermiculite Acoustical Plastic (Non-combustible base)	10-20
Sprayed Asbestos Fiber	15
Sprayed Gypsum Fireproofing Plaster	20
Gypsum, Lime and Portland Cement Plasters	0*

* Assumed Ratings.

FIRE INSURANCE RATE DETERMINATION

When deciding on the materials and construction details to be included in a building, the designer considers not only initial cost but also cost of maintenance over a period of years. From an economy standpoint, it is apparent that use of a material costing $4.00 a square foot and requiring no appreciable maintenance is preferable to one costing only $1.00 a square foot initially but requiring $1.00 per square foot per year to maintain. Fire insurance rates and maintenance costs are roughly analogous, and often prove to be major economic factors in building construction. Fire insurance rates are determined by regional fire insurance company organizations, maintained by stock and mutual insurance company members and subscribers. The National Board of Fire Underwriters, also maintained by stock insurance companies, acts only in an advisory capacity, and has no direct rate-making function. Each regional organization has a certain procedure for grading a building according to the risk involved. Since the primary function of the underwriters organization is to evaluate the risk of property loss resulting from fire, grading criteria vary somewhat from those used by building code authorities.

Although grading systems and criteria vary among the local rating bureaus, the following rate determinants are more or less standard:

A. *Considerations not controlled by designer.*

   1. Occupancy hazard.

   2. Efficiency and number of local fire-fighting organizations.

3. Distance from the nearest fire station.
4. Amount of and distance from the nearest water supply.
5. Building laws.
6. Fire alarm systems.
7. Fire prevention programs.
8. Police and fire department cooperation.
9. Physical conditions of city.
10. Weather conditions prevailing.

B. *Considerations over which designer has some degree of control.*

1. Measures that reduce the risk of fire starting and spreading.
   a. Construction details and materials employed.
      (1) Fire retardance of structure and of enclosure elements capable of confining fire of estimated severity.
      (2) Provision of firestopping partitions, suspended ceilings, etc.
      (3) Combustibility of structural and surface materials.
   b. Planning considerations.
      (1) Subdivision of large spaces with fire barriers.
      (2) Isolation of high hazard areas with respect to fire spread.
2. Measures that provide for rapid and effective extinguishment should a fire start.
   a. Construction details and materials employed.
      (1) Fire protection of structural and other building elements.
      (2) Provision of a sprinkler system.
      (3) Provision of a 24-hour alarm system.
   b. Planning considerations.
      (1) Provision of sufficient open space around the entire building perimeter to allow access to fire fighters.
      (2) Building width not more than effective range of a fire hose stream[*]

---

[*] at 55 psi, a stream from a 1½-inch nozzle will reach 78 feet.[4]

(twice the effective range if accessible from both sides).

An example of the basic difference in approach of building codes and of fire insurance rating organizations is the respective attitude towards combustible versus incombustible construction.

Building codes in general do not differentiate between a rated assembly containing combustible materials and an assembly containing incombustible materials for occupancies where the combustible materials are permitted. On the other hand, insurance companies, generally will allow a substantial reduction in premium rate if the incombustible assembly is used. Also, in general, a two-hour combustible assembly receives no rate reduction consideration over a one-hour combustible assembly.

There is generally a rather sharp rate break at the two-hour rating level in the Midwestern states, and at the three-hour level throughout the rest of the United States. Assemblies having fire resistance ratings at these levels usually involve a sharply reduced premium rate compared with less fire-resistive construction.

For this reason — though the insurance requirement may be more stringent than the applicable code requirement — it may often be advantageous to meet the more severe requirement. An additional one-quarter inch of plaster may increase the fire resistance of an assembly by one hour while increasing construction cost by a negligible amount. However, this additional hour of protection may allow substantial savings in insurance costs.

Consultation with the Fire Insurance Rating Bureau, at an early stage of design may afford considerable savings in insurance and construction costs. Such changes necessary for a favorable insurance rate can be made more easily and at less cost before the design has passed the preliminary phase.

Appendix A includes a Directory of Regional Underwriters Bureaus.

FIRE SAFETY — A DESIGN DETERMINANT

There is much truth in the cliché which states that the degree of fire resistance possessed by a building is determined on the drawing board. To this we can add that the degree of efficiency with which this fire resistance is effected is determined here also. In this sense, efficiency means providing adequate fire protection at a minimum compromise of other design considerations such as location, size, shape, cost, utility, and so on. It can be achieved only through correlation of fire resistance with other major determinants during all stages of the design process.

The process of building design is a continuing analysis of all factors established as pertinent in a particular situation. It may be considered as an environment in which several alternate solutions develop but only the one best adapted to all formative influences ultimately survives. The formative influences in this process are the criteria established as relevant by the designer. Ideally, the characteristics of the design will be determined by each criterion according to its relative importance.

To correlate such dissimilar factors as cost, shape, and circulation pattern, all must be reduced to a common denominator of generality that will allow comparative analysis. After a broad relationship is established, the factors are developed through a series of increasingly specific relationships until the stage of final synthesis is reached.

Establishment of a fire resistance requirement may usually be accomplished in any particular case by analyzing the applicable building code or insurance analytical system with respect to the occupancy involved. Often, certain construction classifications not permitted for that occupancy can be eliminated at the outset. Those that are permitted can be tabulated for further analysis as a series of restrictions on areas, heights, materials, and other factors.

Thus, the degree of fire safety required by a code can be translated into terms of space and construction alternatives so as to make possible direct correlation with other determinants. For example, sizes of undivided areas may be related to costs;

structural economy possible with large undivided areas can be weighed against the increased cost of incombustible structural materials and fireproofing required by the code in this instance.

Analysis of the empirical data included in codes and other authorities produces many useful generalizations which provide the designer with a rational basis for making certain preliminary decisions early in the design process which will orient a building towards fire safety. The need for drastic changes for this purpose later on at the expense of other equally important criteria can thus be greatly reduced.

The preceding section provides a general context for the many specific limitations appearing in any particular code and to supplement them with other pertinent information which, although not under code jurisdiction, is valuable to the designer. The sections that follow are related to the latter part of the design process and include a description of lath and plaster membrane fireproofing. Again, the purpose is to provide the designer with supplementary material which will aid in the efficient incorporation of fire resistance considerations into building design.

As design approaches the final stages, decisions confronting the designer concern selection of specific materials and construction details which will satisfy the requirements of particular structural elements. Fire resistance requirements that were established at an earlier stage must now be met by selecting details which possess the necessary hourly ratings. Efficient selection of details entails consideration of other criteria established for the element in question. In the case of a partition this might include thickness, acoustical properties, stiffness, weight, maintenance cost, and other factors. Since the fire resistance rating can be satisfied only through use of a detail which has been fire tested, it is apparent that overall efficiency of the element increases with the number of alternate details from which the designer can choose.

The fire resistance rating tabulation included in a later section has been made as comprehensive as possible to provide maximum freedom of selection for the designer.

FIRE ENDURANCE OF BUILDING MATERIALS AND CONSTRUCTION

Without some form of protection, most commonly used structural materials will burn or collapse fairly rapidly upon exposure to fire.

When structural steel is exposed to fire, it increases in strength up to temperatures between 400 degrees F. and 600 degrees F. Thereafter, strength decreases as temperatures increase to about 1,000 degrees F., at which point it is about equal to the working stress of 20,000 psi. From this point it loses strength rapidly, until ultimate failure occurs. It should be noted that according to the standard time-temperature curve, the temperature in a fire test reaches 1,000 degrees F. in five minutes and increases somewhat more slowly thereafter.

Failure of steel that has been in direct contact with flame and hot gases is characterized by buckling and severe distortion. A more gradual temperature rise causes a gradual sagging. This difference is important, because severe distortion will often cause adjacent fire walls and other elements to collapse. The less violent failure may result only in collapse of the steel member and the building elements directly supported by it, leaving adjacent construction intact.

Often a reinforced concrete structural element will survive longer than will a comparable exposed steel member due to the protection afforded the reinforcing steel by the concrete. To a large extent, aggregate used in the concrete and coverage over the reinforcing steel determines its fire resistance. Certain aggregates cause rapid and violent spalling which, if severe enough to expose the reinforcing steel, can cause premature failure of the member. Regardless of aggregate used, unequal thermal expansion will cause eventual cracking and spalling, and ultimately failure.

The fire endurance of wood members varies with the relationship of the least dimension to the cross-sectional area. Although equally combustible,

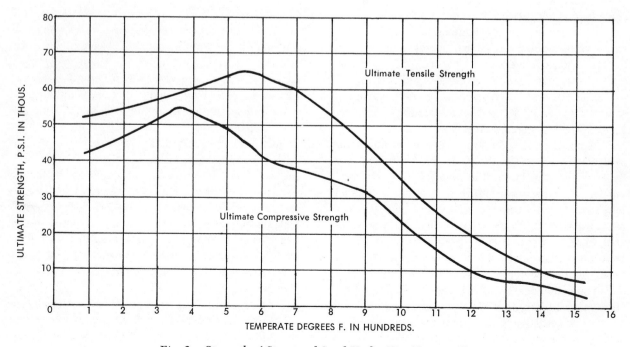

Fig. 2 — Strength of Structural Steel Under Fire Exposure [5]

heavy timber construction is more fire resistant than frame construction. Because of the relative massiveness of the members, a longer time is required for fire to penetrate to a depth that will cause failure under load. Wood, however, regardless of rate of combustion, adds fuel to a fire.

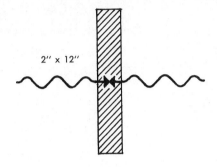

2″ x 12″

Nominal Cross-Sectional Area — 24 Sq. In.
40 Minute Exposure
Rate of Fire Penetration — 1½″ Hr.

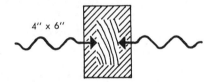

4″ x 6″

Fig. 3 — The Effect of Least Dimension on Fire Endurance of Wood Members

FIREPROOFING METHODS

There are various means for extending the time that a structural member will remain in place and sustain its load during exposure to fire. The most common method consists of surrounding the structural member with a noncombustible material which will retard heat transmission from its exposed surface through to the member. This may be done in three ways: by completely embedding the member in monolithic or unit masonry; by enclosing or covering the member with a membrane of fire resistant material, such as lath and plaster; and by spray application of fire resistant insulating materials directly to the member.

Lath and plaster membrane fireproofing. A lath and plaster membrane is fundamentally a relatively thin slab or shell supported by or attached to furring channels or other light, rigid members. It may be used to protect structural elements such as floors, roofs, joists, columns, beams, and load-bearing studs, or space dividers, such as hollow or solid non-bearing plaster partitions.

This method differs markedly in concept from the so-called mass fireproofing where each member is treated individually, with the protective material becoming physically, although not integrally, a part of the structural system. In the membrane method, the idea of separating the structure from a fire by a semi-independent barrier introduces unusual opportunities for protecting groups of members by a single element. It also allows the use of the protective device for other architectural functions as well, as in the case of ceilings and partitions.

The critical properties which determine fire resistance efficiency are, first, the ability to retard heat transmission from its exposed to its unexposed face; and second, the ability to remain in place and prevent passage of hot gases, flame, and smoke.

The ability of a membrane to resist heat transmission depends on the thermal characteristics of the material, its thickness, and in some instances, its location with respect to the element protected.

Within ordinary temperature ranges, the best types of materials for thermal insulation are those containing a minimum of water.

Usually, the lighter a material, the better it is as an insulator against heat transfer. However, such materials are inferior in their ability to meet the requirements of the standard fire test, when compared to heavier materials with high heat capacity, and materials containing mechanically and chemically combined water. Until all the moisture in a membrane utilizing the latter type of material has been converted into steam, the temperature on the unexposed surface will not significantly exceed 212 degrees F. This is well below the average rise of 250

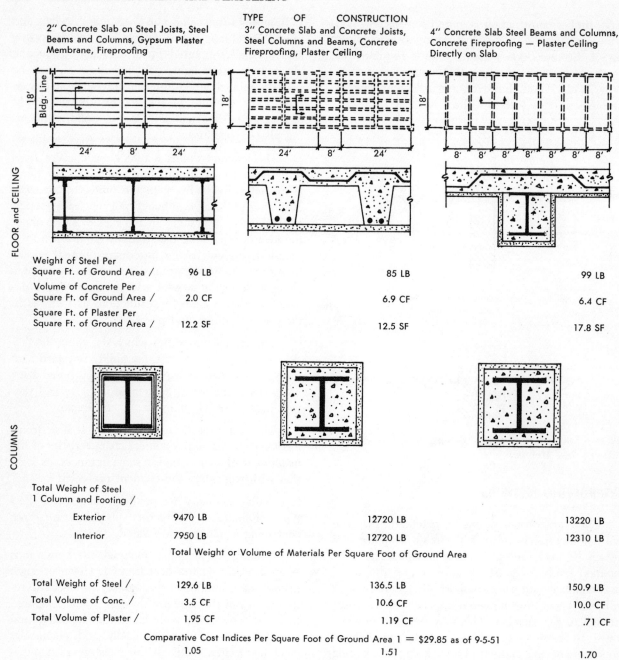

TYPE   OF   CONSTRUCTION

2" Concrete Slab on Steel Joists, Steel Beams and Columns, Gypsum Plaster Membrane, Fireproofing

3" Concrete Slab and Concrete Joists, Steel Columns and Beams, Concrete Fireproofing, Plaster Ceiling

4" Concrete Slab Steel Beams and Columns, Concrete Fireproofing — Plaster Ceiling Directly on Slab

FLOOR and CEILING

Weight of Steel Per Square Ft. of Ground Area /	96 LB	85 LB	99 LB
Volume of Concrete Per Square Ft. of Ground Area /	2.0 CF	6.9 CF	6.4 CF
Square Ft. of Plaster Per Square Ft. of Ground Area /	12.2 SF	12.5 SF	17.8 SF

COLUMNS

Total Weight of Steel 1 Column and Footing /			
Exterior	9470 LB	12720 LB	13220 LB
Interior	7950 LB	12720 LB	12310 LB

Total Weight or Volume of Materials Per Square Foot of Ground Area

Total Weight of Steel /	129.6 LB	136.5 LB	150.9 LB
Total Volume of Conc. /	3.5 CF	10.6 CF	10.0 CF
Total Volume of Plaster /	1.95 CF	1.19 CF	.71 CF

Comparative Cost Indices Per Square Foot of Ground Area 1 = $29.85 as of 9-5-51

1.05	1.51	1.70

Fig. 4 — Comparison of Six Structural Systems Utilizing Mass and Membrane Fireproofing. Comparative Data for 12 Floors of a Hypothetical 12 Story Office or Apartment Building. Live Load: 50 lbs/S.F., — Story Height 10'-0".
Partition Load: 20 lbs/S.F. Fire Protection: Columns — 3 hrs. Floors — 2 hrs. or more.[6]

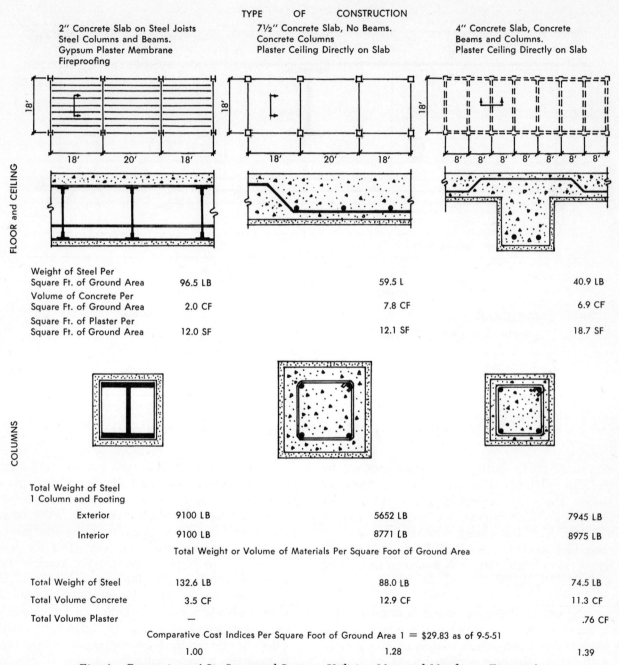

TYPE   OF   CONSTRUCTION

2" Concrete Slab on Steel Joists Steel Columns and Beams. Gypsum Plaster Membrane Fireproofing

7½" Concrete Slab, No Beams. Concrete Columns Plaster Ceiling Directly on Slab

4" Concrete Slab, Concrete Beams and Columns. Plaster Ceiling Directly on Slab

Weight of Steel Per Square Ft. of Ground Area	96.5 LB	59.5 L	40.9 LB
Volume of Concrete Per Square Ft. of Ground Area	2.0 CF	7.8 CF	6.9 CF
Square Ft. of Plaster Per Square Ft. of Ground Area	12.0 SF	12.1 SF	18.7 SF

Total Weight of Steel 1 Column and Footing			
Exterior	9100 LB	5652 LB	7945 LB
Interior	9100 LB	8771 LB	8975 LB

Total Weight or Volume of Materials Per Square Foot of Ground Area

Total Weight of Steel	132.6 LB	88.0 LB	74.5 LB
Total Volume Concrete	3.5 CF	12.9 CF	11.3 CF
Total Volume Plaster	—		.76 CF

Comparative Cost Indices Per Square Foot of Ground Area 1 = $29.83 as of 9-5-51

1.00	1.28	1.39

Fig. 4 — Comparison of Six Structural Systems Utilizing Mass and Membrane Fireproofing. Comparative Data for 12 Floors of a Hypothetical 12 Story Office or Apartment Building. Live Load: 50 lbs/S.F., — Story Height 10'-0".
Partition Load: 20 lbs/S.F. Fire Protection: Columns — 3 hrs. Floors — 2 hrs. or more.[6]

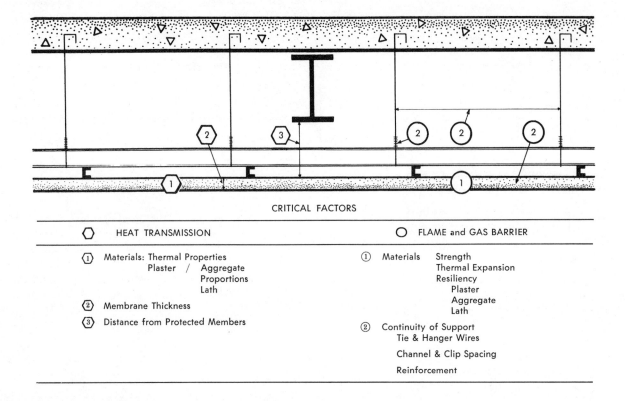

CRITICAL FACTORS

⬡ HEAT TRANSMISSION   ◯ FLAME and GAS BARRIER

① Materials: Thermal Properties   ① Materials   Strength
         Plaster / Aggregate   Thermal Expansion
                   Proportions   Resiliency
                   Lath   Plaster
                                                                              Aggregate
② Membrane Thickness   Lath

③ Distance from Protected Members   ② Continuity of Support
                                                             Tie & Hanger Wires

                                                             Channel & Clip Spacing

                                                             Reinforcement

Fig. 5 — Factors Affecting Fire Retardance of Lath and Plaster Membranes.

degrees F. above starting temperature specified by the standard fire test procedure as a criterion of failure. The water content of gypsum plaster, for example, provides a marked heat transmission lag at 212 degrees F. This phenomenon does not occur in other heat insulating materials. Even after calcination, gypsum plaster serves as insulation for as long as it is held in place.

Gypsum plaster resists heat flow in these ways: as sensible heat is taken up in the course of temperature rise; as latent heat is taken up by the evaporation of mechanically combined water; as the heat of dissociation is taken up by an endothermic chemical reaction as the water of crystallization is driven off. This process is commonly termed *calcination*.[8]

Lime and portland cement plasters exhibit the same phenomena, but to a lesser degree. Gypsum is more effective in this respect because it releases mechanically and chemically combined water more readily and at a lower temperature than the others.

The aggregate used will also affect the heat transmission properties of plaster. For example, the insulation afforded by perlite and vermiculite slows down the rate at which the cementitious material loses combined water by retarding heat flow within the membrane. In the case of lightweight aggregates, the effect of the binder-aggregate ratio on heat transmission is somewhat complex, due to their insulating properties. In the case of sand, however, as the proportion of sand is reduced, the ability of the plaster to resist heat transmission is increased.

The heat insulation value of a membrane is affected to a large degree by plaster thickness. According to the general theory of heat transmission, if one face of a homogeneous wall of a certain thickness is exposed to a constant heat source, and the other side is protected against heat loss, the time required for

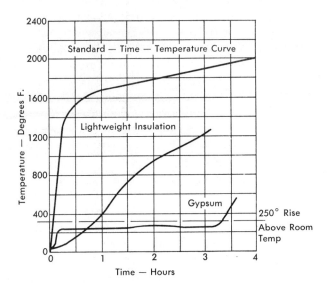

Fig. 6 — Comparison of Gypsum with Lightweight Insulation[7]

a specific temperature rise on the unexposed side varies with the square of the thickness.[9] However, due to the increasing temperature encountered in the standard fire test, the time will vary according to approximately the 1.7 power of the thickness.[10]

The second critical property — ability to remain in place and prevent passage of hot gases and flame — is a function of the materials comprising the membrane and the degree of continuity with which the plaster and lath is supported and tied in to adjacent elements. To be efficient as a fire resistant mem-

brane, plaster must be strong enough to maintain bond between coats and to help resist cracking due to the deformation caused by thermal expansion. A degree of resiliency is also necessary to allow for dimensional changes without excessive cracking or spalling. Finally, the coefficient of thermal expansion should, ideally, be low in order to prevent excessive warping and buckling during temperature rise.

Lath and plaster membranes may be designed to achieve maximum fire resistance by using metal reinforcement, lightweight aggregates, and increased thicknesses of gypsum plaster.

If it is to maintain surface integrity, a membrane should be designed to provide maximum continuity between lath, plaster and stiffeners. To eliminate any potential plane of weakness, joints in lath should be securely wired or clipped. Since thickness is a critical factor, care must be taken to insure that plaster grounds are as specified. On large areas, use of one or more intermediate screeds may aid control. Stability of the entire construction is necessary to counteract movement and warping due to unequal thermal expansion.

Where a membrane intersects with adjacent construction, the joint must be carefully designed to prevent uncontrolled separation during a fire. If flame and hot gases are able to pass around the membrane, its usefulness as fireproofing may be severely impaired. The two elements should be joined together in a way that will prevent separation, yet, if possible, allow room for thermal movements.

Membrane efficiency as a fire retardant is reduced when it is penetrated by large openings for electrical, heating, or ventilating fixtures that are not properly protected. Based on fire test data, most codes allow 100 square inches of opening in 100 square feet of ceiling, providing the opening is protected with a metal damper and fusible link. In cases where lighting fixtures are mounted flush with the ceiling surface, it is often practicable to carry the lath and plaster membrane over the top of the fixtures to provide protected recesses. Where this is not practicable, and the openings exceed the maximum allowed, a double suspended ceiling may be necessary. In this case, the upper membrane acts as the principal fire retardant while the lower provides the finished ceiling that conceals ducts, cables, and other mechanical equipment. A variation of this system involves covering the structural elements and the lower surface of the floor or roof deck with special fire retardant plaster or acoustical plaster or plastic eliminating the need for the upper ceiling.

Lath and plaster membrane fireproofing in its many forms meets the preceding requirements and characteristics. It has been fire-tested more than any other type of fire protection. It is approved by building codes and accepted by fire insurance rating authorities. Suitable for all types of construction, it provides fire-safe, lightweight, economical, and modern building construction, particularly when combined with structural steel.

Recently, fire tests have been performed using various proprietary plasters as fire resistive materials. In some instances, conventional membrane construction consisting of acoustical materials applied to a standard basecoat have been utilized. In others, materials have been sprayed directly on the member to be protected. The latter category consists of materials which generally utilize gypsum or clay-like binders in combination with lightweight aggregates, fibers, or both.

FIRE RESISTANCE RATING TABLES

The fire resistance ratings presented in the following tables have been compiled and edited by a technical subcommittee of the Lathing and Plastering Industry Committee from industry sponsored fire test data produced by recognized fire testing authorities.

Additional information of a more general nature on construction of membrane fireproofing is in Chapter 5.

Under the column titled, "**Plaster materials and proportions**":

1. Where two proportions are given; the first indicates the scratch coat proportions, the second, brown coat proportions.

2. Sanded plaster proportions are given as parts by weights.

3. Lightweight aggregate plaster proportions are given as pounds of cementitious material to cubic feet of aggregate.

4. There have been many fire tests conducted on similar or nearly identical constructions using both perlite and vermiculite plaster aggregate. In all cases it has been found that these two aggregates are essentially equal in terms of fire resistance and therefore most building code authorities allow them to be used interchangeably. In consideration of this established fact, the following tables make reference to the use of either perlite or vermiculite in all gypsum plaster constructions that were tested with lightweight plaster aggregate.

5. It is generally acknowledged that sand aggregate when used with gypsum plaster does not afford as much fire resistance as an equivalent amount (by volume) of lightweight aggregate. However, wherever sand has been used as the aggregate, it is usually permissible to use an equal thickness of lightweight aggregate to attain the same or greater fire resistance. It is also usually permissible to reduce the amount of sand used.

Under the column titled, "**Thickness**":

1. Plaster thickness is measured from the face of the plaster base. Where noted with an asterisk, it is measured from the back plane of metal lath.

2. Total plaster thickness includes the finish coat, usually a $\frac{1}{16}$ inch thickness.

Under the column titled, "**Notes**":

1. Numbers in parentheses refer to test authorities. See list at end of tables.

Under the column titled, "**Fire Resistance Ratings (Hours)**:

1. Hour ratings refer to published retardance periods and do not usually represent the total time achieved in tests.

Floor and Ceiling Constructions	Lath	Plaster Materials and Proportions	Thickness	Notes	Fire Resistance Ratings Hours
Steel Joists or Beams Concrete Slab Deck	Metal	Gypsum: Perlite or Vermiculite 100 : 2 100 : 3	¾″	2½″ concrete slab on corrugated steel form units. Ceiling lath attached to ¾″ furring channels. (1)	4
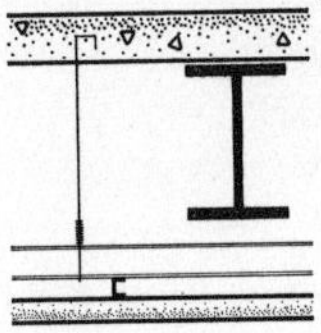	Metal	Gypsum: Perlite or Vermiculite 100 : 2 100 : 3	1″*	2½″ concrete slab on metal lath or 2″ reinforced gypsum slabs covered with ½″ mortar on joists. (2)	4
	Gypsum ⅜″ perforated	Gypsum: Perlite or Vermiculite 100 : 2 100 : 3	1″	2″ concrete slab on metal lath. Ceiling lath attached to ¾″ furring channels spaced 12″ o.c. with transverse wire clips engaging each other, giving continuous support to the lath. Plaster reinforced with 20 ga. wire mesh attached to furring channels at joints in lath. (3)	4
	Gypsum ⅜″ perforated	Gypsum: Perlite or Vermiculite 100 : 2½	½″	2″ concrete slab on metal lath. Ceiling lath attached to ¾″ furring channels spaced 16″ o.c. with transverse wire clips engaging each other, giving continuous support to the lath. Plaster reinforced with 20 ga. wire mesh which is attached to furring channels at joints in lath. (3)	3
	Gypsum ⅜″ perforated	Gypsum: Perlite or Vermiculite 100 : 2 100 : 3	⅝″	2″ concrete slab on metal lath. Ceiling lath attached to ¾″ furring channels spaced 12″ o.c. with transverse wire clips engaging each other, giving continuous support to the lath. Plaster reinforced with 14 ga. galvanized wire secured diagonally to clips or channels at each intersection. (3)	3

Floor and Ceiling Constructions	Lath	Plaster Materials and Proportions	Thickness	Notes	Fire Resistance Ratings Hours
Steel Joists or Beams Concrete Slab Deck	Metal	Gypsum: Perlite or Vermiculite 100 : 2 100 : 3	¾"*	2½" concrete floor slab on metal lath or 2" reinforced gypsum tile covered with ½" mortar. (2)	3
	Metal	Gypsum: Perlite or Vermiculite 100 : 2 100 : 3	1"*	2" concrete floor slab on metal lath or 2¾" reinforced P.C. concrete plank with joints thoroughly grouted; on joists. (5)	3
	Metal	Gypsum, unsanded, wood, fibered	1"*	2½" concrete slab on metal lath or 2" reinforced gypsum tile covered with ½" mortar. (2)	3
	Gypsum ⅜" perforated	Gypsum: Perlite or Vermiculite 100 : 2 100 : 3	⅝"	2" concrete floor slab on metal lath. Ceiling lath attached to ¾" furring channels spaced 12" o.c. with special wire clips at edges of lath and ⅓ points of lath width at each channel. (3)	3
	Metal	Gypsum: Perlite or Vermiculite 100 : 2 100 : 3	¾"	2½" perlite concrete slab on paper backed wire fabric. Ceiling lath secured to joists with wire clips. (1)	3
	Gypsum ⅜" perforated	Gypsum: Perlite or Vermiculite 100 : 2½	½"	2" concrete slab on metal lath. Ceiling lath secured to ¾" furring channels spaced 16" o.c. with transverse wire clips engaging each other, giving continuous support to the lath. 14 ga. galvanized wire secured diagonally to clips or channels at each intersection. (3)	2½

Floor and Ceiling Constructions	Lath	Plaster Materials and Proportions	Thickness	Notes	Fire Resistance Ratings Hours
Steel Joists or Beams Concrete Slab Deck— Continued	Metal	Gypsum, unsanded, wood fibered	1″*	2″ concrete floor slab on metal lath, or 2″ reinforced gypsum tile covered with ¼″ mortar; on joists. (2)	2½
	Metal	Gypsum: Perlite or Vermiculite 100 : 2 100 : 3	¾″*	2″ concrete floor or 2″ gypsum tile; the latter with ¼″ mortar finish. (2)	2½
	Metal	Gypsum: Sand 1 : 2 1 : 3	¾″*	2¼″ concrete floor slab on metal lath or 2″ reinforced gypsum tile covered with ¼″ mortar finish; on joists. (2)	2
	Gypsum ⅜″ perforated	Gypsum: Sand 1 : 2 1 : 3	⅝″	2″ concrete floor on metal lath. Ceiling lath secured to ¾″ furring channels spaced 12″ o.c. with transverse wire clips engaging each other, giving continuous support to the lath. 14 ga. galvanized wire secured diagonally to clips or channels at each intersection. (20)	2
	Metal	Portland Cement: Sand 1 : 2 1 : 3 With 3 lbs. asbestos fiber and 15 lbs. hydrated lime/bag P.C.	¾″*	2″ concrete floor slab on metal lath or 2″ reinforced gypsum tile; on joists. (2)	1½
	Gypsum ⅜″ perforated	Gypsum: Perlite or Vermiculite 100 : 2 100 : 3	1″	2″ concrete slab on metal lath. Ceiling lath attached to ¾″ furring channels spaced 16″ o.c. with transverse wire clips engaging each other, giving continuous support to the lath. (3)	1½
	Metal	Gypsum: Sand 1 : 2 1 : 3	¾″*	2″ concrete floor slab on metal lath or 2″ reinforced gypsum tile; on joists. (2)	1½

Floor and Ceiling Constructions	Lath	Plaster Materials and Proportions	Thickness	Notes	Fire Resistance Ratings Hours
Steel Joists or Beams Concrete Slab Deck— Continued	Metal	Gypsum: Sand 1 : 2 1 : 3	¾″*	⅞″ wood flooring nailed to wood sleepers on covering of asbestos paper weighing 14 lbs./100 sq. ft. cemented on sheet steel deck. (2)	1
	Gypsum ⅜″ perforated	Gypsum: Perlite or Vermiculite 100 : 2½	⅝″	2″ concrete slab on metal lath. Ceiling lath attached to ¾″ furring channels spaced 16″ o.c. with steel wire clips giving continuous support to lath. (3)	1
	Gypsum ⅜″ perforated	Gypsum: Perlite or Vermiculite 100 : 2½	½″	2″ concrete slab on metal lath. Ceiling lath nailed to steel nailing channels spaced 16″ o.c. with barbed nails having 11/32″ heads spaced 5″ o.c. (1)	1
	Gypsum ⅜″ perforated	Gypsum: Perlite or Vermiculite 100 : 2½	½″	2″ concrete floor slab on metal lath. Ceiling lath attached to ¾″ furring channels spaced 16″ o.c. with special wire clips at edges of lath and mid-point of lath width at each channel. (3)	1
Cellular Formed Steel Units	Metal	Gypsum, unsanded, wood fibered	1″*	1½″ concrete + ½″ cement mortar finish, on top of cellular steel units. Lath secured not less than 9″ below bottom of cellular steel units. (2)	4
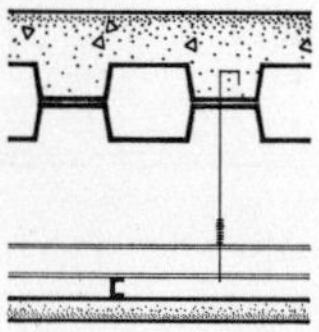	Metal	Gypsum: Perlite or Vermiculite 100 : 2 100 : 3	⅞″	2″ cinder concrete (minimum thickness over cells) on top of cellular steel floor units. Ceiling lath supported by ¾″ furring channels attached to 1½″ runner channels secured to bottom of floor units. Lath 2¼″ below steel deck. (1)	4

Floor and Ceiling Constructions	Lath	Plaster Materials and Proportions	Thickness	Notes	Fire Resistance Ratings Hours
Cellular Formed Steel Units— Continued	Metal	Gypsum: Perlite or Vermiculite 100 : 2 100 : 3	1″	2″ perlite concrete (minimum thickness over cells) on top of cellular steel floor units. Lath supported not less than 3″ from underside of steel floor units. Back plaster not less than 1″. (1)	4
	Metal	Gypsum: Vermiculite 100 : 2 100 : 3 and ½″ Vermiculite Acoustical Plaster or Plastic	⅝″	2½″ (minimum thickness over cells) concrete on top of cellular steel floor units. Lath supported not less than 7¼″ from underside of steel floor units. (1)	4
	Metal	Gypsum: Perlite or Vermiculite 100 : 2 100 : 3	⅞″	2″ reinforced concrete over cellular steel floor units. Lath supported not less than 15½″ from underside of steel floor and spaced at least 3½″ below steel beams. Duct opening in ceiling not larger than 70 sq. in. in each 100 sq. ft. of ceiling area. Protected by fire damper of #12 USS ga. steel covered with two 1/32″ thick layers of asbestos paper. Also #12 USS ga. steel fire damper at junction between branch and main ducts. Not more than 1 electric outlet in each 90 sq. ft. ceiling area. (1)	4
	Metal	Gypsum: Perlite or Vermiculite 100 : 2 100 : 3	1″	3¼″ concrete over cellular floor units. Metal lath attached directly to underside of floor panel. Beams plastered 1½″ thick over face of lath with same mix. (1)	4
	None	Perlite Acoustical Plaster	¾″ (below units)	3¼″ concrete fill (minimum thickness over cells). Plaster applied direct to underside of floor units. (1)	4

Floor and Ceiling Constructions	Lath	Plaster Materials and Proportions	Thickness	Notes	Fire Resistance Ratings Hours
Cellular Formed Steel Units— Continued	None	Vermiculite Acoustical Plastic	11/16″ (below cells)	2½″ concrete fill (minimum thickness over cells) — cellular units 3⅛″ deep. Plastic applied direct to underside of floor units. (1)	4
	None	Special Fire-Retardant Gypsum Plaster	⅝″ (below cells)	2½″ concrete over cellular floor units. Plaster applied directly to underside of floor units in one coat. (1)	4
	None	Vermiculite Acoustical Plastic	¾″ (below fluted units) 1″ (below cells) 1½″ (below junction boxes)	2½″ concrete over cellular floor units. Plastic applied directly to underside of floor units in two coats. (1)	3
	Metal	Gypsum, unsanded, wood fibered	1″*	1½″ concrete + ½″ cement mortar finish on top of cellular steel units. Lath secured not less than 2″ below bottom of cellular steel units. (2)	3
	Metal	Gypsum: Perlite or Vermiculite 100 : 2 100 : 3	⅞″	2″ (minimum thickness over cells) concrete on top of cellular steel floor units. Lath suspended not less than 14¾″ from underside of floor units and spaced at least 2¾″ below steel beams. Lath attached to ¾″ or 1″ furring channels spaced 12″ o.c. which are attached to 1½″ runner channels spaced 48″ o.c. Duct opening in ceiling not to exceed 70 sq. in. in each 100 sq. ft. of ceiling area, protected by fire damper of #12 USS ga. steel (covered each side) with 1/16″ thick layer of asbestos paper. Also, #12 USS ga. steel fire damper at junction between branch and main ducts. (1)	3

Floor and Ceiling Constructions	Lath	Plaster Materials and Proportions	Thickness	Notes	Fire Resistance Ratings Hours
Cellular Formed Steel Units— Continued	Metal	Gypsum: Perlite or Vermiculite 100 : 2 100 : 3	⅞″	2″ (minimum thickness over cells) concrete on top of cellular steel floor units. Lath supported not less than 15⅜″ from underside of floor units and 3½″ under beams. Duct and electrical outlet openings in ceiling not larger than 100 sq. in. in each 100 sq. ft. of ceiling area and duct protected by #14 USS ga. fire damper. (1)	3
	None	Perlite Acoustical Plaster	1″ (below units)	3¼″ concrete fill (minimum thickness over cells). Plaster applied directly to underside of floor units. (1)	3
	Gypsum ⅜″ perforated	Gypsum: Perlite or Vermiculite 100 : 2½	½″	2½″ (minimum thickness over cells) concrete on top of cellular steel deck. Lath suspended below underside of floor units. Furring channels on 12″ centers. Plaster reinforced with 14 ga. wire. Test included 12″ steel "I" beam with plaster applied to ⅞″ thickness. (20)	3
	None	Vermiculite Acoustical Plastic	1-7/16″ (below cells)	2½″ concrete fill (minimum thickness over cells). Plastic applied directly to underside of floor units, following contour. (1)	3
	None	Special Fire-Retardant Gypsum Plaster	⅝″ (on bottom of cells) ¾″ (on top of re-entrant spaces.) 1″ (over header ducts and junction boxes.)	2½″ concrete over cellular floor units. Plaster applied directly to underside of floor panels in one coat. Not more than 1 electrical header duct in each 90 sq. ft. floor area. (1)	3

Floor and Ceiling Constructions	Lath	Plaster Materials and Proportions	Thickness	Notes	Fire Resistance Ratings Hours
Cellular Formed Steel Units— Continued	None	Special Fire-Retardant Gypsum Plaster	⅜″ (below cells)	2½″ concrete over cellular floor units. Plaster applied directly to underside of floor units in one coat. (1)	3
	None	Special Fire-Retardant Gypsum Plaster	½″ (following contours of deck)	2½″ concrete over cellular floor units. Plaster applied directly to underside of floor panels in one coat. (1)	2
	None	Perlite Acoustical Plaster	⅞″ (under header ducts) 2″ (under junction boxes)	3¼″ concrete fill (minimum thickness over cells). Plaster applied directly to underside of floor units, under header ducts and junction boxes. (1)	2
	None	Vermiculite Acoustical Plastic or Plaster	½″ (below cells)	2½″ concrete fill (minimum thickness over cells) Cellular units 3⅛″ deep. Plaster applied directly to underside of floor units. (1)	2
	None	Vermiculite Acoustical Plastic	½″ (below corrugations)	3¼″ concrete over metal deck. Plastic applied direct to underside of steel floor. (1)	4
Corrugated Formed Steel Units	Metal	Gypsum: Perlite or Vermiculite 100 : 2 100 : 3	1″	4½″ (measured from bottom of corrugations) concrete on top of corrugated steel floor units. Lath suspended not less than 14½″ below floor units. (1)	4

Floor and Ceiling Constructions	Lath	Plaster Materials and Proportions	Thickness	Notes	Fire Resistance Ratings Hours
Corrugated Formed Steel Units— Continued	None	Special Fire-Retardant Gypsum Plaster	¾″ (following contours of deck)	4½″ (measured from bottom of corrugations) expanded shale concrete on top of floor units. Plaster applied directly to underside of floor units in one coat. Not more than 1 electrical header duct in each 60 sq. ft. floor area. (1)	4
	Metal	Gypsum: Perlite or Vermiculite 100 : 2	⅜″	4½″ (measured from bottom of corrugations) expanded slag concrete on top of corrugated steel floor units. Lath attached directly to floor units with sufficient plaster pushed through the lath to fill the corrugations of the floor units. 1″ plaster thickness to the face of the lath in an area 3″ square centered below electrical raceway junction box: not more than 1 junction box per 90 sq. ft. floor area. (1)	3
	None	Special Fire-Retardant Gypsum Plaster	¾″ (following contours of deck) 1½″ (under header ducts and junction boxes)	2½″ (minimum thickness over cells) concrete on top of steel floor units. Plaster applied directly to underside of steel floor in one coat. Not more than 1 electrical header duct in each 90 sq. ft. floor area. (1)	3
	None	Vermiculite Acoustical Plastic	⅞″	2⅞″ (measured from bottom of corrugations) vermiculite concrete on top of corrugated steel floor units. Plastic applied directly to underside of floor units. (1)	2

Floor and Ceiling Constructions	Lath	Plaster Materials and Proportions	Thickness	Notes	Fire Resistance Ratings Hours
Flat Plate Formed Steel Units	None	Vermiculite Acoustical Plastic	¾″	2½″ (minimum thickness over cells) concrete on top of cellular steel floor units. Plastic applied directly to underside of floor units. (1)	2
Combination Flat Plate and Fluted Formed Steel Units	None	Vermiculite Acoustical Plastic	1-7/16″	2½″ (minimum thickness over cells) concrete on top of steel floor units. Plastic applied directly to underside of floor units in three coats. (1)	3
	None	Vermiculite — Type MK	⅞″	2½″ (minimum thickness over cells) concrete on top of steel floor units. Plaster applied directly to underside of steel floor in one coat. (1)	3
	None	Special Fire-Retardant Gypsum Plaster	¾″ (following contours of deck) 1¼″ (under header ducts and junction boxes)	2½″ (minimum thickness over cells) concrete on top of steel floor units. Plaster applied directly to underside of steel floor in one coat. Not more than 1 electrical header duct in each 90 sq. ft. floor area. (1)	2
Steel Plate Deck on Steel Joists	Metal	Gypsum: Perlite or Vermiculite 100 : 2 100 : 3	1″	2″ reinforced vermiculite concrete on steel plate deck. Ceiling lath supported at least 7″ below underside of steel floor plates and spaced at least 2½″ from steel members. (1)	4
	Metal	Gypsum: Unsanded, wood fibered	1″*	2½″ concrete on steel plate deck. (2)	3

Floor and Ceiling Constructions	Lath	Plaster Materials and Proportions	Thickness	Notes	Fire Resistance Ratings Hours
Steel Plate Deck on Steel Joists— Continued	Metal	Gypsum: Sand 1 : 1	1⅛″*	2½″ cinder concrete + ½″ cement mortar finish on steel plate deck. Total thickness 3″. (2)	3
	Metal Ribbed	Gypsum: Sand 1 : 2	1½″*	2″ concrete on steel plate deck. (2)	2½
	Metal	Gypsum: Sand 1 : 2	1″*	2½″ concrete on steel plate deck. (2)	2½
	Metal	Gypsum: Sand 1 : 1	1⅛″*	2″ concrete on steel plate deck. (2)	2½
	Metal	Portland Cement: Sand 1 : 2 1 : 2½ +10 lbs. hydrate lime/bag Portland Cement	1″*	2″ concrete on steel plate deck. (2)	2
	Metal	Gypsum: Sand 1 : 2 1 : 3	¾″*	2″ concrete on steel plate deck. (2)	2
	Metal	Gypsum: Sand 1 : 2 1 : 3	¾″*	1½″ concrete on steel plate deck. (2)	1½
	Metal	Gypsum: Sand 1 : 2 1 : 3	¾″*	1″ concrete on steel plate deck. (6)	1
Reinforced Concrete	Metal	Gypsum: Perlite or Vermiculite 100 : 2 100 : 3	1″	5″ slab with limestone aggregate, with electrical raceways and junction boxes. Portions of this slab not containing raceways and junction boxes may be 3″. (1)	4

Floor and Ceiling Constructions	Lath	Plaster Materials and Proportions	Thickness	Notes	Fire Resistance Ratings Hours
Reinforced Concrete— Continued	Metal	Gypsum: Perlite or Vermiculite 100 : 2 100 : 3	¾″	2″ slab with limestone aggregate. Lath supported not less than 13½″ from bottom of slab. (1)	3
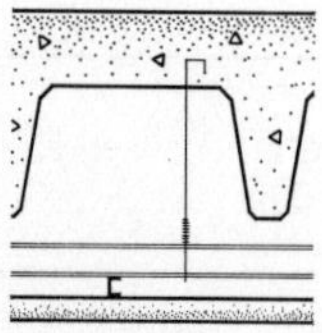	Metal	Gypsum: Perlite or Vermiculite 100 : 2 100 : 3	¾″	4″ slab with limestone aggregate, with electrical raceways and junction boxes. Portions of slab not containing raceways and junction boxes may be 2″. Lath supported not less than 11½″ from bottom of slab. (1)	3
Reinforced Concrete Joists	Metal	Gypsum, unsanded, wood fibered	1″*	2½″ reinforced concrete floor slab on joists not over 30 in. o.c. (e)	3
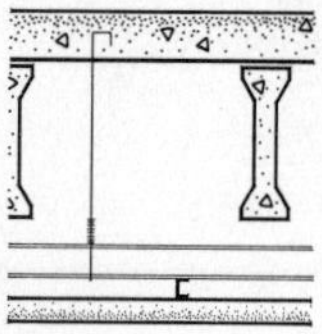	Metal	Gypsum: Perlite or Vermiculite 100 : 2 100 : 3	¾″*	2½″ reinforced concrete floor slab on joists not over 30 in. o.c. (e)	3
	Metal	Gypsum: Sand 1 : 2 1 : 3	¾″*	2¼″ reinforced concrete floor slab on joists not over 30 in. o.c. (e)	2
	None	Vermiculite Acoustical Plastic	⅞″	2⅞″ o.f. vermiculite concrete on formed steel units. Plastic applied directly to the underside of steel units and 1/16″ thick around concrete joists. (1)	2
Wood Joists 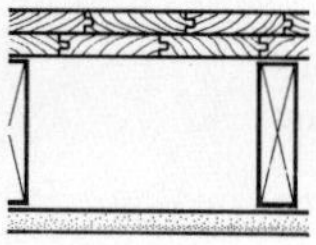	Metal	Gypsum: Perlite or Vermiculite 100 : 2 100 : 3	¾″*	Wood floor consisting of 1″ (nominal) T & G sub and finish flooring with building paper between. Lath nailed to joists with 1½″ barbed roofing nails having 7/16″ heads and spaced 4¾″ o.c. (20)	1½

Floor and Ceiling Constructions	Lath	Plaster Materials and Proportions	Thickness	Notes	Fire Resistance Ratings Hours
Wood Joists— Continued	Gypsum ⅜″	Gypsum: Perlite or Vermiculite 100 : 2½	½″	Wood floor consisting of 1″ (nominal) T & G sub and finish flooring with building paper between. Lath nailed to joists with 1½″ nails having ⅜″ diameter heads. Plaster reinforced with 20 ga. wire mesh nailed to joists through lath with 2⅜″ nails with ¼″ diameter heads. (20)	1½
	Gypsum ⅜″	Gypsum, wood fibered: Sand 2 : 1	½″	Double ⅞″ T & G wood flooring with building paper between. Gypsum lath attached with 1¼″ nails with 7/16″ heads, 12 to each 16″ x 48″ lath; 3″ strips of expanded metal lath nailed over all joints in gypsum lath. (4)	1
	Gypsum ⅜″ perforated	Gypsum: Sand 1 : 2	½″	Wood flooring consisting of ¾″ sub floor and T & G finish flooring with asbestos paper weighing 14 lbs./100 sq. ft. between. Lath attached by 1⅛″ nails with ⅜″ heads and spaced 4″ o.c. 3″ wide strips of expanded metal lath nailed over all joints in gypsum lath using 1¾″ nails with ½″ heads spaced 5″ o.c. along joists and with 2 nails to each joist for joints perpendicular to joists. (2)	1
	Gypsum ⅜″ perforated	Gypsum: Perlite or Vermiculite 100 : 2½	½″	Wood floor consisting of 1″ (nominal) T & G sub and finish flooring with building paper between. Lath nailed to joists with 1-3/16″ nails having 9/32″ diameter heads. (20)	1
	Metal	Gypsum: Sand 1 : 2 1 : 3	¾″ *	Lath attached with 1½″, 11-ga. 7/16″ head barbed roofing nails, 6″ o.c. (2)	1

Floor and Ceiling Constructions	Lath	Plaster Materials and Proportions	Thickness	Notes	Fire Resistance Ratings Hours
Wood Joists— Continued	Metal	Portland Cement: Sand 1 : 2 1 : 3 plus 3 lbs. asbestos fiber and 15 lbs. hydrated lime per bag Portland Cement	¾″ *	Wood floor consisting of ¾″ sub floor and T & G finish floor with asbestos paper weighing 14 lbs./100 sq. ft. between. Lath nailed with 1½″ No. 11 ga. barbed roofing nails having 7/16″ heads and spaced 6″ o.c. (2)	1

Walls and Partitions	Lath	Plaster Materials and Proportions	Thickness	Notes	Fire Resistance Ratings Hours
Solid Plaster Partitions — Steel Framing Embedded	Metal	Gypsum, unsanded, wood fibered	2½″ Total	Lath attached to ¾″ steel channels. Nonbearing. (2)	2½
	Metal	Gypsum: Perlite or Vermiculite 100 : 2 100 : 3	2½″ Total	Lath attached to ¾″ steel channels. Nonbearing. (20) (1)	2
	Metal	Gypsum: Sand 1 : ½	2½″ Total	Lath attached to ¾″ steel channels. Nonbearing. (2)	2
	Metal	Gypsum, unsanded, wood fibered	2″ Total	Lath attached to ¾″ steel channels. Nonbearing. (20)	2
	Metal	Gypsum: Sand 1 : ½	2″ Total	Lath attached to ¾″ steel channels. Nonbearing. (2)	1½
	Metal	Gypsum: Perlite or Vermiculite 100 : 2½	2⅛″ Total	Lath attached to ¾″ steel channels. Nonbearing.	1½
	Metal	Gypsum: Sand 1 : 2	2″ Total	Lath attached to ¾″ steel channels. Nonbearing. (7)	1

Walls and Partitions	Lath	Plaster Materials and Proportions	Thickness	Notes	Fire Resistance Ratings Hours
Solid Plaster Partitions— Steel Framing Embedded— Continued	Metal	Gypsum: Perlite or Vermiculite 100 : 2½	2″ Total	Lath attached to ¾″ steel channels. Nonbearing.	1
	Metal	Gypsum: Sand 1 : 2 1 : 3	2½″ Total	Lath attached to ¾″ steel channels. Nonbearing. (9)	1
Solid Plaster Partitions — without Steel Framing	Gypsum ½″	Gypsum: Perlite or Vermiculite 100 : 2 100 : 3	2½″ Total	Plastered both sides 1″ thick. Nonbearing. (20)	2
	Gypsum ½″	Gypsum: Perlite or Vermiculite 100 : 2 100 : 3	2″ Total	Plastered both sides ¾″ thick. Nonbearing. (20)	1½
	Gypsum 1″	Gypsum: Sand 1 : 2½	2″ Total	Plastered both sides ½″ thick. Nonbearing. (21)	1
	Metal	Gypsum: Sand 1 : 2	2″ Total	Lath attached top and bottom to steel runners. Nonbearing. (11)	1
	Gypsum ½″	Gypsum: Sand 1 : 1 1 : 2	2″ Total	Lath inserted at top and bottom in steel runners. Plastered both sides ¾″ thick. Nonbearing. (12)	1
Wood Stud Partitions — Studs 2 x 4 or Larger	Metal	Gypsum, unsanded, wood fibered	1″*	Nonbearing. (20)	2

Walls and Partitions	Lath	Plaster Materials and Proportions	Thickness Plastered Two Sides	Notes	Fire Resistance Ratings Hours
Wood Stud Partitions — Studs 2 x 4 or Larger— Continued	Gypsum ⅜″ perforated	Gypsum: Perlite or Vermiculite 100 : 2½ 100 : 2½	1″	1″ — 20 ga. hexagonal wire mesh applied over lath with ⅜″ furring nails, 1¾″ long, 8″ o.c. (35)	2
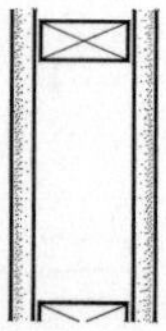	Metal	Gypsum, unsanded, wood fibered	¾″*	(2)	1½
	Metal	Gypsum: Sand 1 : 2	¾″*	Stud spaces filled with mineral wool. (2)	1½
	Metal	Gypsum: Sand 1 : 2 1 : 3	⅞″*	Stud spaces filled with mineral wool. (2)	1½
	Gypsum ⅜″ perforated	Gypsum: Sand 1 : 2	½″	Resilient metal clips and metal end fastening clips. Load bearing. (22)	1½
	Metal	Gypsum: Sand 1 : 2	¾″*	(2)	1
	Metal	Gypsum: Sand 1 : 2 1 : 3	⅞″*	(2)	1
	Metal	Portland Cement: Asbestos fiber: Sand 1 : 1/30 : 2 1 : 1/30 : 3	⅞″*	(2)	1
	Wire Lath (Paper-backed fabric)	Gypsum: Sand 1 : 2	¾″	(1)	1

Walls and Partitions	Lath	Plaster Materials and Proportions	Thickness Plastered Two Sides	Notes	Fire Resistance Ratings Hours
Wood Stud Partitions — Studs 2 x 4 or Larger— Continued	Metal	Gypsum: Sand 1 : 1½ 1 : 3	¾ "	Lath attached by 1½" 4d nails 6" apart or by equivalent staples. Studs 2 x 2 if nonbearing. (1)	1
	Gypsum ⅜" perforated	Gypsum: Perlite or Vermiculite 100 : 2½	½ "	Lath securely attached by metal clips. (20)	1
	Gypsum ⅜" perforated	Gypsum: Sand 1 : 2	½ "	Nailed 4" o.c. (20)	1
	Gypsum ⅜"	Gypsum, unsanded, wood fibered	½ "	(2)	1
	Gypsum ⅜" perforated	Gypsum: Perlite or Vermiculite 100 : 2½	½ "	If load bearing. If Nonbearing. (20)	1 1½
	Metal	Gypsum: Perlite or Vermiculite 100 : 2 100 : 3	¾ "	(1)	1
Steel Stud Hollow Partitions	Metal	Gypsum: Perlite or Vermiculite	1"	Lath attached to ¼" pencil rods on clips fastened to metal studs. (23)	3½
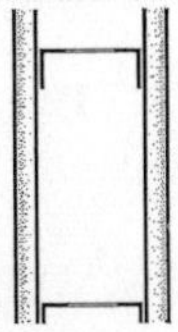	Metal	Gypsum, unsanded, wood fibered	1"*	Where loading exceeds 5120 psi of stud area. Where loading does not exceed 5120 psi of stud area. (2)	2 2½

Walls and Partitions	Lath	Plaster Materials and Proportions	Thickness Plastered Two Sides	Notes	Fire Resistance Ratings Hours
Steel Stud Hollow Partitions— Continued	Metal	Gypsum: Sand 1 : ½	1″*	Nonbearing. (2)	2
	Metal	Gypsum: Perlite or Vermiculite 100 : 2 100 : 3	1″*	Nonbearing. (20)	2
	Metal	Gypsum, unsanded, wood fibered	⅞″*	Nonbearing. (2)	2
	Metal	Gypsum, unsanded, wood fibered	¾″*	Load bearing steel studs. (2)	1½
	Metal	Gypsum: Sand 1 : ½	⅞″*	Nonbearing. (2)	1½
	Gypsum ⅜″ perforated	Gypsum: Sand 1 : 2	½″	¼″ pencil rods attached to studs with resilient metal clips. Gypsum lath attached to pencil rods with wire clips and at adjacent pieces with metal end fastening clips. (26)	1½
	Gypsum ⅜″ perforated	Gypsum: Sand 1 : 2	½″	Lath secured to studs by special clips across lath. Abutting ends of lath secured to each other with metal clips. Nonbearing. (24)	1½
	Gypsum ⅜″ perforated	Gypsum: Sand 1 : 2	½″	Lath attached to studs by tie wires and wire clips. Abutting ends of lath secured to each other with metal clips. Nonbearing. (25)	1½

Walls and Partitions	Lath	Plaster Materials and Proportions	Thickness Plastered Two Sides	Notes	Fire Resistance Ratings Hours
Steel Stud Hollow Partitions— Continued	Gypsum 3/8" perforated	Gypsum: Sand 1 : 2	1/2"	Lath attached to steel studs by metal clips across lath. Abutting ends of lath secured to each other with metal wire clips. Nonbearing. (31)	1½
	Metal	Gypsum: Sand 1 : 2 1 : 3	7/8"*	Bearing or nonbearing. (2)	1
	Metal	Gypsum: Sand 1 : 2 1 : 3	3/4"	1/4" pencil rods attached to studs with resilient metal clips. Metal lath wire tied to pencil rods. (27)	1
	Gypsum 3/8" plain	Gypsum: Perlite or Vermiculite 100 : 2½	1/2"	Lath attached to studs by wire clips. Abutting ends of lath secured to each other with metal clips. Nonbearing. (28)	1
	Gypsum 3/8" perforated	Gypsum: Sand 1 : 2½	1/2"	Lath attached to studs by wire clips. Abutting ends of lath secured to each other with metal clips. Nonbearing. (29)	1
	Gypsum 3/8" perforated	Gypsum: Sand 1 : 2½	1/2"	Lath attached directly to steel stud with resilient metal clip. (30)	1
	Gypsum 3/8"	Gypsum: Sand 1 : 1	1/2"	Lath on steel studs providing 1¼" central air space. Nonbearing. (20)	1
	Metal	Gypsum: Sand 1 : 2	3/4"*	Bearing or nonbearing. (2)	1

Walls and Partitions	Lath	Plaster Materials and Proportions	Thickness Plastered Two Sides	Notes	Fire Resistance Ratings Hours
Steel Stud Hollow Partitions— Continued	Gypsum ½″	Gypsum: Sand 1 : 1 1 : 2	¾″	3¼″ total thickness. Lath attached tightly to ¾″ channel frame by wire ties. ¾″ channels spaced 30″ o.c. horizontally and 5′ o.c. vertically; tied at intersections. Channel frame attached to ¾″ runner channels at floor, ceiling and wall edge. (1)	1
	Metal	Portland Cement: Asbestos fiber: Sand 1 : 1/30 : 2 1 : 1/30 : 3	⅞″*	Nonbearing. (2)	1
Steel Stud Brick Veneered Walls (Bearing) 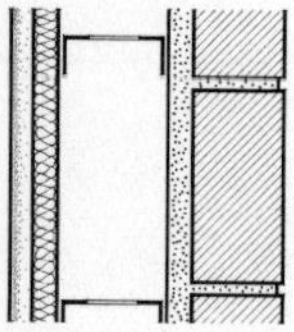	Metal	Gypsum: Sand 1 : 2 1 : 3	¾″*	One side sheathed with paper-backed wire lath and 3¾″ brick veneer secured by filling 1″ space between brick and lath with mortar. Other side faced with 1″ paper-enclosed mineral wool blanket weighing 0.6 lbs./sq. ft. attached to studs; metal lath laid over blanket and attached to studs. (2)	4
	Gypsum ½″ perforated	Gypsum: Sand 1 : 2	½″	One side with ½″ gypsum sheathing nailed to 2-5/16″ studs, and 3¾″ brick veneer secured with metal ties to studs every fifth course. (20)	2
	Metal	Gypsum: Sand 1 : 2	⅞″*	One side sheathed with 1″ magnesium oxysulphate wood fiber board attached to studs, 1″ air space, 3¾″ brick secured with metal ties to studs every fifth course. (2)	1½

Walls and Partitions	Lath	Plaster Materials and Proportions	Thickness	Notes	Fire Resistance Ratings Hours
Masonry Back-Up Brick Veneered Walls		Gypsum: Sand 1 : 3	½″	Brick faced, concrete masonry units, expanded slag aggregate. 4″ units, 63% solid (rated as load bearing with noncombustible or no members framed into wall), one side plastered and other faced with 3¾″ brick. (2)	4
		Gypsum: Sand 1 : 3	½″	Brick faced, concrete masonry units, cinder aggregate. 4″ units, 63% solid (rated as load bearing with noncombustible or no members framed into wall). Plastered one side, other faced with 3¾″ brick. (2)	4
Spandrel Walls		Portland Cement: Perlite 1 : 4	4″	4″ portland cement perlite plaster on paper-backed wire fabric on one face; 1″ gypsum perlite plaster on paper and aluminum foil-backed wire fabric on interior face, with furring channels forming 1″ air space between the two sections. (1)	4
		Gypsum: Perlite 100 : 2 100 : 3	1″		
		Portland Cement: Vermiculite 1 : 4	4¼″	Portland cement - vermiculite plaster on paper-backed wire fabric attached to a steel frame. (1)	4
Wood Stud Exterior Walls	Gypsum ⅜″ perforated	Gypsum: Sand 1 : 2	½″ plastered one side	One side sheathed with ½″ gypsum sheathing and covered with wood drop siding. (20)	1
Concrete Block — Plastered as Noted		Gypsum: Sand 1 : 3	½″ plastered two sides	Concrete masonry units, expanded shale aggregate. 3″ units, 76% solid. Nonbearing. (2)	2

Walls and Partitions	Lath	Plaster Materials and Proportions	Thickness	Notes	Fire Resistance Ratings Hours
Concrete Block— Plastered as Noted— Continued		Gypsum: Sand 1 : 3	½″ plastered one side	Concrete masonry units, expanded shale aggregate. 4″ units, 76% solid. Nonbearing. (13)	2
		Gypsum: Sand 1 : 3	½″ plastered two sides	Concrete masonry units, cinder aggregate. 6″ units, 50% solid. Nonbearing. (2)	2
		Gypsum: Sand 1 : 3	½″ plastered one side	Concrete masonry units, expanded slag aggregate. 6″ units, 50% solid. Nonbearing. (2)	2
		Gypsum: Sand 1 : 3	½″ plastered one side	Concrete masonry units, cinder aggregate. 6″ units, 61% solid. Nonbearing. (2)	2
		Gypsum: Sand 1 : 3	½″ plastered two sides	Concrete masonry units, calcerous gravel aggregate. 4″ units, 63% solid. Nonbearing. (2)	1½
Terra Cotta — Plastered as Noted		Vermiculite — Type MK	3″	3-3/16″ terra cotta panel with vermiculite Type MK applied directly to inside face. Bearing. (32)	2½
		Gypsum: Perlite or Vermiculite 100 : 2 100 : 3	1″	2½″ terra cotta panel with plaster applied directly to inside face. Nonbearing. (33)	2
Clay Tile — Plastered as Noted		Gypsum: Sand 1 : 3	¾″ plastered side not exposed to fire	6″ partition consisting of 4″ tile, cored not to exceed 41%, faced on fire exposed side with 1¾″ tile, cored not to exceed 15%, with ⅜″ mortar filled joint between. Nonbearing. (20)	3

Walls and Partitions	Lath	Plaster Materials and Proportions	Thickness	Notes	Fire Resistance Ratings Hours
Clay Tile — Plastered as Noted— Continued		Gypsum: Sand 1 : 3	¾″ plastered back side only	4″ facing tile cored not to exceed 25%. Nonbearing. (20)	2
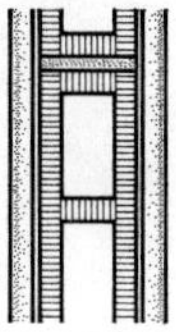		Gypsum: Sand 1 : 3	⅝″ plastered two sides	6″ hollow tile of medium burned clay, not less than 45% solid, 2 cells in thickness. Nonbearing (2)	2
		Gypsum: Sand 1 : 3	⅝″ plastered two sides	6″ hollow tile of medium burned clay, not less than 30% solid. Nonbearing. (2)	1½
		Gypsum: Sand 1 : 3	¾″ plastered back side	4″ facing tile cored not to exceed 47%. Nonbearing. (20)	1
		Gypsum: Sand 1 : 3	⅝″ plastered two sides	3″ hollow tile not less than 50% solid or 4″ hollow tile not less than 40% solid of medium burned clay. Nonbearing. (2)	1
		Gypsum: Sand 1 : 3	¾″ plastered two sides	4″ hollow tile. Nonbearing. (14)	1
		Gypsum: Sand 1 : 3	⅝″ plastered two sides	6″ hollow tile. Nonbearing. (2)	1
		Gypsum: Sand 1 : 3	⅝″ plastered two sides	4″ hollow tile having 2 cells in wall thickness. Nonbearing. (2)	1

Walls and Partitions	Lath	Plaster Materials and Proportions	Thickness	Notes	Fire Resistance Ratings Hours
Gypsum Block — Plastered as Noted		Gypsum: Sand 1 : 3	½″ plastered two sides	4″ hollow blocks. Nonbearing. (15)	4
		Gypsum: Sand 1 : 3	½″ plastered two sides	3″ hollow. Nonbearing. (15)	3
		Gypsum: Sand 1 : 3	½″ plastered one side	4″ hollow block. Nonbearing. (20)	3
		Gypsum: Sand 1 : 3	⅝″ plastered one side	3″ hollow blocks. Nonbearing. (34)	3
		Gypsum: Sand 1 : 3	½″ plastered one side	3″ hollow blocks. Nonbearing. (20)	1½

Steel Column Protections	Lath	Plaster Materials and Proportions	Thickness	Notes	Fire Resistance Ratings Hours
Gypsum Block — Plastered as Noted		Gypsum-Sand 1 : 3	½″	Solid 2″ block; wire lath strips laid in horizontal joints; fill of gypsum block and mortar with ½″ mortar between columns and blocks. (16)	4
		Gypsum-Sand 1 : 3	½″	Solid 2″ block; ⅞″ 12 gauge metal cramps set in holes drilled in blocks to link adjacent blocks of same course together. (16)	4

Steel Column Protections	Lath	Plaster Materials and Proportions	Thickness	Notes	Fire Resistance Ratings Hours
Gypsum Block —Plastered as Noted— Continued		Gypsum-Sand 1 : 3	½″	Solid 3″ block; ⅞″ 12 gauge metal cramps linking adjacent blocks of same course; ¼″ mortar between column flange and block. (16)	4
Clay Tile — Plastered as Noted		Lime: Sand 1 : 2½ (vol)	⅝″	4″ hollow tile with 1⅛″ mortar between tile and column, ⅜″ metal mesh in horizontal joints; limestone concrete fill. (1)	4
		Gypsum: Sand 1 : 3 (vol)	¾″	2″ hollow tile with ¾″ mortar between tile and columns, ⅜″ metal mesh in horizontal joints; limestone concrete fill. (17)	4
Wire Fabric — Plastered as Noted	#16 ga. Wire Fabric Paper-backed	Portland Cement: Vermiculite 94 : 4	2″	Plaster reinforced with plain wire fabric. (1)	4
	#16 ga. Wire Fabric Paper-backed	Portland Cement: Perlite 94 : 3½	2⅛″	Plaster reinforced with plain wire fabric. (1)	4
Metal Lath — Plastered as Noted	Metal	Gypsum: Perlite or Vermiculite 100 : 2 100 : 3	1½″	Lath spaced 1¼″ from column with plaster pushed through to column flanges. (1)	4
	Metal	Gypsum: Perlite or Vermiculite 100 : 2 100 : 3	1½″	Lath spaced 7/16″ from flanges by ¾″ steel furring channels at approximately 2 feet vertical spacings. (1)	4
	Metal	Gypsum: Perlite or Vermiculite 100 : 2½	1″	Loose vermiculite fill. Lath spaced 1″ from column. (18)	4

Steel Column Protections	Lath	Plaster Materials and Proportions	Thickness	Notes	Fire Resistance Ratings Hours
Metal Lath — Plastered as Noted— Continued	Metal Self-Furring	Gypsum: Perlite or Vermiculite 100 : 2 100 : 3	1¾″	(1)	4
	Metal Self-Furring	Gypsum: Perlite or Vermiculite 100 : 2 100 : 3	1⅜″	(1)	3
	Metal	Gypsum: Perlite or Vermiculite 100 : 2 100 : 3	1″	Lath spaced 1¼″ from column with plaster pushed through to column flanges. (1)	3
	Metal Self-Furring	Gypsum: Perlite or Vermiculite 100 : 2 100 : 3	1″	(1)	2
	Metal	Gypsum: Perlite or Vermiculite 100 : 2 100 : 3	1″	Lath spaced 1¼″ from column. (1)	2
	Metal	Portland Cement: Lime: Sand 1 : 1/10 : 2½ (vol)	1″*	(17)	1
	Metal	Portland Cement: Sand 1 : 2½	1″*	(2)	1
	Metal	Gypsum: Sand 1 : 3	¾″*	(2)	1
Gypsum Lath — Plastered as Noted	Gypsum ½″ Two Layers	Gypsum: Perlite or Vermiculite 100 : 2 100 : 3	1½″	1″ hexagonal 20 gauge mesh wrapped around lath. (19)	4
	Gypsum ⅜″ perforated	Gypsum: Perlite or Vermiculite 100 : 2 100 : 3	1⅜″	Lath boxed around column and fastened with wire ties. (20)	3

Steel Column Protections	Lath	Plaster Materials and Proportions	Thickness	Notes	Fire Resistance Ratings Hours
Gypsum Lath — Plastered as Noted— Continued	Gypsum 3⁄8″ perforated	Gypsum: Sand 1 : 2 1 : 3	2″	Lath boxed around column and fastened with wire ties. (20)	3
	Gypsum 3⁄8″ perforated	Gypsum: Sand 1 : 2 1 : 3	13⁄8″	Lath boxed around column and fastened with wire ties. (20)	2
	Gypsum 3⁄8″ perforated	Gypsum: Perlite or Vermiculite 100 : 2½	1″	Lath boxed around column and fastened with wire ties. (19)	2
	Gypsum 3⁄8″ perforated	Gypsum: Sand 1 : 2½	5⁄8″	Lath boxed around column and fastened with wire ties. (19)	1½
	Gypsum 3⁄8″ perforated	Gypsum: Sand 1 : 2½	½″	Lath boxed around column and fastened with wire ties. (19)	1

Beams, Girders and Trusses Protected By A Ceiling of	Lath	Plaster Materials and Proportions	Thickness	Notes	Fire Resistance Ratings Hours
Note		Any beams, girders or trusses above the ceiling construction, described under Floor and Ceiling Constructions, will have the same rating as the floor, provided there are no combustible materials above the ceiling, and the bottom flange of the beam does not extend more than 6″ below the ceiling and is protected. (36)			
Metal Lath — Plastered as Noted	Metal	Gypsum: Perlite or Vermiculite 100 : 2	1″	Minimum 3″ space between lath and structural member. Steel member to project not more than 8″ below ceiling surface. Back plaster on ceiling lath not less than 1″ and on beam 1½″-3″ especially at corners. (1)	4

Beams, Girders and Trusses Protected By A Ceiling of	Lath	Plaster Materials and Proportions	Thickness	Notes	Fire Resistance Ratings Hours
Metal Lath— Plastered as Noted— Continued	Metal	Gypsum: Perlite or Vermiculite 100 : 2 100 : 3	1″	2½″ air space between lath and structural member. (1)	4
	Metal	Gypsum: Perlite or Vermiculite 100 : 2½	1″*	Lath suspended, furred or in contact with lower flanges of supporting members. (2)	4
	Metal	Gypsum: Perlite or Vermiculite 100 : 2½	¾″*	Lath suspended, furred or in contact with lower flanges of supporting members. (2)	3
Gypsum Lath — Plastered as Noted	Gypsum ⅜″ perforated	Gypsum: Perlite or Vermiculite 100 : 2½	⅞″	Lath applied to ¾″ furring channels spaced 12″ o.c. with transverse wire clips engaging each other, giving continuous support to the lath. Plaster reinforced with 14 gauge galvanized wire secured diagonally to the clips. (20)	3
Metal Lath- Membrane Penetrated as Indicated 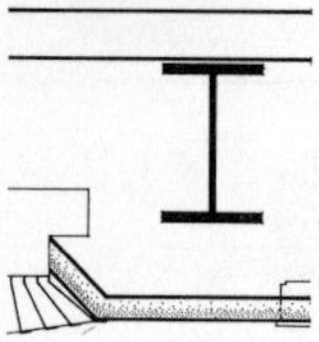	Metal	Gypsum: Perlite or Vermiculite 100 : 2 100 : 3	⅞″	Lath suspended not less than 3½″ below structural member and ducts. Duct openings not to exceed 70 square inches in each 100 square feet of ceiling area. Not more than 1 electrical outlet in each 90 square feet of ceiling area. Damper protections, duct locations, etc., as specified in U.L. Fire Protection Equipment List. (1)	4
	Metal	Gypsum: Perlite or Vermiculite 100 : 2 100 : 3	⅞″	Lath suspended not less than 2¾″ below structural member and ducts. Duct openings not to exceed 70 square inches in each 100 square feet of ceiling area. Damper protection and other details as specified in U.L. Fire Protection Equipment List. (1)	4

Beams, Girders and Trusses Individually Protected By	Lath	Plaster Materials and Proportions	Thickness	Notes	Fire Resistance Ratings Hours
Metal Lath— Membrane Penetrated as Indicated— Continued	Metal	Gypsum: Perlite or Vermiculite 100 : 2 100 : 3	7/8 "	Lath suspended not less than 3½" below structural members. Duct and electrical outlet openings not to exceed 100 square inches in each 100 square feet of ceiling area. Damper protections, duct locations, etc., as specified in U.L. Fire Protection Equipment List. (1)	3
Metal Lath — Plastered as Indicated	Metal Self-Furring	Gypsum: Perlite or Vermiculite 100 : 2	1½"	Lath cage — back of lath ¼" from steel. (1)	4
	Metal	Gypsum: Perlite or Vermiculite 100 : 2 100 : 3	1⅛"	Lath supported on wire or channel hangers. (1)	4
	Metal Self-Furring	Special Fire Retardant Gypsum Plaster	1"	Lath wrapped around beam. (1)	4
	Metal Self-Furring	Gypsum: Perlite or Vermiculite 100 : 2½	1½"	Lath clipped to beam flanges. (1)	4
	Metal	Gypsum: Perlite or Vermiculite 100 : 2½	1¼"	Lath clipped to beam flanges. (1)	3
	Metal Self-Furring	Gypsum: Perlite or Vermiculite 100 : 2½	1⅛"	Lath clipped to beam flanges. (1)	2
	Metal Self-Furring	Gypsum: Perlite (mill-mixed)	1"	Lath wrapped around beam. (1)	2

Beams, Girders and Trusses Individually Protected By	Lath	Plaster Materials and Proportions	Thickness	Notes	Fire Resistance Ratings Hours
Metal Lath — Plastered as Indicated— Continued	Metal	Gypsum: Perlite or Vermiculite 100 : 2 100 : 3	1″	Lath supported by metal lath hangers. (1)	2
	Metal	Gypsum: Perlite or Vermiculite 100 : 2 100 : 3	1″	Lath supported by ¾″ channels boxed around beam. Back of lath at least 1½″ from bottom and 1⅛″ from edges of structural member. (1)	2
	Metal	Gypsum: Perlite or Vermiculite 100 : 2 100 : 3	⅞″	(1)	2
	Metal	Gypsum: Perlite or Vermiculite 100 : 2 100 : 3	⅞″	Lath supported by metal with hangers anchored in concrete pads over beams. (1)	1½
	Metal	Gypsum: Perlite or Vermiculite 100 : 2 100 : 3	1″	(1)	1
	Metal	Gypsum: Sand 1 : 3	¾″	(e)	1
	Metal	Portland Cement: Sand 1 : 2½	1″	(e)	1
Direct Applied Plaster	None	Special Fire Retardant Gypsum Plaster	1½″	Plaster applied in two coats following contour of beam. (1)	4
	None	Vermiculite — Type MK	1⅞″	Vermiculite Type MK machine applied directly to structural member in one coat following contour of beam. (1)	3

Beams, Girders and Trusses Individually Protected By	Lath	Plaster Materials and Proportions	Thickness	Notes	Fire Resistance Ratings Hours
Tile or Block — Plastered as Indicated		Gypsum Plaster	½″	2″ Gypsum blocks (hollow). 3″ Gypsum blocks (hollow). (e)	2 3
		Gypsum Plaster	½″	2″ solid gypsum blocks. (e)	4
		Gypsum or Portland Cement Plaster	½″	2″ clay tile or concrete block. (e)	2
		Gypsum or Portland Cement Plaster	½″	2″ clay tile or concrete block; all spaces between member and tile or block filled solid. (e)	3

TEST AUTHORITIES AND REFERENCES

1. Underwriter's Laboratories, Inc.
2. "Fire Resistance Classifications of Building Constructions," National Bureau of Standards Report, BMS 92, 1942.
3. "Fire Endurance of Open-Web Steel Joist Floors with Concrete Slabs and Gypsum Ceilings," National Bureau of Standards Report, BMS 141, 1954.
4. Columbia University Testing Laboratory Report No. FW 59, August, 1930.
5. Report of Committee on Test Re: Cal. No. 163-46 SM, Bulletin of the Board of Standards and Appeals of the City of New York, December 17, 1946.
6. "Fire Resistance and Sound-Insulation Ratings for Walls, Partitions and Floors," National Bureau of Standards Technical Report on Building Materials, TRBM-44, June 24, 1946.
7. Ohio State University Engineering Experiment Station Report Project No. T-129, January 24, 1948. (Unpublished)

8. Ohio State University Engineering Experiment Station Report Project No. T-147, July, 1949. (Unpublished)

9. "Fire Tests of Wood and Metal-Framed Partitions," National Bureau of Standards Report BMS 71, 1941.

10. Ohio State University Engineering Experiment Station Report Project No. T-118, March 10, 1947. (Unpublished)

11. Ohio State University Engineering Experiment Station Report Project No. T-162, December, 1950. (Unpublished)

12. Ohio State University Engineering Experiment Station Report Project No. T-118, March, 1948. (Unpublished)

13. "Fire Resistance of Walls of Lightweight Aggregate Concrete Masonry Units," National Bureau of Standards Report, BMS 117, 1950.

14. "A Study of the Fire Resistance of Building Materials," Bulletin No. 104 of the Engineering Experiment Station of Ohio State University. (January, 1940)

15. Ohio State University Engineering Experiment Station Report No. T-26, Bulletin of the Board of Standards and Appeals of the City of New York. July 19, 1941.

16. "Fire Tests of Columns Protected with Gypsum," National Bureau of Standards Research Paper No. RP563, 1933.

17. "Fire Tests of Building Columns," A Joint Report of Underwriters' Laboratories, Inc., The Associated Factory Mutual Fire Insurance Companies and The National Bureau of Standards, 1920.

18. Report of Committee on Tests Re: Cal. No. 163-46 SM, Bulletin of the Board of Standards and Appeals of the City of New York, December 17, 1946.

19. "Fire Tests of Steel Columns Encased with Gypsum Lath and Plaster," National Bureau of Standards Report, BMS 135, 1953.

20. Based on Test Data Obtained From Unpublished Report of Recognized Testing Laboratory.

21. Ohio State University Engineering Experiment Station Report. Project No. T-737.

22. Ohio State University Engineering Experiment Station Report. Project No. T-1329.

23. Ohio State University Engineering Experiment Station Report. Project No. T-799.

24. Ohio State University Engineering Experiment Station Report. Project No. T-346.

25. Ohio State University Engineering Experiment Station Report. Project No. T-347.

26. Ohio State University Engineering Experiment Station Report. Project No. T-948.

27. Ohio State University Engineering Experiment Station Report. Project No. T-1262, T-650.

28. Ohio State University Engineering Experiment Station Report. Project No. T-397.

29. Ohio State University Engineering Experiment Station Report. Project No. T-1332.

30. Ohio State University Engineering Experiment Station Report. Project No. T-1330.

31. Ohio State University Engineering Experiment Station Report. Project No. T-304.

32. Ohio State University, 1959.

33. Ohio State University Engineering Experiment Station Report. Project No. T-1167.

34. Ohio State University Engineering Experiment Station Report. Project No. T-1315.

35. Ohio State University Engineering Experiment Station Report. Project No. T-961.

36. National Board of Fire Underwriters.

e — refers to estimated ratings.

FIRE INSURANCE INSPECTION AND RATING ORGANIZATIONS

ALABAMA
Alabama Inspection and Rating Bureau
Washington Building, P.O. Box 80
Montgomery 1, Alabama

ALASKA
Pacific Fire Rating Bureau
465 California Street
San Francisco 4, California

ARIZONA
Arizona Fire Rating Bureau
45 W. Jefferson Street
P.O. Box 2831
Phoenix, Arizona

ARKANSAS
Arkansas Inspection and Rating Bureau
512 Hall Building, P.O. Box 2661
Little Rock, Arkansas

CALIFORNIA
Pacific Fire Rating Bureau
465 California Street
San Francisco 4, California

COLORADO
Mountain States Inspection Bureau
801 Gas and Electric Building
P.O. Box 1740
Denver 1, Colorado

CONNECTICUT
New England Fire Insurance Rating
   Association
89 Broad Street, P.O. Box 2057
Boston 6, Massachusetts

DELAWARE
Middle Department Association of
    Fire Underwriters
401 Walnut Street
Philadelphia 6, Pennsylvania

DISTRICT OF COLUMBIA
Insurance Rating Bureau of D.C.
840 Woodward Building
Washington 5, D.C.

FLORIDA
Florida Inspection and Rating Bureau
35 South Hogan Street, P.O. Box 539
Jacksonville 1, Florida

GEORGIA
Georgia Inspection and Rating Bureau
300 Trust Company of Georgia
    Building, P.O. Box 4809
Atlanta 2, Georgia

HAWAII
Hawaii Fire Rating Bureau
250 South King Street — Room 320
Honolulu 13, Hawaii

IDAHO
Idaho Surveying and Rating Bureau, Inc.
1007 West Jefferson, P.O. Box 1069
Boise, Idaho

ILLINOIS (Cook County only)
Cook County Inspection Bureau
175 West Jackson Boulevard
Chicago 4, Illinois

ILLINOIS (Except Cook County)
Illinois Inspection Bureau
309 West Jackson Boulevard
Chicago 6, Illinois

INDIANA
Indiana Rating Bureau
320 North Meridian Street
Indianapolis 9, Indiana

IOWA
Iowa Inspection Bureau
414 Insurance Exchange Building
Des Moines 8, Iowa

KANSAS
Kansas Inspection Bureau
701 Jackson Street, P.O. Box 949
Topeka, Kansas

KENTUCKY
Kentucky Inspection Bureau
940 Starks Building
Louisville 2, Kentucky

LOUISIANA
Louisiana Rating and Fire Prevention
    Bureau
Pere Marquette Building, P.O. Box 730
New Orleans 2, Louisiana

MAINE
New England Fire Insurance Rating
    Association
89 Broad Street, P.O. Box 2057
Boston 6, Massachusetts

MARYLAND
Maryland Fire Underwriters Rating
    Bureau
Garrett Building
Redwood and South Streets
Baltimore 2, Maryland

MASSACHUSETTS
New England Fire Insurance Rating
    Association
89 Broad Street, P.O. Box 2057
Boston 6, Massachusetts

MICHIGAN
Michigan Inspection Bureau
Cadillac Tower, P.O. Box 2719
Detroit 31, Michigan

MINNESOTA
Fire Underwriters Inspection Bureau
1229 Plymouth Building
Minneapolis 3, Minnesota

MISSISSIPPI
Mississippi State Rating Bureau
901 Plaza Building, P.O. Box 1790
Jackson 5, Mississippi

MISSOURI
Missouri Inspection Bureau
1330 Pierce Building
St. Louis 2, Missouri

MONTANA
Montana Fire Rating Bureau
708-11 Metals Bank Building
P.O. Box 1973
Butte, Montana

NEBRASKA
Nebraska Inspection Bureau
3016 Harney Street
Omaha 31, Nebraska

NEVADA
Pacific Fire Rating Bureau
465 California Street
San Francisco 4, California

NEW HAMPSHIRE
New Hampshire Board of Underwriters
3 Capitol Street
Concord, New Hampshire

NEW JERSEY
Fire Insurance Rating Organization of
   New Jersey
520 Broad Street
Newark 2, New Jersey

NEW MEXICO
Mountain States Inspection Bureau
801 Gas and Electric Building,
P.O. Box 1740
Denver 1, Colorado

NEW YORK
New York Fire Insurance Rating
   Organization
85 John Street
New York 38, New York

NORTH CAROLINA
North Carolina Fire Insurance Rating
   Bureau
226 South Dawson Street,
P.O. Box 2021
Raleigh, North Carolina

NORTH DAKOTA
Fire Underwriters Inspection Bureau
1229 Plymouth Building
Minneapolis 3, Minnesota

OHIO
Ohio Inspection Bureau
431 East Broad Street, P.O. Box 1290
Columbus 16, Ohio

OKLAHOMA
Oklahoma Inspection Bureau
801 Mercantile Building, P.O. Box 559
Oklahoma City 1, Oklahoma

OREGON
Oregon Insurance Rating Bureau
721 S.W. Oak Street, P.O. Box 70
Portland 7, Oregon

PACIFIC FIRE RATING BUREAU
Pacific Fire Rating Bureau
465 California Street
San Francisco 4, California

PENNSYLVANIA
Middle Department Association of
   Fire Underwriters
401 Walnut Street
Philadelphia 6, Pennsylvania

PUERTO RICO
Puerto Rico Inspection and Rating
   Bureau
P.O. Box 1333
San Juan 7, Puerto Rico

RHODE ISLAND
New England Fire Insurance Rating
   Association
89 Broad Street, P.O. Box 2057
Boston 6, Massachusetts

SOUTH-EASTERN
UNDERWRITERS ASSOCIATION
South-Eastern Underwriters Association
327 Trust Company of Georgia Building,
P.O. Box 5048
Atlanta 2, Georgia

SOUTH CAROLINA
South Carolina Inspection and Rating
   Bureau
1332 Sumter Street, P.O. Box 1379
Columbia, South Carolina

SOUTH DAKOTA
Fire Underwriters Inspection Bureau
1229 Plymouth Building
Minneapolis 3, Minnesota

TENNESSEE
Tennessee Inspection Bureau
1000 Stahlman Building
Nashville 3, Tennessee

TEXAS
Texas Insurance Advisory Association
812 Brazos Street, P.O. Box 15
Austin 1, Texas

TEXAS
Fire Prevention and Engineering Bureau
520 Mercantile Securities Building
1810 Main Street
Dallas 1, Texas

UTAH
Utah Fire Rating Bureau
1106 Boston Building
Salt Lake City 1, Utah

VERMONT
New England Fire Insurance Rating
   Association
89 Broad Street, P.O. Box 2057
Boston 6, Massachusetts

VIRGINIA
Virginia Insurance Rating Bureau
American Building, P.O. Box 1198
Richmond 9, Virginia

WASHINGTON
Washington Surveying & Rating Bureau
Alaska Building, P.O. Box 1818
Seattle 11, Washington

WEST VIRGINIA
West Virginia Rating Bureau
1210 Kanawha Valley Building
308 Capitol Street, P.O. Box 626
Charleston 22, West Virginia

WISCONSIN
Fire Insurance Rating Bureau
210 West Michigan Street
Milwaukee 3, Wisconsin

WYOMING
Mountain States Inspection Bureau
801 Gas and Electric Building,
P.O. Box 1740
Denver 1, Colorado

DEFINITIONS

The definitions that follow apply to terms used in this text. Although they follow the definitions listed by most authorities as to general content, they do not necessarily agree with any particular publication.

Fire hazard classification
  a. *With respect to occupancy:* a classification of building uses based on fire load or danger of explosion.
  b. *With respect to building materials:* a classification of surfacing materials based on flame spread over their surfaces, fuel contributed, and density of smoke produced during fire exposure.

Fire limits. Boundary lines establishing an area in which there exists, or is likely to exist, a fire hazard requiring special protection.

Fire zone. Area within fire limits.

Fire load. An estimate of the intensity and duration of a fire derived from measurement of the total combustible contents of a building, or space subdivisions therein.

Fireproof, fire resistive, fire retardant. The quality of materials, construction or structures to resist fire and prevent its spread. (Many codes utilize one or more of these terms as construction classifications and assign each a specific series of hourly ratings).

* "National Building Code," National Board of Fire Underwriters, 1955.

Fire resistance. That property of materials, construction or assembly of materials which, during a fire, prevents or retards the passage of excessive heat, hot gases, or flames.

Fire resistance rating. The time in hours that a material or construction will withstand fire exposure as determined by a fire test made in conformity with accepted standards.

Incombustible, noncombustible.* As applied to a building construction material this means a material which, in the form in which it is used, falls in one of the groups described in (a) through (c) below. It does not apply to surface finish materials nor to the determination of whether a material is noncombustible from the standpoint of clearances to heating appliances, flues or other sources of high temperature. No material shall be classed as noncombustible which is subject to increase in combustibility or flame spread rating beyond the limits herein established through the effects of age, moisture or other atmospheric conditions. "Flame spread rating," as used here, refers to ratings obtained according to ASTM E-84.

  (a) Materials no part of which will ignite and burn when subjected to fire. Any material which liberates flammable gas when heated to a temperature of 1,380 degrees F., for 5 minutes shall not be considered noncombustible within the meaning of this paragraph.

(b) Materials having a structural base of non-combustible material as defined in (a), with a surfacing not more than ⅛ inch thick which has a flame spread rating not higher than 50.

(c) Materials, other than as described in (a) or (b), having a surface flame spread rating not higher than 25 without evidence of continued progressive combustion and of such composition that surfaces that would be exposed by cutting through the material in any way would not have a flame spread rating higher than 25 without evidence of continued progressive combustion.

Glossary of Terms

GLOSSARY OF TERMS

ACCELERATOR — An admixture that will hasten the setting action of stucco, plaster, or mortar.

ACOUSTICAL — Related to, pertaining to, or associated with sound, but not having its properties or characteristics.

ACOUSTICAL PLASTER & PLASTIC — Sound absorbing finishing materials mill-formulated for application in areas where a reduction in sound reverberation or noise intensity is desired. These materials usually are applied to a minimum thickness of ½″ and generally provide a noise reduction coefficient of at least .45 decibels.

ACOUSTICS — The science of sound including its production, transmission and effects.

ADDITIVE — (See "Admixtures")

ADHESIVE BOND — A relationship between two materials in contact with each other causing them to stick or adhere together by means other than cohesion.

ADMIXTURE — Any substance added to a plaster component or to plaster mortar for the purpose of altering its properties.

AGGREGATE — An inert material used as a filler with cementitious material and water to produce plaster, concrete, etc. The term used in conjunction with plaster usually implies sand, vermiculite or perlite.

AIR-ENTRAINMENT — The process by which air is introduced into a material while in a liquid or plastic state in the form of small isolated bubbles.

ALABASTER — A massive densely crystalline, softly textured form of practically pure gypsum.

ALPHA GYPSUM — A term denoting a class of specially processed calcined gypsums having properties of low consistency and high strength. Alpha Gypsums can be produced having strengths in excess of 10,000 PSI.

ANGLE FLOAT — A finishing tool having a surface bent to form a right angle. Used to finish re-entrant angles.

ANHYDROUS CALCIUM SULPHATE — A stable form of gypsum from which practically all of the water of crystallization has been removed. Described by the term dead-burned gypsum.

ARCH CORNER BEAD — A job-shaped length of corner bead used to define the curved portion of arched openings.

BACKING — (See "Plaster Base")

BACK-PLASTERING — A term denoting plaster applied to one face of a lath system following application and subsequent hardening of plaster applied to the opposite face. Back-Plastering is used primarily in construction of solid plaster partitions and certain exterior wall systems.

BASE — (See "Plaster Base")

BASE BEAD — (See "Base Screed")

BASECOAT — Any plaster coat or coats applied prior to application of the finish coat.

BASE SCREED — A preformed metal screed with perforated or expanded flanges. Provides a ground for plaster and separates areas of dissimilar materials.

BEAD — A strip of sheet metal usually formed with a projecting nosing and 2 perforated or expanded flanges. The nosing serves to establish plaster grounds while the flanges provide for attachment to the plaster base. Used at the perimeter of a plaster membrane as a stop or at projecting angles to define and reinforce the edge. Types are corner beads, base beads, casing beads, etc.

BINDER — (See "Cementitious Material")

BLISTERING — A condition usually characterized by a bulging of the finish plaster coat as it separates and draws away from the basecoat. The resulting protuberances are often termed "turtle backs."

BOND — The state of adherence between plaster coats or between plaster and a plaster base produced by adhesive and/or cohesive properties of plaster or special supplementary materials.

BONDING AGENT — A substance applied to a surface to improve the quality of the bond between it and succeeding plaster application.

BOND PLASTER — A specially formulated gypsum plaster designed as a first coat application over monolithic concrete.

BROWN COAT — The second coat in three coat plaster application.

BROWN OUT — To complete application of basecoat plastering.

BUILDING LIME — A lime whose chemical and physical characteristics and method of processing make it suitable for ordinary or special construction uses; also called construction lime.

BULK DENSITY — The weight of a material per unit of volume.

BUTTERFLIES — Color imperfections in a lime-putty finish coat which smear out under pressure of the trowel.

CALCINE — To drive off or lose chemically combined water by action of heat thereby altering the chemical and physical characteristics of a material.

CALCINED GYPSUM — Gypsum that has been partially dehydrated by heat.

CASTS — Finished products from a mold sometimes referred to as staff.

CASING BEAD — A Bead used at the perimeter of a plaster membrane or around openings to provide a stop and, to provide separation from adjacent materials.

CATFACE — Blemish or rough depression in the finish coat caused by variations in base coat thickness.

CONTACT CEILING — A ceiling which is secured in direct contact with the construction above without use of furring.

CEMENT — A material or mixture of materials which when in a plastic state, possesses adhesive and cohesive properties and which will set in place. Note: The word cement is used without regard to the composition of the material.

CEMENTITIOUS MATERIAL — A component material of plaster which when mixed with water provides plasticity necessary for placement. Upon subsequent setting or hardening it serves to bind aggregate particles together into a rigid heterogeneous mass.

CEMENT PLASTER — A variously defined term used in some localities to denote plaster containing portland cement, in other localities to denote calcined gypsum.

CHECK CRACKS — (See "Craze Cracks")

CHECKING — (See "Craze Cracks")

CHEMICAL BOND — A term denoting bond produced by cohesion between separate laminae of similar crystalline materials. Based on formation and subsequent interlocking of crystals.

CHIP CRACKS — Fine cracks, similar to check cracks except that bond is partially destroyed producing a series of concave fragments of the surface material. The condition is also termed "egg shelling", fire cracking, etc.

CLIPS — A classification of devices usually made of wire or sheet metal used to attach various types of lath to supports or to secure adjacent lath sheets.

COAT — A thickness, covering, or layer of plaster applied in a single operation.

COLORED FINISHES — Plaster finish coats containing integrally mixed color pigments or colored aggregates.

COMPOUND PLASTER — A regional term denoting neat calcined gypsum for use in basecoat plasters.

CONSISTENCY — A term literally denoting the fluidity or viscosity of a plaster mortar or cementitious paste. The term is often used to denote the quantity of water required to bring a given quantity of dry cementitious material or mixture of cementitious material and aggregate to a given state of fluidity.

CORNER BEAD — A metal bead used at projecting or external angles to define and reinforce the corner.

CORNER REINFORCEMENT — Plaster reinforcement used at reentrant or internal angles to provide continuity between two intersecting plaster planes. Usually a strip of diamond mesh metal lath bent to form a right angle. Other names "cornerite", corner lath.

CRAZE CRACKS — Fine, random fissures or cracks which may appear in a plaster surface caused by plaster shrinkage. Also termed check cracking, these cracks are generally associated with a lime finish coat that has not been properly gauged or troweled.

CROSS FURRING — Term used to denote furring members attached to other structural components to support lath in suspended ceilings. Generally ¾″ steel channels or pencil rods.

CURE — To provide conditions conducive to completion of the hydration process. Generally used in conjunction with portland cement plaster: To maintain a sufficient quantity of water in contact with portland cement plaster to insure complete hydration throughout the period required for this process to take place.

DARBY — A flat wooden or metal tool about 4″ wide and 42″ long with handles; used to smooth or float the brown coat; also used on finished coat to give a preliminary true and even surface.

DASH-BOND COAT — A thick slurry of portland cement, sand and water dashed on smooth monolithic concrete surfaces with a paddle or whisk-broom to provide a key for subsequent portland cement plaster coats.

DECIBEL — A unit measure of sound intensity which can be used in expressing sound volume or loudness.

DEVIL'S FLOAT — A wooden float with two nails protruding from the toe. Usually used to roughen the surface of the brown coat.

DIAMOND MESH — One of the common types of metal lath having a characteristic geometrical pattern produced by the slitting and expansion of metal sheets.

DOLOMITIC — Term used to denote a type of lime or limestone containing calcium carbonate in combination with up to 50% magnesium carbonate.

DOPE — A term used by plasterers for mortar additives of any type, such as those used to retard or accelerate set.

DOT — A small lump of plaster placed on a surface between grounds to assist the plasterer in obtaining the proper plaster thickness and aid in aligning the surface.

DOUBLE-UP — A method of plaster placement characterized by application in successive operations with no setting or drying time allowed between coats. Also called: double-back, doubled-up, laid off, laid on, or two coat work.

DRY-OUT — A condition occasionally occurring in gypsum plaster work which by excessive evaporation or suction has lost some or all of the water necessary for crystallization. Appears as a light colored, friable area.

EFFLORESCENCE — White, fleecy surface deposits sometimes found on plaster or masonry. Also referred to as "whiskering" or "saltpetering."

EGGSHELLING — (See "Chip Cracks")

EXPANDED METAL — Term used to denote sheet metal which has been slit and drawn out to form diamond-shaped or herringbone openings. This, when used as a plaster base, is termed "metal lath."

EXPANSION JOINT — A device usually formed from sheet metal and having a "W" shaped cross section. Used to provide controlled discontinuity at locations in a plaster membrane where high stresses may be encountered. Also known as a "relief joint" or "control joint."

FAT — Material accumulated on the trowel during the finishing operation often used to fill in small imperfections. Also a term used to describe working characteristics of a mortar containing a high proportion of cementitious material. Also used to describe working characteristics of highly plastic mortars.

FEATHER EDGE — A tool of metal or wood having a bevelled edge: Used in finish coat work to straighten reentrant angles.

FIBER — Animal hair or sisal, manilla or glass fibers of appropriate length added to plaster mortar to increase its cohesiveness.

FIBERED — Term pertaining to basecoat plaster containing animal, vegetable or glass fiber. Note: not included in this definition is neat gypsum basecoat plaster containing wood fiber as an aggregate and designed for use either with or without addition of other aggregates which is termed "wood-fibered plaster."

FINES — Term usually pertaining to small aggregate particles capable of passing through a #200 sieve.

FINISHING BRUSHES — Brushes used to apply water to a smooth lime finish coat during final troweling.

FINENESS MODULUS — An abstract number used to compare different particles or graduations of aggregate. The fineness modulus is computed by adding the cumulative percentages retained on the six standard screens (#4, #8, #16, #30, #50 and #100) and dividing the sum by 100.

FINISH COAT — The last layer of plaster applied. Usually providing a decorative surface or a base for further decoration.

FISH EYES — A term used to describe small blemishes occasionally found in lime finish coats. Approximately ¼″ in diameter, they are caused by lumpy lime.

FLOAT — A tool or procedure used by the plasterer to straighten and level the finish coat surface, to correct surface irregularities produced by other tools and to impart a distinctive surface texture.

FLOAT FINISH — A finish coat texture which is rougher than a trowel finish. The roughness is derived primarily from aggregate particles contained in the plaster mortar.

FRESCO — An artistic or decorative medium consisting of a water-soluble paint applied to freshly applied plaster.

FURRED CEILING — A ceiling having spacer elements, (usually furring channels, round rods, or wood strips) interposed between it and the supporting structure above.

FURRING — Term applied to spacer elements used to maintain a space between a finish and the structural elements behind it.

FURRING CHANNELS — Term generally applied to ¾″ cold or hot rolled steel channels used in plaster base construction.

GAUGING — Another cementitious material (usually calcined gypsum, Keene's cement, or portland cement) added to lime putty to provide and control set. Also the act of adding gauging material.

GESSO — A plaster surface composed of gypsum plaster, whiting and glue; used as a base for decorative painting.

GRADATION — The particle size distribution of aggregate as determined by separation with standard screens. Sieve analysis, screen analysis, and mechanical analysis are terms used synonomously in referring to gradation of aggregate. Gradation of aggregate is expressed in terms of the individual percentages retained on U. S. standard screens designated by the numbers 4-8-16-30-50 and 100.

GREEN — A term used to describe newly applied plaster that has not dried.

GROUNDS — A piece of wood or metal attached to the plaster base so that its exposed surface acts as a gauge to determine the thickness of plaster to be applied. Also used by the carpenter as a nailing base or spacer for attachment of trim. A term denoting plaster thickness.

GYPSITE — An earthy deposit found at or near the surface of the ground, consisting of finely crystalline gypsum mixed with loam, clay, sand, and humus. Gypsum content generally ranges from 60% to more than 90%.

GYPSUM — A naturally occurring mineral consisting of calcium sulphate combined with two molecules of water, in crystalline form, having the approximate chemical formula $CaSo_4 2H_2O$.

GYPSUM LATH — A plaster base manufactured in the form of sheets or slabs of various sizes and either ⅜″ or ½″ thick, having an incombustible core (essentially gypsum) and surfaced with special paper suitable for receiving gypsum plaster.

GYPSUM PLASTER — Ground calcined gypsum combined with various additives to control set. Also used to denote applied gypsum plaster mixtures.

GYPSUM TROWEL FINISH — Various proprietary ready-mixed finish coat materials consisting essentially of calcined gypsum.

HANGERS — Tensile members used to attach the framework of a suspended ceiling to the supporting structure above.

HARD WALL — A regional term denoting neat gypsum basecoat plaster.

HAWK — A tool used by plasterers to hold and carry plaster mortar. The hawk consists of a flat piece of wood or metal approximately 10″-14″ square, with a wooden handle centered and fixed to the underside.

HEMIHYDRATE — A hydrate containing half a molecule of water to one of the material forming the hydrate. A term used to describe the form of calcined gypsum generally used for plaster.

HIGH CALCIUM LIME — A type of lime containing principally calcium oxide or hydroxide and not more than 5% magnesium oxide or hydroxide.

HIGH MAGNESIUM LIME — A type of lime containing more than 5% magnesium oxide or hydroxide.

HODDABILITY — A term descriptive of the ease with which a plaster mortar may be handled with a hod or hawk. Dependent upon flow characteristics and angle of repose of the mortar.

HYDRATE — To combine with water or elements of water. A term used to denote hydrated lime.

HYDRATED LIME — The dry, relatively stable material produced by treating quicklime with just enough water to satisfy its chemical affinity for water under the conditions of its hydration.

JOINING — Sometimes termed a jointing, denotes the juncture of two separate plaster applications usually within a single surface plane.

JOURNEYMAN — A term applicable to a plasterer or lather who through training and experience has become thoroughly skilled in his trade. Distinguished from an apprentice or a laborer.

KEENE'S CEMENT — A cementitious material used principally in finish coats as gauging for lime putty. Capable of producing a very hard, smooth surface. Keene's Cement consists of gypsum, calcined to a point where all but 0.1% to 1% of the water of crystallization has been removed, and compounded with an accelerator. Also termed anhydrous calcined gypsum.

LAKE SAND — Sand consisting predominantly of fine, rounded particles.

LAND PLASTER — A term used to describe coarsely ground natural gypsum used agriculturally as a soil conditioner.

LATH — A material applied separately to a structure whose primary function is that of a plaster base. Lath is generally classified as metallic, gypsum, wood, or insulation board.

LATH AND PLASTER MEMBRANE — A thin slab of lath and plaster including any integral supporting and stiffening members. A term describing lath and plaster as a unit of structure.

LEAN MIXTURE — A term denoting any plaster mortar containing a relatively high ratio of aggregate to cementitious material. The term "harsh" is often used to describe the working properties of a mortar mix that is too lean.

LIGHTWEIGHT AGGREGATES — A term generally applied to vermiculite and perlite distinguished from sand and middle weight aggregates such as pumice, expanded slag, etc.

LIME — A general term applicable to the principal product derived from burning various types of limestone: Consisting essentially of the oxides or hydroxides of calcium and magnesium.

LIME PLASTER — A term generally referring to basecoat plaster consisting essentially of lime and an aggregate.

LIME PUTTY — A plastering material resulting from slaking quicklime or soaking and mixing hydrated lime with a sufficient quantity of water to form a thick paste.

LOW-CONSISTENCY PLASTER — A neat gypsum base coat plaster that has been specially processed during manufacture so that less mixing water is required to produce workability than in standard gypsum basecoat plaster.

LUMP LIME — Quicklime as it comes from the kiln.

MAIN RUNNERS — The heaviest integral supporting members in a suspended ceiling. Main runners are supported by hangers attached to the building structure and in turn support furring channels or rods to which lath is fastened.

MAREZZO — An imitation marble produced with Keene's cement to which color pigments have been added.

MECHANICAL APPLICATION — Application of plaster mortar by mechanical means: Generally pumping and spraying. Distinguished from hand application with a trowel.

MECHANICAL BOND — A term used to describe the physical keying of one plaster coat to another or to the plaster base. Examples of mechanical bond are the clinching of plaster keys to metallic laths, and the interlock obtained between adjacent plaster coats by scratching or cross raking. Distinguished from "chemical bond" which implies formation of interlocking crystals or fusion.

MECHANICAL TROWEL — A power machine used to smooth and compact plaster finish coats: Capable of producing an extremely smooth, dense surface. Consisting of revolving metal or rubber blades. Also termed "power trowel."

MEMBRANE FIREPROOFING — A lath and plaster membrane having among its functions that of providing a barrier to fire and intense heat.

METAL LATH — A term denoting a metallic plaster base manufactured from sheet metal by slotting and subsequent expansion or by punching and forming. Types are diamond mesh, rib lath and sheet lath. Distinguished from wire lath, ·or wire fabric lath which is a welded or woven wire mesh.

MILL-MIXED — Term referring to plaster materials that have been formulated and dry-mixed by the manufacturer, requiring only the addition and mixture of water at the job.

MORTAR — A material used in a plastic state, which can be troweled and becomes hard in place. The term is used without regard to the composition of the material or its specific use.

PARGE — To coat with plaster: Particularly foundation walls and rough masonry.

PARGETING — A term originally applicable to all plaster work. Now generally applied only to elaborate ornamental work.

PERLITE — A siliceous volcanic glass. When expanded by heat it is used as a lightweight plaster aggregate.

PLASTER — From Greek, emplastron, to daub on; Latin, emplastrum; French, platre; old English, plaister.
1. A cementitious material or combination of cementitious materials and aggregate that, when mixed with a suitable amount of water, forms a plastic mass or paste which applied to a surface, adheres to it and subsequently sets or hardens, preserving in a rigid state the form or texture imposed during the period of plasticity.
   The term "plaster" is used with regard to the specific composition of the material and does not explicitly denote either interior or exterior use. The term "stucco," however, is generally used to describe plaster applied on the exterior.
2. The term "plaster" is used regionally to denote specifically neat calcined gypsum, lime-sand mixtures, etc.
3. To plaster (v). The act of applying plaster.

PLASTER WORK — The finished product of the plasterer.

PLASTER OF PARIS — Calcined Gypsum (calcium sulphate hermihydrate) without addition of material to control set. Principal use is in casting and industrial applications.

PLASTICITY — That property of plaster mortar that permits continuous and permanent deformation in any direction. A plastic material is distinct from a fluid material in that it requires a measurable force (yield value) to start flow. The property exists in varying degrees in different materials and in plaster mortar is sometimes regarded as an index of working characteristics.

PORTLAND CEMENT — A binder material commonly used in plaster. Portland cement alone or in combination with lime is the cementitious material generally used for exposed exterior plaster work.

PULP — A term used in some areas to denote wood fiber added as an aggregate to neat calcined gypsum.

PUTTY-COAT — A term generally denoting a smooth-troweled finish coat containing lime putty and a gauging material.

QUICKLIME — An unstable material generally produced by burning limestone, the major part of which is calcium oxide or calcium oxide in natural association with a lesser amount of magnesium oxide.

Before it can be used in construction, quicklime must be slaked in water and aged for at least 2 weeks.

READY-MIXED — A term denoting a plaster which is mixed at the mill with mineral aggregate and other ingredients which control time of set.

Generally used in conjunction with gypsum plasters. Also termed mill-mixed, pre-mixed.

RETARDER — An admixture used to delay the setting action of plaster.

Generally used only with gypsum plasters or finish coat plaster containing calcined gypsum gauging.

SAND — Loose granular material resulting from the natural disintegration of rock or from the crushing of friable sandstone.

Manufactured sand is the fine material resulting from the crushing and classification by screening, or otherwise, of rock, gravel or blast furnace slag.

SCAGLIOLA — An imitation marble made by the plasterer. Composed of a combination of Keene's cement, glue, isinglass and coloring material. It takes a high durable polish.

SCRATCH COAT — The first coat of plaster applied to a surface in three coat work. The term "scratch coat" originates from the practice of cross-raking or scratching the surface of this coat with a comb-like tool to provide a mechanical key to aid bond with the brown coat.

SCRATCH DOUBLE-UP — (See "Double-Up")

SCREEDS — Devices or materials run across the base surface of a wall or ceiling to serve as thickness and alignment guides for the plasterer in subsequent applications. Plaster screeds are generally about 4″ wide and of full basecoat thickness.

SCRIM — Rough textured woven cloth worked into brown or finish coat to add crack resistance to the plaster. Its use is now very rare.

SGRAFFITO — A decorative and artistic medium generally consisting of two layers of differently colored plaster. While still soft, the uppermost layer is scratched away, exposing the base or ground layer. Countless variations on the process are possible by modulation of pigments and combination with fresco techniques. Sgraffito in Italian means "scratched."

SHEET LATH — A type of metal lath formed by punching geometrical perforations in steel sheets. Made from heavier gauge steel than expanded laths, they consequently have greater stiffness.

SIEVE ANALYSIS — A method of classifying aggregates according to proportional content of particles of various sizes. Classification is done with standard sieves. (See gradation).

SKIM COAT — A term denoting a thin finish coat. Usually containing lime putty and troweled to a smooth surface.

SLAKE — A term denoting the process whereby lime putty is produced from quicklime. Slaking consists of adding quicklime to water and allowing the resulting slurry to age for at least two weeks.

SLICKER — A tool often used by the plasterer in place of the darby. It is made of a thin board bevelled on both sides, about 4 feet long and 6″ to 8″ wide, held by the thicker edge.

SPOT GROUNDS — Pieces of wood attached to the plaster base at various intervals for gauging plaster thickness.

STAFF — Plaster casts of ornamental details made in molds and reinforced with fiber. Usually wired or nailed into place.

STRIP LATH — A narrow strip of diamond mesh metal lath sometimes applied as reinforcement over joints between sheets of gypsum lath, at the juncture of two different base materials, at corners of openings, etc.

STRIPITE — (See "Strip Lath")

STUCCO —
1. A term denoting plaster used on exposed exterior locations. The term stucco is used without regard to specific composition of the material. Also termed "exterior plaster."
2. A term used within the manufacturing segment of the plaster industry to denote gypsum that has been partially or fully calcined but not yet processed into finished plaster. Also used to denote gypsum formulations for certain special industrial uses.

SUSPENDED CEILING — A ceiling which is suspended from and is not in direct contact with the floor or roof construction above.

SWEAT OUT — A defective condition occasionally occurring in gypsum plaster. Characterized by a soft, damp area remaining after the surrounding area has set hard. Often caused by insufficient ventilation which inhibits normal drying.

TEMPER — To mix plaster to a workable consistency.

TORPEDO SAND — A natural well-graded plastering sand obtained from pits along the Fox River, west of Chicago, Illinois.

THREE COAT PLASTERING — The application of plaster in three successive coats, leaving time between coats for setting and/or drying of the plaster.

TROWEL — A tool used by the plasterer to apply, spread, shape and smooth the various plastering mortars. The size of the trowel varies according to the mechanics preference with regard to the tool's feel and balance. Common sizes are 10½″ x 4½″ and 11½″ x 4¾″. There are three parts of a trowel: These are called the blade, the mounting, and the handle. The following trowels are commonly used — margin trowel, angle trowel. Other trowels — joint trowel, panel trowel, and texture trowel.

TROWEL FINISH — A term denoting the smooth finish coat surface produced by troweling.

TWO COAT PLASTERING — (See "Double-Up" method)

"TURTLE BACK" —
1. A term often used synonomously with blistering.
2. A term used regionally to denote a small localized area of craze-cracking.

VERMICULITE — A mineral that when expanded by heat is used as a lightweight aggregate for plaster.

WOOD FIBER — Ground or shredded, non-staining wood used as an aggregate with gypsum plaster.

WORKABILITY — A property of plaster mortar closely related to plasticity which determines the ease and speed with which the mortar can be applied and finished.

WHITE COAT — A term denoting a gauged lime putty trowel finish.

Notes, References and General Bibliography

NOTES, REFERENCES, AND GENERAL BIBLIOGRAPHY

CHAPTER 2

Notes and References

1. Best, John C. *The Rock Nobody Knows* (National Gypsum Company), p. 7.

2. U. S. Department of the Interior, Bureau of Mines. *Mineral Industry Surveys (Mineral Market Report* MMS No. 2692, 1957), p. 1.

3. Portland Cement Association. *Cement and Concrete Reference Book* (Chicago, 1957), p. 8-9.

4. Zonolite Company.*Vermiculite, Chemical and Physical Properties* (Chicago, 1954), p. 3.

5. North, Oliver S. *Vermiculite.* A chapter from *Mineral Facts and Problems.* (Preprint from Bureau of Mines Bulletin 556, 1955), p. 1.

6. Zonolite Company, *Vermiculite, Chemical and Physical Properties,* (Chicago, 1954), op. cit.

7. North, Oliver S. *Perlite.* A chapter from *Mineral Facts and Problems.* (Preprint from Bureau of Mines Bulletin 556, 1955), p. 1.

8. Hill, R. D., *The Long-term Expansion of Perlite Plaster and Concrete* (Australian Journal of Applied Science, Volume 9, Number 2, 1958), pp. 141-162.

9. *Standardized Lathing and Plastering Practices,* page 67, Final Report dated December 28, 1948. Prepared by Armour Research Foundation of the Illinois Institute of Technology for the U. S. Department of Commerce, Industrial Research and Development Division, contract number CAC. 47-18.

10. Metal Lath Manufacturers Association. *Peter Naylor, Man of Vision* (Metal Lath News, Volume 20, Number 3, 1956.)

General Bibliography

Mantell, Charles L. (ed.) *Engineering Materials Handbook* (McGraw-Hill, 1958).

Brady, George S., *Materials Handbook,* eighth edition (McGraw-Hill, 1956).

Van Den Branden, Felicien, and Knowles, Mark, *Plastering, Skill and Practice* (American Technical Society, Chicago, 1954), Chapter Three.

Dalton, Byron W., *Practical Plastering, Cement Finishing, and Related Subjects* (1949).

Standardized Lathing and Plastering Practices. Final Report, dated December 28, 1948, prepared by Armour Research Foundation of the Illinois Institute of Technology for the U. S. Department of Commerce, Industrial Research and Development Division, Contract Number CAC-47-18.

United States Gypsum Company, *Directory of Building Materials* (1953).

United States Gypsum Company, *U.S.G. Gypsum Plasters and Finishing Limes* (1959).

National Gypsum Company, *Gold Bond Gypsum Plasters and Lime* (1958).

Finishing Lime Association of Ohio, *Plaster With Finishing Hydrated Lime.*

Andrews, H., *The Production, Properties, and Uses of Calcium Sulphate Plasters* (Reprint from Building Research Congress, 1951), Part F, pp. 135-144.

Voss, Walter C., *Lime Characteristics and Their Effect on Construction* (Reprint from *Symposium on Lime,* American Society for Testing Materials, Philadelphia, 1939).

Ohio Lime Company, *Ohio Hydrate Lime for Plaster and Stucco.*

Portland Cement Association, *Cement and Concrete Reference Handbook* (Chicago, 1956).

Brunauer, Stephen, *Some Aspects of The Physics and Chemistry of Cement* (Portland Cement Association, Research Department, Bulletin 80, 1957).

U. S. Dept. of the Interior, Bureau of Mines, *Gypsum and Gypsum Products* (Mineral Market Report MMS No. 2692, 1957).

Cowper, A. D., *Sands for Plasters, Mortars and External Rendering*, National Building Studies, Bulletin No. 7 (Department of Scientific and Industrial Research, London, 1950).

North, O. S. and Chandler, H. P., *Vermiculite*, Bureau of Mines Information Circular 7668 (U. S. Department of the Interior, 1953).

Myers, John B., *Vermiculite* (Reprint from *Industrial Minerals and Rocks*, Chapter 51).

Zonolite Company, *Vermiculite, Chemical and Physical Properties* (Chicago, 1954).

Perlite Institute, *Perlite Design Manual* (New York, 1959).

North, Oliver S., *Perlite*, Bureau of Mines, U. S. Dept. of the Interior (Preprint of Chapter from Bulletin 556, Mineral Facts and Problems, 1955).

Metal Lath Manufacturers Association, *Types of Metal Lath and Their Uses*, Technical Bulletin No. 1 (Cleveland, 1956).

United States Gypsum Company, *Rocklath Plaster Base, Metal Lath and Accessories* (1959).

National Gypsum Co., *Gold Bond, Metal Lath, Gypsum Lath, Wall and Ceiling Systems and Accessories* (1958).

Larsen Products Corporation, *Larsen Bonding Agents* (1959).

CHAPTER 3

General Bibliography

American Standards Association. *American Standard Specifications For Gypsum Plastering and Interior Lathing and Furring* (New York: ASA, January 11, 1955). ASA A42.1, 1955; ASA A42.4, 1955.

California Lathing and Plastering Contractors Association, Inc. *Reference Specifications for Lathing, Furring, and Plastering in California*, second edition (Los Angeles, 1958).

Lurie, Erwin M. *Handbook of Recommended Specifications for Lathing, Furring and Plastering*, second edition. National Foundation for Lathing and Plastering, Inc. (Chicago, 1949).

Gypsum Association. *Gypsum Lath: Floating Angle Construction and Nailing and Stapling Recommendations* (Chicago, 1959).

The Wood, Wire, and Metal Lathers' International Union. *Manual of Training and Instruction with Recommended Outline of Course of Study for Apprentices* (Cleveland, n. d.).

Van Den Branden, Felicien and Knowles, Mark. *Plastering Skill and Practice* (Chicago: American Technical Society, 1954).

Metal Lath Manufacturers Association. *Technical Bulletin Number 4* (Cleveland, revised 1956).

Metal Lath Manufacturers Association. *Technical Bulletin Number 12* (Cleveland, 1956).

Metal Lath Manufacturers Association. *Supplement Number 1 to Technical Bulletin Number 12* (Cleveland, 1957).

Metal Lath Manufacturers Association. *Supplement Number 1 to Technical Bulletin Number 14* (Cleveland, 1958).

Portland Cement Association. *Plasterer's Manual for Applying Portland Cement Stucco and Plaster* (Chicago: The Association, 1958).

The Dow Chemical Company. *Styrofoam-Insulation-Plaster Base Construction* (Midland, Michigan, 1957).

CHAPTER 4

Notes and References

1. U. S. Department of Labor, Bureau of Apprenticeship, *Apprentice Training*, Washington, D. C. G.P.O., 1956

2. Santa Anita Manufacturing Corporation, *Plaster Master*, Number 1, 1957, File No. 20.52, p.2.

3. Millar, William, *Plastering Plain and Decorative*, B. T. Batsford, London, 1899, p.537.

4. *Ibid.*, p.7.

5. *Ibid.*, p.7.

6. *Standardized Lathing and Plastering Practices*, Final Report Dated December 28, 1958, prepared by Armour Research Foundation of the Illinois Institute of Technology for the U.S. Department of Commerce, Industrial Research and Development Division, Contract Number CAC-47-18, p.127.

7. American Standards Association, *American Standard Specifications for Gypsum Plastering*, New York: ASA, January 11, 1955, ASA No.: A42.1-1955, p.4.

8. Millar, *Plastering Plain and Decorative*, p.4.

9. California Lathing and Plastering Contractors Association, Inc., *Reference Specifications: Lathing, Furring and Plastering in California*, 2nd Ed., Los Angeles, 1958, p.29.

10. Princeton University, School of Architecture, *Curtain Walls of Stainless Steel*, New York, American Iron and Steel Institute, 1955, p.99-100.

11. *Standardized Lathing and Plastering Practices*, p.175.

12. *Ibid.*, p.174.

13. Gypsum Association, Concluding Report — *Research Program on Plaster Cracking*, Chicago, 1946, p.7.

14. ASA No.: A42.1-1955, p.4.

15. *Adhesion of Gypsum Plaster to Various Backings*, "American Architect," September, 1925, p.234.

16. Johnson, S. L. and others, *Adhesion of Plaster, Stucco, and Mortar to Various Structural Backings*, Bulletin of the Virginia Polytechnic Institute, V. 41, No. 5, July, 1948, p.34.

17. *Standardized Lathing and Plastering Practices*, p.94. Quotation on pages 106-107 should read: "Scratch marks have negligible effect on the strength of bond between the scratch and brown coats as determined by direct short time tension tests. Scratch marks appear to constitute a region of weakness in the scratch coat as evidenced by the development of cracks in the scratch coat, which originate from the roots of these marks, both during the curing period of the scratch coat and upon structural deformation of the finished cured construction. Cracks developing in the under coat from these weak regions may be transmitted to the brown and finish coats."

18. ASA, A42.1, p.5.

19. *Ibid.*, p.4.

20. *Ibid.*, p.5.

21. *Ibid.*, p.6.

22. *Ibid.*

23. *Ibid.*

24. Finishing Lime Association of Ohio, *Specification for Lime Plastering.*

25. Finishing Lime Association of Ohio, *Fibered Basecoat Finishing Hydrated Lime: Hydrated Lime for Plaster*, Toledo, Ohio, p.6-7; and *Specifications for Lime Stucco*, No. 6.

26. ASA A42.2-3, p.12.

27. The Universal Atlas Cement Company, *Universal Atlas Handbook of Atlas White Non-Staining Portland Cements*, New York, 1951, p.26.

28. ASA A42.2-3.

29. Hall, Bert A., *Crack Control in Portland Cement Plaster Panels,* Journal of the American Concrete Institute, V.19, No. 2, October, 1947, p.139.

30. U.S. Department of Commerce, National Bureau of Standards, *Stucco Investigations at the Bureau of Standards*, Circular No. 311. 1926.

31. American Technical Society, Chicago, 1954, p.189-194.

32. Wells, Clark and others, *Investigation of Failures of White Coat Plaster*, National Bureau of Standards, BMS 121, 1951.

CHAPTER 5

Notes and References

1. Fitch, James Morton. *American Building* (Boston: Hougton, Mifflin Co., 1948).

2. O'Heir, Richard J. *Perlite Insulating Concrete: Curtain Wall Design, Progressive Architecture*, March, 1957, p. 143.

3. Severud-Elstad-Krueger. Report to the Vermiculite Institute on the design of 4″ and 2″ cast-in-place vermiculite concrete panel or spandrel walls (Chicago: Vermiculite Institute, 1954).

4. *Ibid.*

5. Princeton University, School of Architecture. *Curtain Walls of Stainless Steel.* (New York: American Iron and Steel Institute, 1955), pp. 99-100.

6. Rogers, Tyler S. *Performance Requirements in Panel Design.* Building Research Institute. Proceedings. Metal curtain walls. (Washington, D. C., 1955), pp. 72-73.

7. Koppes, W., Callender, J. H. and McLaughlin, R. W. *Joints in Metal Curtain Wall Construction.* Study No. 2 Curtain Wall Research Project, School of Architecture, Princeton University, Princeton, N. J. (Committee of Stainless Steel Producers, American Iron and Steel Institute, 1957).

8. Princeton University, *op. cit.*, p. 148.

9. Rogers, *op. cit.*, p. 65.

10. Queer, Elmer R. *Thermal Insulation and Condensation Control in Metal Curtain Walls.* Building Research Institute. Proceedings. Metal Curtain Wall. (Washington, D. C., 1955), p. 127.

11. *Ibid,* p. 129.

12. Pennsylvania State University. *A Test of Several Wall Systems Exposed to Controlled Temperatures and Humidities.* Report No. TRL5006-H, p. 1.

CHAPTER 6

Notes and References

1. Garston, England. Building Research Station. *External Rendered Finishes for Walls*, by G. E. Bessey (London, HMSO, 1951). (National Building Studies, Bulletin No. 10), p. 22.

2. Llewellyn, H. M. *Painting Plaster. Journal of the Royal Institute of British Architects,* March 1946, pp. 169-170.

3. Pittsburgh Plate Glass Company. *Improved Practices in Painting Plaster.* Technical Bulletin No. 17. (Published from the Research Laboratories by the Paint and Advisory Board, 1929), pp. 11-12.

4. Armour Research Foundation of the Illinois Institute of Technology. *Report . . . Standardized Lathing and Plastering Practices.* Final Report, December 28, 1948 (Chicago, The Foundation, c.1949), pp. 168-169.

5. Vermiculite Institute. *Impact Tests on Vermiculite Plaster With Keene's Cement Finish Coat* (Chicago, The Institute, 1948).

6. U. S. Department of Commerce. National Bureau of Standards. *Wall Plaster: Its Ingredients, Preparation and Properties* (Washington, GPO, 1924). NBS Circular #151), p. 53.

7. *Loc. cit.*

8. Armour Research Foundation, *op. cit.,* p. 223.

9. *Ibid.,* p. 224.

10. American Standards Association. *American Standard Specifications for Gypsum Plastering and Interior Lathing and Furring* (New York, ASA, January 11, 1955). A42.1-1955, A42.4-1955), p. 4.

11. Andrews, H. *The Production, Properties and Uses of Calcium Sulphate Plasters* (Building Research Congress, 1951). Division 2, part F. (Building Research Station, Watford), p. 140, Table III.

12. Perlite Institute. *Perlite Institute Plaster Strength Investigation.* Conducted at the Cleveland Gypsum Company's laboratory. Final report. October 1954.

13. Andrews, H. *The Effect of Water Contents on the Strength of Calcium Sulphate Plaster Products.* (Reprint from *Journal of the Society of Chemical Industry,* v.LXV:125-128).

14. American Society for Testing Materials. *Methods of Testing Gypsum.* C-26.

15. Andrews, H. *The Production, Properties and Uses of Calcium Sulphate Plasters,* op. cit., p. 141.

16. *Loc. cit.*

17. Armour Research Foundation, op. cit., p. 144.

18. U. S. Department of Commerce. Bureau of Standards. *Wall Plaster,* op. cit., p. 54.

19. Peter, J. P. C. *Adhesion of Gypsum Plaster to Various Backings. The American Architect,* September 9, 1925, p. 234.

20. National Lime Association. Construction data sheet No. 3. *Staining and Discoloration of Plaster,* p. 2.

21. Rogers, T. S. *Design of Insulated Buildings for Various Climates* (New York, F. W. Dodge Corporation, 1951), p. 25.

CHAPTER 8

Notes and References

1. Data averaged from tables of several references.

2. Acoustics Conference (Gypsum Association, Chicago, April 28, 1958).

3. Burris-Meyer, Harold, and Goodfriend, Lewis S. *Acoustics For The Architect.* (N. Y.; Reinhold, c.1957), p. 2.

4. Sabine, H. J. *Less Noise — Better Hearing.* (Chicago, The Celotex Corporation, c.1950), p. 1.

5. Burris-Meyer, *op. cit.,* p. 7.

6. Sabine, H. J., *op. cit.,* p. 4.

7. *Ibid.,* p. 7.

8. Allison, David. *Acoustics for Modern Interiors, Arch. Forum,* April 1959, p. 146.

9. Burris-Meyer, *op. cit.,* p. 37.

10. *Ibid.,* p. 9.

11. Sabine, H. J., *op. cit.,* pp. 18-19.

12. Harris, C. M. *Handbook of Noise Control.* (N. Y.: McGraw-Hill c. 1957), p. 13.

13. The Sabine formula is shown by some references as: $T = \dfrac{0.05V}{a}$ where the constant 0.05 has been taken to the nearest 1/100.

14. Excerpted from *Less Noise — Better Hearing, op. cit.*

15. Burris-Meyer, *op. cit.,* Chapter 5.

16. Knudsen, V. O. *Modern Acoustics and Culture.* (Berkeley, California: University of California Press), 1937.

17. Newman, Robert B. *Sound Transmission,* Building Research Institute, *Metal Curtain Walls.* Proceedings. December 1955, p. 132.

18. Data compiled from industry consultation, general references and manufacturers' literature.

19. McNulty, J. D. *Perlites . . . Vermiculites . . . and the Plastering Machine.* A panel discussion . . . Dr. Huntzicker . . . *Plastering Industries,* April 1956, p. 20.

20. Sabine, H. J., *op. cit.,* p. 84.

21. Bolt, Richard H., and Ingard, K. Uno. *System Considerations in Noise-Control Problems*, Harris, C. M. *Handbook of Noise Control*. (N. Y.: McGraw-Hill, c.1957), p. 22-7, 22-8.
    The partitions as indicated in the charts of Figures 11*a* and 11*b* have been selected from published test ratings of Riverbank Laboratories and the National Bureau of Standards (BMS Report 144 and supplements).

22. Armour Research Foundation Laboratories, Riverbank, Illinois.

23. *Heating, Ventilating, Air-Conditioning Guide*. (N. Y.: American Society of Heating and Air Conditioning Engineers, Inc., c.1958).

24. *Ibid.*

25. *Ibid.*

26. Rogers, T. S. *Design of Insulated Buildings for Various Climates*. (N. Y.: F. W. Dodge Corporation, c.1951), p. 16, 17.

27. *Ibid.*, p. 17.

28. *Ibid.*, pp. 28, 29.

29. *Ibid.*, p. 20.

30. O'Heir, Richard J. *Perlite Insulating Concrete: Curtain Wall Design*. Reprinted from March 1957 *Progressive Architecture*

31. Rogers, T. S., *op. cit.*, p. 29.

32. *Ibid.*, p. 23-25.

33. *Thermal Resistance of Wallboard. Power Plant Engineering*, June 1936, p. 359.

34. Rogers, T. S., *op. cit.*, p. 42.

35. *Ibid.*

36. *HVAC Guide, op. cit.*, p.7.

37. Adlam, T. Napier. *Radiant Heating*. (N. Y.: Industrial Pr., 1949), p. 187.

38. Pratt Institute, School of Architecture. *Radiant Heating-Radiant Cooling: A Forum Series*. Bulletin No. 1, 1954, p. 28.

39. Adlam, *op. cit.*, p. 44.

40. *Ibid.*, pp. 45, 47.

41. Chase Brass and Copper Co. *Suggestions for Designing Radiant Panel Heating With Copper Tube*. (Waterbury, Conn., The Company, n.d.), p. 10.

42. Pratt Institute, *op. cit.*, p. 28.

43. *Ibid.*, pp. 17-18.

44. Gypsum Association. *Radiant Heating*, in *Time Saver Standards*. (N. Y.: F. W. Dodge Corp., 1954), pp. 768-69.

45. Rogers, Tyler S. *Design of Insulated Buildings for Various Climates*. (N. Y.: F. W. Dodge Corp., 1951) p. 29.

46. Schutrum, L. F., and Humphreys, C. M. *Further Studies of the Thermal Characteristics of Plaster Panels. Heating, Piping and Air Conditioning*, June 1953, p. 125.

47. Rogers, Tyler S., *op. cit.*, p. 29.

48. *Loc. cit.*

49. Invisible Panel Warming Association. *Distempering and Painting Warming Panels* (London: The Association, n.d.), Pamphlet #DP38.

50. *Ibid.*

51. *Ibid.*

52. Raber, B. F. and Hutchinson, F. W. *Experimental Studies on Panel Heating Tube Spacing. Heating, Piping, and Air Conditioning*, August 1947, p. 111.

53. Adlam, *op. cit.*, p. 81.

54. *Radiant Heating in Ceilings. Metal Lath News*, Vol. 17, No. 4, p. 10.

55. Gypsum Association. *Panel Heating as Allied With Gypsum Products*. (Chicago: The Association, n.d.), p. 4.

56. *Ibid.*

57. The Finishing Lime Association of Ohio. *How to Plaster Radiant Heat Ceiling Panels*. (Toledo, Ohio: The Association, n.d.)

58. Pratt Institute, *op. cit.*, p. 25.

59. National Warm Air Heating and Air Conditioning Association. *Code and Manual for the Design and Installation of Warm Air Ceiling Panel Systems (Radiant Panel Heating)*. (Cleveland: The Association, 1950), p. 36.

60. For complete information regarding the design and installation of warm air ceiling panel systems, refer to Manual 7A, published by the National Warm Air Heating and Air Conditioning Association, 640 Engineers Building, Cleveland 14, Ohio.

61. National Board of Fire Underwriters. *National Electrical Code*. (N. Y.: The Board, 1957), Sec. 4283.c.

62. *Ibid.*

CHAPTER 9

Notes and References

1. *Fire-Resistance Classifications of Building Construction, BMS 92.* National Bureau of Standards, 1942.

2. *Ibid.*

3. *Ibid.*

4. National Fire Protection Association, *NFPA Handbook of Fire Protection.* 11th Edition. Copyrighted 1954.

5. *Ibid.*

6. Based on a comparison of structural systems made for the Gypsum Association in 1951 by Holabird, Root and Burgee, Architects.

7. National Research Council, National Academy of Sciences. Proceedings. BRAB Conference Report No. 2 *Fire Resistance of Non-Load-Bearing Exterior Walls.* (From the comments of Robert L. Davidson, entitled "The Viewpoint of the Research Director," made at the Research Correlation Conference, November 21, 1950.

8. Hull, W. A., *A Comparison of the Heat-insulating Properties of Some of the Materials Used in Fire Resistive Construction.* Technical Paper BS 12, National Bureau of Standards, 1919.

9. McAdams, William H., *Heat Transmission,* 1st Edition. Copyright 1933. McGraw-Hill Book Co.

10. *Fire-Resistance Classifications of Building Construction, BMS 92,* National Bureau of Standards, 1942.

Index

INDEX